FUNDAMENTALS
OF
T'AI CHI CH'UAN

by Wen-shan Huang

With a new Introduction

by Laura Huxley

and a Forward

by James C. Ingebretsen

**Revised Fifth Edition
1984**

First Edition, June, 1973
Second Edition, October, 1974
Third Edition, January, 1979
Fourth Edition, March, 1982
Fifth Revised Edition, April, 1984

Distributor: American Academy
of Chinese Culture, Inc.,
1493 Galveston Street,
Los Angeles, Calif, 90026
Phone (213) 628–8656

Publisher:

South Sky Book Company

5-7, O'Brien Road,
Hong Kong.
TEL. H-8937608
CABLE: "SOUTHSKYBC"

South Sky Book Company Ltd

5501-5503 UNIVERSITY WAY N. E.
SEATTLE WASHINGTON 98105 U.S.A.
TEL: 206-523-4904

張三丰遺像

張三丰祖師真像

摹自湖北武當山玄天觀石壁

Chang San-feng, the founder of Tai Chi Ch'uan. Based on the rubbing taken from the stone engraving at the Monastary of Hsun Tien in Wu Tang Mountain, Hupei Province, China.

WEN-SHAN HUANG

Taken at the First U.S. Conference

on

CHINESE Total HEALTH and Fitness

Disneyland Hotel

Anaheim, California

September 9—11, 1977

Sponsored by

Center for Chinese Medicine

In cooperation with

College of Oriental Studies

Wen-Shan Huang
Taken at Cité Université, Paris

CONTENTS

A NEW INTRODUCTION TO THE REVISED EDITION
by Laura Huxley
Prelude to Silence

To be able to portray in a book the manifold aspects of life is an almost impossible accomplishment, achieved once in a while by a genius — the same can be said of Tai Chi Ch'uan and of Prof. Huang's imposing achievement in this book — for Tai Chi means "The Great Ultimate" or "The Great Primal Beginning". Only a scholar with the depth of knowledge and devotion of Prof. Huang could make such a masterful elucidation.

A planet is only a little part of a galaxy, yet it is complete in itself. Tai Chi Ch'uan is a complete system of exercise but this is only a part of its galaxy of psychological, philosophical, metaphysical and other aspects. In fact, if a group of people would be asked: "What is Tai Chi Ch'uan?" each person would be right in answering: it is a system of: gymnastics — philosophy — rejuvenation — breathing — symbology — self-defense — changing body image — will training — therapy — dancing — meditation — mind expansion — energy balancing — and more. This versatility, combined with the ongoing evolutionary quickening of our awareness level, accounts for the amazing increase in the number (probably one hundred to one) of Tai Chi Ch'uan students in the last ten years.

For the serious student of oriental culture *The Fundamentals of Tai Chi Ch'uan* is essential. To those, like myself, lovers of Tai Chi Chuan, this book gives a clarification and background of whatever aspect or level of Tai Chi Ch'uan to which one is oriented at the time. For those interested in the form and m ment, there are the diagrams and photographs — explan how and why health and endurance are remarkably i Other readers will be fascinated by the derivation of Tai Cl from the *I-Ching* or the *Book of Changes.*

Scientists, sociologists, philosophers, historians — each will find valuable material correlating their different disciplines into an organismic whole. For the basic orientation in this book is a union, or rather a re-union of body and mind essential not only to the healing of most of our diseases, but also to the realization of that untarnished state of being which reveals the wonder of our Body/Mind.

Aldous stressed this point in *Island**, his presentation of a possible and feasible Utopia:

" 'What sort of dancing does he teach?' Mrs. Naravan tried to describe it: 'No leaps, no high kicks, no running. The feet always firmly on the ground . . . . movements intrinsically beautiful and at the same time charged with symbolic meaning. Thought taking shape in ritual and stylized gesture. The whole body transformed into a hieroglyph, a succession of hieroglyphs, of attitudes modulating from significance to signficance like a poem or a piece of music. Movements of the muscles representing movements of consciousness . . . . It's meditation in action. She concluded. It's the metaphysics of the Mahayana expressed, not in words, but through symbolic movements and gestures.' " Not in words, sounds or music — for Tai Chi Ch'uan is experienced in total silence — ushering at times transcendent Silence. Like all the educational methods in Island's enlightened society, this meditation in action is practiced from the elementary grades on for the purpose of actualizing the potentialities of intelligence and good will of its people. Aldous' interest in, and practice of, oriental psychophysical disciplines, of which Tai Chi Ch'uan is one, was due to this fact, which he often pointed out in his writing, that they are not abstract but

---

**Island*, by Aldous Huxley published by Harper & Row, 1962.

pragmatic, not conceptual only but intensely practical and experiential. This is true of Tai Chi Ch'uan which unites Body, Will and Imagination in a triangle of unsuspected power. It is the most fluid of disciplines as it adapts itself to each person's temperament, body type, and thinking/feeling level.

In the field of relationship Tai Chi Ch'uan puts us in contact with the space outside and the space inside ourselves, making us increasingly aware that the quality of those two immensities and their relationship determines the quality of our life. It is hard to imagine a subtler form of relationship with another person than the joint-hands Operations where the non-verbal response of sensation and rhythm, intention and feeling is perceived through the silent emanation of the adhering wrists. The expansion of consciousness often experienced in practicing Tai Chi Ch'uan is subtly but definitely dissimilar from the "high" produced by more sensational means. Probably one of the reasons is that in Tai Chi Ch'uan, while the upper part of the body is as light and evanescent as a heavenly caress, the feet and legs are solidly planted on Earth. This basic posture facilitates the realization that we are creatures between Heaven and Earth and from the infinitely varied blend of these two sources of energy, we create our own individualized existence. The most important factor in Tai Chi Ch'uan is the balancing of the two universal energies, Yin and Yang, positive and negative, substantial and insubstantial, soft and hard, Heaven and Earth and their eternal interplay. Through *Fundamentals of Tai Chi Ch'uan* and with the guidance of an enlightened teacher like Janice Seaman, who portrays the Tai Chi Ch'uan postures in this book, it becomes clear that the opposites need not be antagonists but, indeed, are necessary to each other's balance. The dawning realization emerges that the harmonious play and finally even the union of these two opposite energies are not necessarily the privilege of solitary mystics but a possibility for us all, living in a conflicting and bewildering world, here and now. What would happen if the harmony that Tai Chi Ch'uan can create was realized by even a minority of human beings on this planet? The urgently needed answer might be: survival — expansion — love.

NOTE TO THE REVISED EDITION

With the increasing interest among the public and universities in the United States, the need for an authoritative book on Tai Chi Ch'uan from the Chinese source has grown from chronic to acute. To answer the immediate demand of American students, the American Academy of Chinese Culture, Inc., in Los Angeles has undertaken to revise the first edition of my *Fundamentals of Tai Chi Ch'uan,* and has asked the publisher to reprint it.

With the assistance of many friends, typographical errors have been corrected, many pictures have been changed, the index enlarged, and new entries inserted. A list of page numbers concerning the Forms is included for quick reference.

Professor S. Y. Wan of Hong Kong, Mrs. Janice Seaman, Mr. Daniel Lee (Engineer at Jet Propulsion Laboratory, and Instructor of Tai Chi Ch'uan at U.C.L.A., El Monte), and Michael Arno are responsibe for the mechanical details of preparing the book for reproduction after the exhausion of the first edition in a short span of five months. I am very grateful for the generous help that I have received from Mr. Joe McCaffree who has made the index for this edition. I want to mention particularly that Mrs. Laura Huxley*, a world renowned writer, had kindly written an Introduction — "Prelude to Silence" — for this Revised Edition. To her, and to all the good friends mentioned above, I am deeply grateful.

The book is now sent forth in the hope that it will contribute

---

* Laura Archera Huxley (Mrs. Aldous Huxley) is the author of "You Are Not The Target, A Practical Manual On How To Cope With A World Of Bewildering Change And Uncertainty", (with an introduction of Aldous Huxley), and "The Timeless Moment — A Personal View Of Aldous Huxley", both published by Farrar, Straus and Giroux, New York, 2nd edition, 1968.

something to lighten the task of learning this great art, and by its use students will become more proficient in learning and practicing it.

Furthermore, I would like to add that in the studying of Tai Chi Ch'uan, there are three stages, which I did not point out in this book, and which should be observed strictly. They are as follows:

Stage I. The learning of the Forms, Patterns or Structure of Tai Chi Ch'uan:

Stage II. The learning of 'Ching' (intrinsic energy) by the constant practicing of Joint-Hands Operations, Ta Lu (Great Pulling), the 'Free Hands' System, and many of the Secrets, songs and guidances, in order to master the art of self defence.

Stage III. But for the purpose of attaining the objective of glowing health and longevity, one must pay much attention to the highest stage — the study of Chi Kung (or Nei Kung), the Breathing System, which is known sometimes as "Meditation in Action". As the Chinese motto goes: "The practicing of Ch'uan (pugilism) without studying 'Kung' (Breathing system), it would certainly end in failure when one comes to old age". But, as a matter of fact, most of the teachers have usually neglected this aspect of the art. This is a great mistake, which should be corrected.

Finally, it may be added that after practicing this eminent art for several decades, I have come to believe firmly that Tai Chi Ch'uan, a sophisticated system having synthesized the major streams of thought such as Confucianism, Neo-Confucianism, Taoism, Zen-Buddhism, and modern science and philosophy, is a path of life. The essential characteristic of the Tai Chi personality, if I may conclude, lies in its need to accept and to integrate all the features of of human self which are variously given unequal supremacy in the other types of personality in different cultures. He is at once strongly Confucian, Taoist, Zennist, Christian, Dionysian, Apollonian Promethean and Maitreyan. Such is the path of life which I named the Path of INTEGRAL TAI CHI, a theory which I have attempted to formulate in my Epilogue written especially for the Chinese part of this book. It lays the foundation of the art of integrated living aiming at the unity of mankind and cultures — the collective community of Tatung, "The Great Harmony" in the sense of Confucius. This is not an ideal of Utopia, but a practical necessity.

Wen-shan Huang

American Academy of Chinese Culture, Inc.
Los Angeles, California, 90026.
December, 1973.

Acknowledgements

for the Third Edition

The author wishes to express his gratitude to the many friends who contributed their work and knowledge to the preparation of the Third Edition of this book in 1977. Special thanks go to Mrs. Janice Seaman who prepared the whole set of pictures of the Tai Chi Ch'uan movements. He is deeply obliged to Michael Arno who revised the texts of the Joint Hands and Ta Lu for the guidance of new students. The author wishes also very much to thank Susan Berlin Irving George Saunders, and James Pyles for their cooperation in making the pictures.

Los Angeles, California
1978.

FORWARD
THIRD EDITION OF FUNDAMENTALS OF TAI CHI CH'UAN
By James C. Ingebretsen, J.D.

It is with deep appreciation, both for the man and his wide-ranging scholarship, that I add this brief forward to the third edition of this landmark publication which, almost alone and unchallenged in its field, provides for us of the western world as deep an understanding of the ancient roots of Tai Chi Ch'uan as our quite different traditional views of the universe, and the man's place in it, permit.

It seems appropriate to include the following tribute, excerpted from a talk delivered at a large dinner held in Professor Huang's honor on the 12th of June, 1977, in Los Angeles, California, celebrating the 15th anniversary of the founding by him of the national Tai Chi Ch'uan association in the United States.

"Other speakers have already testified to the important pioneering of Professor Huang in bringing the practice of Tai Chi Ch'uan from China to this, his adopted land. Today there are thousands of practioners who owe their increased good health and spirits to Professor Huang and the leaders whom he helped to train.

"But even today there are very few, indeed, even of those who teach others, who have the command of the underlying and inherent medical, cultural, religious, philosophical, psychological and esoteric concepts and principles from which the practice of Tai Chi Ch'uan has evolved, and upon which its deepest virtues rest. The fruit from the seeds planted by Professor Huang in his teachings and exhaustive writings on the subject, will be harvested over many years by those westerners who have been encouraged to delve ever more deeply for themselves into the fountains of wisdom to which Professor Huang has pointed the way.

"Mrs. Ingebretsen and I were students in the very first class in Tai Chi Ch'uan which Professor Huang offered in 1959 just after his arrival in Los Angeles to join the faculty at U.S.C.

"Our friendship has ripened through the years to include many interests other than our continued study and practice of Tai Chi Ch'uan. we have, in particular, been intensely interested in his far-reaching and illuminating work at the growing edges of one of the newest of all the social sciences —— culturology.*

"Professor Huang's writings on culturology are unfortunately, mostly still untranslated from the Chinese in which they are now to be found. Nevertheless, we know from the excerpts which have been translated that his contributions are such that the current concepts of anthropology, archeology, sociology, psychology, and even religion, will, in time, be significantly transformed.

"I have no doubt that in the long run his distinguished contributions in the field of culturology, will be seen to have been even more noteworthy than the contributions to the study and practice of Tai Chi Ch'uan for which we honor him this evening."

* For general refrences on Culturology, please see:

White, Lesile A. White, Culturology, Article in the International Ercyclopedia of the Social Sciences, The Macmillan Company & The Free Press, 1968, pp. 547—551.

Huang Wen-Shan, Culturology, Yuen Wu Encyclopedia of Social Sciences.,
Vol. 10, Anthropology, Commercial Press, Taipei, 1971, pp. 55—56 (in Chinese).

Huang Wen-Shan, Culturology — Its Evolution and Prospects, Bulletin of the Institute of Ethnology, Academia Sinica, No. 27, Spring 1969. See also Bulletin, VIIth Congress of Anthrapological and Ethnological Sciences, 1968, Tokyo, pp. 6—10.

Huang Wen-Shan, System of Culturology, Chung Hwa Book company, Taipei, Third Edition, 1971. (in Chinese)

Chang I-hon, A Symposium on Wen-Shan Huang's "System of Culturology," Chung Hwa Book Company, Taipei, 1977. (in Chinese)

Los Angeles California, 1978.

FOREWORD

As one views the world today, change is the dominant order of things. In the complexities of modern living, conflicting ideologies and shifting standards of value, man is surrounded with mounting and ever increasing stresses and tensions. As Western man and his science break through barrier after barrier and penetrate deeper and deeper into the unknown, that which he seeks ever eludes his quest. Western man has sought happiness and security in external things; that is, things outside of himself. When man loses touch with the inner core of his being, he becomes lost on the periphery of reality in the world of change and circumstance.

It is only in recent time that the West has become aware of the rich cultural heritage to be found in the East in the fields of religion, philosophy, literature, art, science, and medicine. The depth of subdety and the lovely vistas of transcendental heights of these Ancient Sages far surpass any modern writings. One need only substitute the nomenclature of science or medicine for these ancient poetic terms and there is before us a modern text book of nuclear physics, or physiology, or of psychosomatic medicine. Western science and medicine with a plethora of terminology, words, and ambiguity of thought, have become lost in a maze of its own creation and is unable to see the forest for the trees.

Science first discovered the molecule, then the atoms with its electrons, protons, positrons and neutrons. Matter in its final analysis is an organized aggregation of electrical changes of Energy capable of a twofold function of attraction and repulsion. This was intuitively perceived by the Chinese Mystics 2,500 years ago, and in like manner by the Mystics of other lands, — only they called it — God. Even the "anti-matter" of the most advanced scientific concepts finds its place in perfect accord with the philosophical mystical views of matter and space by the Chinese Taoists.

Therefore, may we not with great profit direct our attention to Ancient Chinese culture? Among nations of the Far East, China throughout a long period of history has held a most unique position. The Chinese were acquainted with the importance of blood and circulation thousands of years before it was rediscovered in Europe. The Chinese had a system of medicine which goes back 5,000 years of recorded history and is still used by the majority of the Chinese people today. Mental illness and high blood pressure were unknown to these ancient people. Longevity, tranquility, and emotional maturity were outstanding virtues among these ancient people but are so grieviously lacking in our modern 'civilized' life today. If one were to ask for a single word to describe the flowering of Ancient Chinese life, it would be Serenity.

The mind of the Western man was directed outward, but the mind of the man of the Far East was turned inwards and, in introspection, contemplated on the wonders of the Universe, of Nature, and of his own being. All the great religions of the world, both past and present, have stressed the reality of the inner world and the Great Peace, or Serenity, which can only be sensed and realized by one whose mind has become calm and quiet and his emotions unruffled like the waters of a placid lake. There can be no true happiness, no security, or lasting peace until a condition of inner Serenity and Balance is attained.

Man's purpose here on earth is to achieve Wholeness and this is the full development of all the potentialities of his nature. There can be no perfect Wholeness without good health, or well-being. Good health is the result of a balancing of the energies of all the component parts of man's nature. Or to express it more simply — health and well-being is the condition resulting from a mind and body calm, or psychosomatic equilibrium. Now ill-health, sickness, fatigue, neuroses, or even more serious derangements can originate and develop from any of the separate parts of man's inner nature. Man's nature is complex and he exists simultaneously in different states or conditions of being. The Ancient Chinese developed 1,000 years ago, possibly 1,300 years, it may be even longer, a peculiar system of psychosomatic development known as Tai Chi Ch'uan.

It was my good fortune some time ago to become acquainted with a very learned and erudite Chinese Scholar — Professor Wen-Shan Huang. In addition to his many accomplishments Professor Huang is a Master of the Ancient Chinese Art of Tai Chi Ch'uan. Our friendship strengthened with the passing years and now that Professor Huang has prepared a book delineating the steps along this great Highway to Eternal Youth, or the Ancient Art of Tai Chi Ch'uan, I was honored to be asked to write a preface for his book. It is with a sense of great humility that these few words have been written to serve as an introduction to one of the richest experiences that can come into our life. If its reading has served to arouse your interest and increase your desire to learn more about the practice of Tai Chi Ch'uan, the time spent has been worth while.

Preston Kline Caye, Ph. D.

Los Angeles, California
1966.

PREFACE

To call Tai Chi Ch'uan a form of exercise would be to completely miss the mark; it would be more appropriate to refer to it as a Chinese form of Yoga. Unlike exercise, Tai Chi Ch'uan will not tire you. Indeed, as one continues in it, he will find himself actually deriving energy from the practice. Sixteen minutes of Tai Chi Ch'uan — a recommended time for performing the three sections — will serve to "charge the batteries" in much the same way Hatha Yoga does.

In the West we make dichotomies where none previously existed. Thus we speak of the "mental, physical, and spiritual approach", as though these were three different things. The Japanese word "Kororo" and the Chinese "Hsin" can be translated as "heart", "mind", or "spirit", and realizing these are the same is a great step forward to Enlightenment. In Tai Chi Ch'uan we cannot say whether we feel so good because of the physical tone acquired from this best-of-exercises, because of the tranquility of mind that comes (much like the Zen state of "Mushin", no-mind, the pure state unbothered by conceptual thinking), or because of the "spiritual development". Actually, we are dealing with the "whole man" here in what Professor Huang refers to as the "Organism", without attempting to compartmentalize that which is without division. One is tempted to remember the sage's advice to think of the space between the ears as being infinite; all things thus exist within us and we realize our true, unlimited identity.

Despite Western translations (by those who do not understand the Chinese mentality), in which "God" is substituted for the "Tao", the Western anthropomorphic Jehovah, the Moslem Allah, and the Hindu Ishvara do not appear in Chinese thought at all. The Tao is completely impersonal, without characteristics, and to praise this abstraction in hymn and prayer would be meaningless. Thus is the analogy between Tai Chi Ch'uan and Yoga. The latter simply means "Union", though it is often expanded to "seeking Union with the Divine". Just as definitely, Tai Chi Ch'uan, properly practised, will draw one to "Union", though Union with what will depend on the preconditioning of the individual culture. Perhaps it is best to say that Tai Chi Ch'uan will make one's body feel good, almost as though there had been an inner bath; it will bring a sense of well-being, much like the spiritual states described by mystics; and it will tranquilize the mind, tending to make it one-pointed in the same manner as deep meditation. It would not be far wrong to say that T'ai Chi Ch'uan is a "walking meditation".

We in the West are the doubting ones. From a philosophic standpoint, this is admirable. All philosophy begins with doubt, taking nothing for granted in the manner of Descartes and Socrates. This is in no way a religious attitude, however, calling for faith in our ability to evolve and become what the sages tell us we always have been. Thus, to learn Tai Chi Ch'uan, one must practice wholeheartedly. Talk will not bring results any more than the most erudite musical criticism can produce pleasing sounds. The longest journey starts with the first step. In Tai Chi Ch'uan it is enough to learn the movements one at a time, and to perfect them by constant practice, without anticipating the other movements still to come. To think in terms of process, and to enjoy the process as it unfolds, will serve a much better purpose than to always use things merely as means to a goal. No one ever reaches perfection in Tai Chi Ch'uan

— indeed, no two will ever perform it in exactly the same way, as it is a living evolving practice — and the Joy lies in the journey itself.

In this book, the reader will be exposed to far more than Tai Chi Ch'uan. Professor Huang's deep understanding of Confucianism, Taoism and Chan (Zen) Buddhism underlie his exposition, and the reader will continually find rich observations that he will want to go back and re-read. If the reader understands this, the book itself will have proved a step on the way to Mastery. As such, it is of a value not to be reckoned.

Justin F. Stone

Los Angeles, California
January 12, 1966.

INTRODUCTION

Tai Chi Ch'uan, an ancient Chinese exercise or art for the harmony of the mind and body, is believed to have a history of more than fifteen centuries. It is often considered an art of extreme value for attaining longevity; indeed, we do not know of any nation where so much respect is paid to such an art except, perhaps, India, where much attention has been drawn to Yoga.

Based upon the principles of the *I-Ching* or *Book of Changes*. Tai Chi Ch'uan is also widely considered one of the best martial systems for self defense. Because of its long historical development through the many centuries since the T'ang (A.D. 618-906) up to the present, it naturally has emerged as an integral system in its own right, both in theory and technique. In fact, it has been gradually recognized that this system comprises one of the greatest contributions to humanity and civilization by the collective genius of the Chinese people.

Since the publication of Joseph Needham's monumental volumes on Science and Civilization in China (1956-   ), Westerners have come to admire the contributions of the Chinese people to philosophy and science, contributions which were not properly appreciated in the past. And with the long list of books published in Western languages during this century on Chinese art forms — e.g., pottery, bronze, jade. lacquer, porcelain, sculpture, silk, painting, architecture and even calligraphy — Westerners have be----   only to recognize China as the c   ehistoric times, but also to take /   ⸨interrelationship and accul-tura/   for the cultural development of China, but for the West as well. Yet, paradoxically, not much has been scientifically known about the various great systems of martial art, among which Tai Chi Ch'uan is considered to have dynamism and movement par excellence.

The reasons are simple enough; under the medieval Chinese society, the practice of this art was, to some extent, limited to the circles of aristocrats and intelligentsia. Because the philosophy on which it is based was enveloped in a mist of metaphysics, the fundamental principles of the art were not easily comprehended by the common people, only by the scholars. Moreover, the art was usually kept in secret, for many of the masters in the past generations considered this a national technique which ought not to be transmitted to foreigners.

In this space age of the twentieth century, the world's cultures are everywhere resurgent, and the greater interpenetration and acculturation of Oriental and Occidental cultures have rendered it necessary to bring forth the important features in Chinese culture. Being myself profoundly interested in all types of Chinese philosophy and art, which are really the essence of Chinese civilization, I was recently asked to teach or transmit the art, philosophy and science of this ancient system to friends in the United States. And in order to meet the increasing interest of the American people in Tai Chi Ch'uan, which is growing at an amazing rate, I was also persuaded to write this book, the aims of which are as follows:

1. To point out that the philosophy of organism of *I Ching,* or the *Book of Changes* and of the Neo-Confucianism on which Tai Chi Ch'uan is based is essential for the construction of modern science. Although its present and common form was derived from the bureaucratic society of ancient and medieval China, the disciplines of Tai Chi

Ch'uan have a scientific basis rather than a metaphysical one.

2. To show that Tai Chi Ch'uan is also a synthesis or a crystalization of the philosophy of Confucianism, Taoism, and Zen Buddhism — the Tao or Way of Chinese life. The mastery of this eminent art, based on natural laws as expounded by Lao Tzu and Tao Chia, is the very key to happiness, longevity, and eternal youth. It also embodies meditation (Zen) in its movement, and one is likely to be rid of tension and disequilibrium, as well as to have one's physical health restored.

3. To bring every one into a simple appreciation of the beauty of the movement of the postures, and to help everyone to have an enjoyment of this art without putting them to the labor of over-exerting themselves in strenuous sports, and eventually to adopt this healthy exercise as a part of life.

4. To supply a more or less complete guide to those who wish to discover the origins, history and fundamental principles of Chinese martial arts — from which many of the Japanese systems, such as Judo and Aikido have drawn their spiritual sources.

5. Finally, to familiarize people with the applied techniques of Tai Chi Ch'uan for self-defense, and to give assistance to those who wish to practice them, even though they know nothing of the martial arts in China.

It is well to note that, in China, martial art is one of the most popular arts among the people. A man of intelligence is generally expected to master not only the literary arts, but also the martial arts. This is what is called "Wen" and "Wu," each complementing the other. Besides, martial art is a national taste, a common folklore known to every Chinese from childhood up. Numerous songs, poems, maxims, classics and books pertaining to the various phases and aspects of this art have been published. In addition to the simplified forms which are being practiced by groups among young students, it is no exaggeration to say that millions of the intellectual, older and younger people in China, Hongkong and Southeast Asia understand the details of this art, and a great number look upon it as a way to health and longevity, as well as a hobby and pastime.

The greatest desire of men is to attain eternal youth. In the West from Merlin down to Cagleiostro, Brown-Sequard, and Voronoff, charlatans and scientists have entertained the same desire. In the East, the Taoists paid much attention to the techniques of how to attain "hsienship" or material immortality, among which are the respiratory, heliotherapeutic, sexual, alchemical, pharmaceutical, dietary and gymnastic techniques. All these techniques went under the collective name of "nourishing the Chi." The *Tao Teh Ching* of Lao Tzu seems to recommend the respiratory techniques. Apparently the founders of Tai Chi Ch'uan, most of whom were Taoists, have absorbed the elements of their creation, for they considered mental and nervous strength definitely more important than muscular strength.

The Chinese practice of mild gymnastics, which was called Tao Yin, that is, extending and contracting the body, and later known as "Kung-fu" and "Nei-kung," implying inwardly-directed work, is undoubtedly very old. It may be pointed out here that a knowledge of Chinese therapeutic gymnastics came to Europe in the 18th century and seems to have played a part of capital importance in the development of modern hygienic and remedial methods. P. H. Ling, a Swedish pioneer of medical gymnastics, was stimulated by the works of the Jesuits who first introduced Chinese philosophy into the West in the 17th and 18th centuries. Professor Needham is also tempted to wonder whether the heliotherapeutic ideas of the Taoists, transmitted in similar Jesuit articles and books, did not exert an effect on the growth of modern physiotherapy. In fact, modern treatment by forms of radiant energy did not start until the 18th century.

Although our knowledge of the human body is still rudimentary, and no man has succeeded in discovering the secret of immortality, nevertheless, rejuvenation, as is known to those of us who have been practicing Tai Chi Ch'uan persistently for many years, is, indeed, possible. Despite the fact that we will not attain immortality, because we are bound by certain laws of organic constitution, we can actually succeed in retarding the inexorable advance of physiological time. In this sense, Tai Chi Ch'uan, based on physical and psychological factors, can produce profound modifications and improvements of the body and of the mind.

Finally, it does not require a Toynbee or a Sorokin to point out the many ills, defects, or even the decline, of modern civilization. On the one hand, the mastery of the outer world, with a relative contempt for the inner, must inevitably lead to great catastrophe. On the other hand, the toll and havoc of compartmentalizing human activities into unrelated fragments, and of turning individuals into unharmonized spiritual, emotional, mental and physical selves, deliver us to the daemonic forces, despite all outward forms of culture. The hope of humanity lies in the organic whole. The restoration of man to the harmony and integrity of his physiological and mental self will transform this universe. We are therefore strongly convinced that modern man, with his personal deterioration and mental frustration, will find substantial answers in the many dimensions of the art of Tai Chi Ch'uan.

At the very least, an individual's good health depends upon the free flow of vital energy to all parts of his organism. Unrestricted flow of this energy produces a balance or equilibrium of the tri-part nature of man. As the nature of man is threefold, so is the nervous system, which is recognized as comprising the Cerebro-spinal, Sympathetic, and Para-sympathetic. When Tai Chi Ch'uan is taught by a competent teacher and correctly performed, these three nervous systems function together in a state of balance (or equilibrium) for the unification of the individual. Thus does man's nature — the inner and the outer, the mind and the body — become integrated and synthesized, enabling him to realize the "Holism" or the Organismic Whole of his Being — the new approach to the development of "Unitary Man."

At the optimum, we should not forget that the universe modifies all aspects according to the conditions of our body. The firm, yet harmonious, free, yet reciprocal way, will certainly induce integration and unity someday in its larger scope — that of all mankind.

Tai Chi Ch'uan has pointed to humanity the goal and has placed at its disposal the means of reaching it. A new approach, new philosophy of life, a new world view, and a new health will transform the individual as well as the universe. May all disciples be benefited and have their lives rebuilt by the study of the philosophy and practice of this most ancient and proven Chinese dynamic system of health, well-being and longevity.

WEN-SHAN HUANG

American Academy of
Chinese Culture, Inc.
Los Angeles, California
1968

ACKNOWLEDGEMENTS

In writing this book, I am grateful to many friends for assistance and encouragement. Dr. Preston Kline Caye's inspiration and his encyclopedic knowledge of Oriental philosophy have been of inestimable value. I am particularly indebted to my friends, James C. Ingebretsen and Justin Stone, who read part of the manuscript and made many constructive suggestions. For the correcting of my many mistakes I must thank Miss Pauline Marfoe, and Professor Chang Yick Wen. I am also deeply grateful to Helena M. Migdalik, Fred G. Bauer, Lyn M. Hite, Marlyse Kusik, Martha Ovaska, June Yuer and Clarence and Ceola Collier, for their magnificant support of an author attempting the impossible.

Finally, I wish to thank my colleagues and members of my classes in U.C.L.A.; the National Tai Chi Ch'uan Institute, Inc.; the Academy of Creative Education, Inc. and the American Academy of Chinese Culture, Inc., for their cooperation and encouragement; and especially Marshall Ho'o, James C. Ingebretsen, Judith Tyberg, C.L.J. Damme, S.S. Jung, Frank S.T. Wong and Ernst Chin, the spiritual leaders of this movement in Los Angeles, California. The author also wishes to express his gratitude to Sophia Delza, Edward Maisel and Y.T. Liu of New York for their inspiration in the teaching of Tai Chi Ch'uan. It would be impossible to mention here everyone who has helped me one way or the other. However, I always feel grateful to many faculty members of the National Peking University, Yau Fu Chun of the National Martial Art Institute in Shanghai, Tung Ying Chieh and Tung Fu-ling of the Ying Chieh Tai Chi Ch'uan

Institute in Hong Kong, Choy Hok-peng, the Founder of the Tai Chi Ch'uan Studio in San Francisco, Yang Shiu-chung of Canton, Cheng Man-Ch'ing, Y.T. Liu, Da Liu, T.T. Liang, T.C. Wong, Kuo Ling Yin, Hui-Ching Lu, Liu Shih-lung, Choy Kam-man, and other masters of Tai Chi Ch'uan in New York and San Francisco, Han Chin-sheng, Hsiung Yang-ho, Kuo Ting-ch'uen of Taipei, for having imparted their knowledge to me with great generosity.

I am indebted to my friend, Mr. Yung-cheng Kwang, an eminent expert in Taiwan for the collaboration of taking the valuable pictures on Joint Hands Operations and the Application of the thirty-seven basic patterns in the Tai Chi Ch'uan postures. A profound debt of gratitude must be expressed here by the author to the many friends, students and colleagues who have lightened his task in preparing this book. To Mrs. Janice Seaman, I should like to acknowledge a special debt for her generously making available the pictures on the whole set of Tai Chi Ch'uan postures, which form the basis of illustrations, along with those of Mr. Kwong's, of this book. For the serviceable photographing of Seaman's postures, I wish to thank Donald McIntosh and Clarance Collier for their valuable collaborations.

In spite of the innumerable books that have been written about Tai Chi Ch'uan in recent years, it is remarkable how little really authentic knowledge we in the United States have about the history, philosophy, and technique of this art. The number of books and articles in English on the subject is steadily growing but, with few exceptions, they are too popular or too superficial to have much value. I sincerely hope that this volume will be the first in English attempting to give a really comprehensive and systematic account of this eminent Chinese art of life as a whole.

The Bibliography of Tai Chi Ch'uan, both in Chinese and English, although not intended to be inclusive, contains examples of how Chinese works have influenced the minds of so many millions of human beings.

Finally the assistances of Mr. Y. T. Liu in supplying part of the bibliography in English, and Mr. S. W. Sung of the Wo Kee Printing Company in handling the manscript for printing are gratefully acknowledged. Thanks are due to Mr. Lee Gut U, General Manager of the South Sky Book Company, Hong Kong for the publication of this book. I also want to thank Professor S. Y. Wan for having provided me with many useful comments and corrections on the subsequent drafts of manuscript.

Wen-shan Huang

Office of the Dean of the Faculty of Liberal Arts
Chu Hai College
Kowloon, Hong Kong
1972

INTRODUCING THE AUTHOR

Professor Wen-shan Huang, who has been a living exponent of this great art — Tai Chi Ch'uan — in modern China, received his instructions from great Masters in Peking, Nanking, Shanghai, Lo-Shan, Chunking, Canton, and Hong Kong, when China enjoyed the richness of her heritage and glory. In the twenties, when he studied philosophy under the late Dr. Hu Shih and Bertrand Russell, he learned the art of Tai Chi Chien (Sword) at the National Peking University where he received his B.A. degree in philosophy. After obtaining his Master's degree from Columbia University, and as Dean of the National Labor University at Shanghai, he·entered the National Institute of Martial Arts and took up Tai Chi Ch'uan in the thirties. One of the foremost masters whom he followed in Canton, China was the late Tung Ying Chieh, one of the most eminent pupils of Yang Ching-fu of Peking immediately after World War II. He has also recently been appointed as Academician by the China Academy.

In recent years, Tai Chi Ch'uan has attracted an ever-widening circle of interest in the United States, particularly in New York, San Francisco and Los Angeles. The credit for this is partly due to Professor Huang, who, besides being the greatest authority on the Philosophy of Tai Chi Ch'uan, is the chief Chinese interpreter of this great art to western people. Professor Huang is a distinguished sociologist and one of the founders of the new discipline "Culturology" — the Science of Culture. His cultural theory has been cited by Professor Pitrim A. Sorokin in his epoch-making book — *Sociological Theories, Today,* (Harper & Row, New York, 1966).

Following a number of academic positions, he was made Head of the Department of Sociology, National Central University at Nanking; President of Chien Sheh University at Shanghai; President, Provincial College of Law and Commerce in Kwang-tung; Dean of the Law School, National Sun Yat-sen University at Canton. During this time he published a number of important books, and, in war time, was a member of the Legislative Yuan and Representative of the National Congress, the Republic of China.

He came to the United States as visiting scholar of Columbia University in 1951, and lecturer in Chinese Art, Chinese Culture, and Culturology at the New School for Social Research (New College), New York. He also lectured on Chinese Art History at the University of Southern California. He was a delegate representing the Republic of China at the 6th International Congress of Anthropological and Ethnological Sciences, Paris, 1960, and a representative of the Chinese Sociological Society attending the 5th World Congress of Sociology in Washington, D.C., 1962. He is an editor of the Bulletin of the Institute of Ethnology, Academia Sinica, and Research Professor of the College of Chinese Culture, Taipei, Taiwan. His stay in the United States has been marked by immense production of both major works and scientific articles for journals, including Academia Sinica. In other activities, he founded the Pan American Chinese Press, Inc.; the American Academy of Chinese Culture, Inc.; and the National Tai Chi Ch'uan Institute, Inc., all of which aim to study and teach knowledge of Asiatic civilization and Chinese art and philosophy.

His books on *"The System of Culturology,"* Chunghua Book Co., Taipei, Taiwan, 3rd ed. 1971, *"Essays on Contemporary Culture,"* Chu Hai College, Hong Kong, 1972, have been highly admired. Besides, he has translated many books into Chinese, such as Pitrim A. Sorokin, *Contemporary Sociological Theories, Sociological Theories,*

Today, Har, *Social Law,* Betrand Russell, *The Problems of Philosophy, Roads to Freedom* and Joseph Needham, *The Science and Civilization in China,* Vol. 1. (all published by the Commercial Press, Shanghai and Taipei.)

Recently, he has been visiting Professor of National Taiwan University, Hong Kong Chinese University, New Asia College (1968-1970), and Dean of the Faculty of Liberal Arts and Professor of the Institute of Chinese Culture, Chu Hai College, Kowloon, Hong Kong (1971-1973).

Returning to the U.S. in the fall of 1973, Dr. Huang is now the President of the American Academy of Chinese Culture; President Emeritus, National Tai Chi Ch'uan Association, Inc., Professor and Chairman of the Department of Arts East and West, College of Oriental Studies — Graduate School, Los Angeles, California, 90006.

PART I: HISTORICAL AND PHILOSOPHICAL

CHARTER I

WHAT IS TAI CHI CH'UAN

1. THE ART OF LIFE

Tai Chi Ch'uan is a Chinese system of exercise or an art of life, the practice of which provides valuable help in extending man's life span, eliminating tension and increasing opportunities of physical, spiritual, and mental well-being and equilibrium. The modern system of this art, or exercise, is a result of the development of a more thorough and rational organization of the ancient techniques. However, the tendencies in the current practice of the present-day Tai Chi Ch'uan — as a health movement, an art of self-defense and a sport — have their basis on the same fundamental principles and techniques.

Analytically speaking, the system consists of three important components: that is, the form or structure, the internal merit or the art of inhalation and exhalation, and the self-defense techniques in application.

2. THE FORM OR STRUCTURE

In the first place, the whole system consists of thirty-seven movement patterns which can be developed into some one hundred and eight postures. However, the original Yang system has only eighty-one forms at its command. These are not static positions but dynamic patterns of action flowing imperceptibly into each other like rising waves of a calm sea, yet retaining their individuality, continuity, and evenness as parts of an integral whole.

The entire composition, both in the manner of moving and in the forms of pattern, is regulated by the principle of Yin (陰) and Yang (陽), or the forces of negative and positive, contained in the Tai Chi (太極) (or the "Supreme Ultimate"), which was originally expounded in the I Ching (易經) *(The Book of Changes)*. It is the Chinese philosophic theory of the interplay and harmony of opposites — such as firmness and softness, strength and lightness, insubstantiality and substantiality, activity and passivity, motion and quiescence. The first principle is the T'ai Chi, the source of phenomena in the whole universe.[1]

[1] The principle for T'ai Chi Ch'uan is the synthetical and analytical Yin-Yang Key, the practical dialectic born in Ancient China from the contemplation and understanding of the universal law of Unity, the complementary of two opposite cosmic forces, positive and negative, constrictive and expanding. Many modern scholars are attempting to apply this principle to all sciences and arts. See the *Philosophy of Oriental Medicine, The Book of Judgment* by G. Ohsawa, 1956, Ohsawa Foundation, N.Y.C.; and his *Principle Unique de la Philosophie et la Science d'Extreme-Orient*, Paris; *Zen Macrobiotics. The Art of Longevity and Rejuvenation*, Ohsawa Foundation, N.Y.C. *A Practical Introduction to Zen, Eastern Psychology for Western Man* by Manly P. Hall, Philosophical Research Society, Los Angeles, California.

The whole set of movements, or exercises, usually requires fifteen to twenty minutes. The fastest that it can be done is in three minutes, whereas the slowest may last for half an hour. They are basically slow, continuous, light, gentle, circular, rhythmic, energetic and graceful movements which are capable of developing an "intrinsic energy" (內勁), ready to tune up the body, slow down the aging processes, and stretch out the life span of the human being.

As Max Müller, the eminent philosopher of religion, said: "The greatest of all arts is the art of life, and the best of all music the harmony of the spirits." Tai Chi Ch'uan is indeed the art of life and the harmony of the spirits, the beauty of which lies in the aesthetic principles of all genuine movements. The "lively movements" which are contrary to motionless shapes or positions, and which are expressed in every part of the human organism, are not a mystery; they are a coordination of the artist's Chi, or energy, with the muscular movements as a means of projecting it to every cell of the organism. It is a very personal faculty, achieved by continuous practice and meditation, and by a discipline that is spiritual in addition to being physical. There are many little rules to be learned in order to bring into our lives harmony and melody as well as dynamic equilibrium, but the eternal law must be love and non-aggression.

3. THE TECHNIQUES OF BODILY MOVEMENT

The thirty-seven basic pattern movements which extend to eighty-one or eighty-seven or even one hundred and eight postures have been devised by great masters to meet the requirements for the constant readjustment, improvement, re-vitalization and upkeep of the human body's principal physio-biological systems. With regard to the operation of these techniques, T. Y. Liu has this to say:

"As both of these systems, especially their extensions in the peripheral tissues which are more susceptible to deterioration and degeneration, are activated by contraction of the muscles, the Tai Chi Ch'uan postures and their transition movements from one to another are performed in such a way as to stretch, reflex and twist every and all of the 710 odd muscles throughout the body, giving each an equal chance of work and, where certain muscles require more attention, a number of postures are repeated. Movement starts from the feet (toes, soles, heels), ankles and legs, ascending along the spine (vertebral column) and concentrating around the waist — the main pillar and axis for sustaining the body weight and the body's equilibrium. It extends further upward to the neck and head and along the shoulders and arms to end at the fingers. Each change of posture comprising from two to four minor movements involves alternately, the raising or lowering of the body, shifting forward or backward, or swinging an angle of 45 to 180 degrees to the right or left, and/or to a full circle around. These rather complicated acts are intended not only to effectively contract all the main and peripheral muscles and nerves but also to improve and vitalize the keenness and sensitivity of the whole nervous system.

"Each movement also involves the alternate shifting of the body weight from one leg to another and is always synchronized with breathing. In the course of slow movement, only by long practice can the body be balanced on one leg steadily and enduringly. Movements are performed slowly, lightly and calmly in a naturally effortless manner of ease and continuity throughout the whole course, which may take from 15 to 30 minutes without any lapse of time and sequence. As each movement must be synchronized with each breathing, slow and deep breathing (the essential aspect of the exercise) can only be accomplished by equally slow movement. A continuous succession of slow, light, calm and steady movements can only be executed with the spine always maintained upright, and the mind consciously concentrated and totally relaxed, throughout the whole course, to the exclusion of all irrelevant thoughts. Movements are also performed with all parts of the body in unison and harmony to constitute a concerted act of the feet (toes, soles, heels), legs (knees), waist, abdomen, shoulders, necks, head (with eyes watching and ears listening), arms, elbows and hands (palms, fingers). With the spine and waist as sustaining pillar and axis and the feet firmly rooted aground, all other parts of the body are maneuvered, in pairs and fours, simultaneously and rhythmically, feeling yourself like a fish propelling under the water or a bird sailing above the air, forgetting all world worries and attaining a heavenly state of serenity. After completion of the whole course of exercise, not only will there be an absence of fatigue but also a feeling of renewed vigor, and the entire body will be charged and warmed up from toes to fingers, with profuse perspiration if performed in warm weather or indoors but without puffing and panting, nor undue heart-beating. It is the combined effect of activated nervous communication, stimulated blood circulation, intensified flowing and draining of the lymphatic fluid and integrated mental relaxation."[2]

---

[2] Y.T. Liu, *Tai-Chi-Ch'uan, Health Exercise: For Advanced Pupils,* quoted with permission.

The above passages summarize admirably how this health art and exercise help a man or woman condition the mind by exercising the body and exercise the body under the direction and impact of the mind.

4. THE BREATHING SYSTEM

Without over-exerting oneself in the stress and strain of tense exercises and sports, as we have seen in the occident, all postures are done in circular and light movements, which have to be coordinated with internal breathing, that is, inhalation and exhalation within the human body. It is the basic principle of Tai Chi breathing, that we exhale whenever our hands are stretched, raised or pushed forward, and that we inhale whenever they are contracted, down or pulled backward. The practice of this breathing system is often called the "internal merit" or "Nei Kung" (內功). With the rhythmic breathing, a sort of "intrinsic energy" or "Ching" (勁) is expected to develop gradually as one arrives at an advanced stage. It is exertable and formless, concentrated and collected, circular and elastic. Where achievement is attained, it is comparable to the toughness of steel, and yet, after each performance, we feel refreshed as if every cell in our body was charged with new energy. Our mind is harmonious and our spirit lifted. We feel a joy, a serene strength and a sense of tranquility within ourselves. Furthermore, we carry these newly acquired faculties into our daily activities. They increase our daily work efficiency, improve our mental alertness, and calm our nervous tension.

In fact, Tai Chi Ch'uan bases its principles not only on the philosophy of the *I Ching,* or *Book of Changes,* but also on the great

Oriental philosophy of Taoism originated by Lao Tzu, who was greatly admired by Confucius. The Taoistic breathing system, which is widely practiced both by the Taoists and the Buddhists for longevity and meditation, was taken over by Tai Chi Ch'uan for the development of "intrinsic energy." The highest stage of the latter is believed to be beyond the reach of other practices of exercise in the Orient, and the calisthenics or gymnastics taught in the Occident. No wonder it is generally considered as the most successful system of internal and external training, embracing the best principles of modern psychology, physiology, biology, mental hygiene, and dynamics for the promotion of health.

5. THE ART OF SELF-DEFENSE

Being an art of exercise, the techniques of Tai Chi Ch'uan are applicable to self-defense. In addition to the common structures or postures, there are the joint hands operations (Tui Shiu) (推手), four corners joint hands operations, Ta Lu (大擺) and free hands operations (Shan Shiu) (散手), which, employing all the techniques of this art, plus some extras, are to be practiced by two persons. They, too, make good exercises. For self-defense, the general principles adopted are the law of "non-aggression" and the law of "non-opposition"; hence, all the techniques can only be employed strategically, without the exertion of awkward force or strength. This is one of the extraordinary characteristics of this martial art. It is also considered as a revolutionary approach to physical culture and pugilism.

6. THE ORIGINS OF TAI CHI CH'UAN

Such are the components of Tai Chi Ch'uan, which, viewed as an art of life, are actually the synthesis and crystalization of what is best in Taoism, Confucianism, Neo-Confucianism, Zen (Ch'an) Buddhism, and the Chinese way of life itself. It teaches us a simple, natural, and healthy formula of living. In ancient times, this system was originally called "Mien Ch'uan" (綿拳) (cotton fist), because of its emphasis on softness or suppleness. Because of this, the system makes it possible for man to be in tune with nature's vibrations while in motion. Its composition is quite complex; its forms highly symbolic; its rhythms very melodic; its motions always cyclic; its movements extremely light and soft; and, above all, its therapeutic value far superior to any known exercise, ancient or modern, east or west.

7. THE THERAPEUTIC VALUE

The primary objective of Tai Chi Ch'uan is concerned with man's well-being, with a view towards everlasting youth, while the aim at self-defense is only secondary. Hence, its stress differs totally from other gymnastics, such as those planned solely for muscle building or those designed solely for exhibition purposes. The accent is on the technique of breathing. Proper and deep breathing is an integral part of this art of life, as music is the integral part of a dance. Furthermore, Tai Chi Ch'uan is a perfect weaving of the dynamic of form and tranquility in motion, in that every aspect of man's well-being is considered; it concentrates the mind and calms the emotions; it regulates the blood circulation; it mobilizes all joints, ligaments, and muscles, and makes one alert and energetic; it absorbs accounts of discoveries relating to the principle of life and of efforts to recreate life naturally. In short, the constant practice of this art and movement certainly increases the respiratory capacity, stimulates and stabilizes the nervous system, and improves the function of all the organs of the body. When all the principles, techniques, and rules are mastered, the results and effects will revolutionize the spirit and the body, leading one to a new sense of harmony and the equilibrium of the Yin and Yang forces in the body. This is what is known as "Tao", or the way of "Life" from the Chinese point of view, or a "unitary man" from a Westerner's point of view.

8. CONCLUSION

Tai Chi Ch'uan dates back to the T'ang (唐) Dynasty in Chinese history (A.D. 618-906), but the historical evolution since Chang San-Feng (張三丰), the alleged creator of this system began in the Sung (960-1279), or Yuan (1206-1368), or even Ming Dynasty (1368-1644). In the last several centuries, it has become the most revolutionary health exercise and art of self-defense, representing the collective creation of Chinese civilization itself rather than the creation of a single man. In recent years, the techniques which have been handed down have been scientifically studied and principles evolved for the most effective use of the various movements for bodily health.

Having heard of the Chen system (陳派), Yang system (楊派),

Wu system (吳派), Sun system (孫派), etc., the average student is led to believe that there are many different schools of Tai Chi Ch'uan. But, in reality, there is only one kind of Tai Chi Ch'uan. There are, however, variations of Tai Chi Ch'uan; for instance, some systems omit certain forms or employ variations of the fundamental movements. All variations are beneficial when taught with understanding, although the Yang system is known as the only systematized or orthodox Tai Chi Ch'uan.

Lastly, this unique and most celebrated system, which has benefited the Chinese people for centuries, is now being practiced in China, Hong Kong, and Southeast Asia by millions — the young as well as the old, men as well as women — all of whom consider it as part of their life and enjoy the results therefrom. Hundreds of books on the into western languages, except a few.[3] Probably this is due to the fact that great masters tried to keep this art a national secret. Memfact that ancient masters tried to keep this art a national secret. Members outside of their own clan were taught not to mention this to the people of other nations. However, in this fast moving world of ours, where art, science and technology are the common heritage of mankind, it seems to be more urgent, now than ever, to have this type of exercise serve the whole of humanity.

---

[3] Yearning K. Chen, *T'ai Chi Ch'uan, Its Effects and Practical Applications,* 1st Ed. 1947, Shanghai; Cheng Man-Ching, *T'ai Chi Ch'uan, A Simplified Method of Calisthenics for Health and Self Defense,* Taipei, Taiwan, China, 1956.

CHAPTER II

HISTORICAL BACKGROUND OF

TAI CHI CH'UAN

Tai Chi Ch'uan in its course of development has completed a form which distinguished it from its original type, Shao-Lin (少林), so greatly, indeed, that we are justified in emphasizing its historical division into the two schools, Shao-Lin and Wu-Tang (武當) (Tai Chi) of the Chinese system of martial arts. As a matter of fact, the Shao-Lin, with all its varied structures, is no more than a form of Chinese pugilism developed by Hua T'u (華佗) (b. 190 A.D.), a famous Chinese physician, who lived during the period of the Three Kingdoms (A.D. 220-265),[1] and wrote a treatise on pugilism, which is considered as the foremost boxing system in China. It also traces back its final authority to its Indian founder, the great Bodhidharma, (known as Ta-Mo) (菩提達摩) (arriving as early as A.D. 475 at Canton, he died A.D. 536), chief of the sect of Dhyana (28th Patriarch of Indian Buddhism), known as Ch'an in China and later Zen in Japan. While this form of the Shao-Lin system was created by Ta-Mo, it achieved further development by other Chinese leaders, who knew

---

[1] See biography of Hua T'u, in *Hou Han Shu,* or the official history of the Later Han dynasty, 25 B.C.-A.D. 220. His treatise is entitled: *The Recreation of the Five Animals.*

how to apply the principles of their system to the ever-varying conditions of their life and to the practical needs of the people. Thus enriched in experience and matured in reflection, Chang San-Feng (張 三丰), a Taoist, achieved a fundamental change of the Shao-Lin system into the great system of Tai Chi. It was a revolution, not only in principles, but also in techniques in the history of Chinese martial art.

Among the many schools or sects of martial art that have grown up in the last eighteen centuries or so, especially in China and finally in Japan, we find many orders claiming to transmit the essence and spirit of Buddhism and Taoism directly from Ta-Mo and Chang San-Feng. But from our point of view, we venture to repeat that Tai Chi Ch'uan is found to have systematized, or rather crystallized, all the philosophies and religions of China, such as Taoism, Confucianism and Buddhism as well as the very life conception itself of the Chinese people. Hence this school is unique in various ways in the history of martial art.4

4 With regard to the historical development of T'ai Chi Ch'uan, in modern times, Y.T. Liu says:
"The T'ai Chi Ch'uan Health Exercise was created and founded by the Chinese Taoism some 700 years ago and originally comprised three parts — Body and Mind Conditioning, Hands Combatting and Weapons Fighting — which had been adopted and practiced by certain sects of the Chinese warriors before the introduction of more sophisticated fire arms. The Japanese Judo is the derivation and modification of the second part of Tai Chi Ch'uan (Hands Combatting). As generally recognized, the Japanese people have acquired much of the Chinese ancient civilization and culture to their benefit from the early times. When obsolete war weapons lost their usefulness to more sophisticated fire arms, the Tai Chi Ch'uan was retained by the Chinese masses for body-and-mind conditioning and self-defense, and by the Chinese sports and showmen for exhibition and competition. Subsequently, the first part for body-and-mind conditioning of the exercise has been extensively adopted by the Chinese health-

seekers, especially the infirm and aged, with remarkable results. It is now more widespread in Taiwan and the mainland China and amongst the Chinese overseas. In the public parks and private open spaces in Taiwan and the mainland, and Hong Kong and Singapore where Chinese overseas are concentrated, you will find numerous masters of Tai Chi Ch'uan teaching classes of various sizes and masses of accomplished pupils practicing themselves, either individually or in groups. They are mixed groups of men and women, young and old.

"More recently, this art of health exercise has been introduced in the United States, mainly in the metropolitan cities of New York, San Francisco, Los Angeles, etc., Mr. Edward Maisel is the founder of the Tai Chi Ch'uan Institute of America in New York and Professor Wen-Shan Huang, founder of the National Tai Chi Ch'uan Institute in Los Angeles. In San Francisco. Dr. Hui-Ching Lu, a Chinese lady educator, has been teaching classes of Tai Chi Ch'uan for many years. Miss Sophia Delza, a creator of modern dance, who had learned the Tai Chi Ch'uan from a Grand Master — Mr. Ma Yueh-liang — in Shanghai, China, has been teaching classes in the U.N. T'ai Chi Ch'uan Club in New York. Mr. Da Liu, on the U.N. Secretariat, has been also teaching T'ai Chi Ch'uan classes in New York for years. About a year ago, three visitors from Taiwan — Prof. Cheng Man-Ching and his two accomplished pupils, Prof. T. T. Liang and Mr. William Chen have remained in New York, to conduct classes of Tai Chi Ch'uan for primary and advanced pupils. They are also experts of T'ai Chi Ch'uan for Hand Combatting and Medieval Weapons Fighting, which are more appealing to youngsters and sportsmen here. Doubtlessly, there are other masters of Tai Chi Ch'uan and classes unknown to the writer." op. cit.

*   *   *   *   *

It may be added that T'ai Chi Ch'uan had actually been taught and introduced to the United States by Choy Hok-Peng (1886-1957) who established the T'ai Chi Ch'uan Institute first in San Francisco in 1941, and branches were set up in Los Angeles and New York at the same period. The author happened to be in San Francisco at that time, and a "Declaration" for the Institute was written by him at the request of Mr. Choy, who, as a good teacher, had trained quite a few hundred pupils in the West and East coasts before the termination of the second world war. He died in Hong Kong in the fifties. A book on Tai Chi Ch'uan published in Hong Kong in 1956, was written by him. His son Choy Kam-man is teaching this art in the Y.M.C.A. in San Francisco, California. (W.S.H.)

Prior to the study of the life of Chang San-Feng and the controversies regarding the historical transmission of this system, it is probably advisable to give a schematic representation of the development of the various schools and sects of martial art in China. Briefly, they are as follows:

1. FREE HANDS (the use of fists and feet)

A. Southern School

Its chief characteristics: softness.

Originated at Wu Tang Mountain (武當山).

Hence, Tai Chi Ch'uan is usually called the pugilism of Wu Tang, which again can be divided into the northern and southern school itself. Basing their main principle on Tai Chi, there are such sects as Pa Kua (八卦), and Hsing I (形意) in China, and Judo and Aikido in Japan.[1]

B. Northern School

Its chief characteristics: firmness.

Owing to the creation of this art at the Shao-Lin Monastery,

---

[1] For the history of the various styles of Kung-Fu — the Tsoi, Li, Mawk, Fut and Hung styles — and animal styles such as the Crane School and the Tiger School — see "The Tiger, the Dragon and the Crane", Black Belt, Vol. III, No. 1, Jan. 1965. Also see Ed. Parker, *Secrets of Chinese Karate*, Prentice Hall, N.Y. 1963. Juchi Wat-an abe & Lindy Avakian, *The Secrets of Judo*, Charles E. Tuttle, Vermont and Tokyo, 1960; and Robert W. Smoth, *Secrets of Shaolin Temple Boxing*, Tuttle, 1964.

it is known as the system of Shao-Lin (少林), from which we have different branches such as Tan T'ui (彈腿), Chia Ch'uan (查拳), Pa Fan (八番), Long Boxing (長拳), Mi Chung (迷蹤), Tuan Ta (短打), Ti Tang (地鐺), Pa Chi (八極), Pei Kua (批卦), etc. The Japanese Karate may have derived its source from this later school.

2. WRESTLING (摔角), or the techniques of "twisting down" (蹟跤術). According to record, these techniques had been transmitted to Japan by Chan Yuan-Pin (陳元斌), a great teacher living at the end of the Ming Dynasty (1368-1644). Hence, we have the present system of Judo which has been admirably evolved and much improved by the Japanese, particularly its application-aspect.

3. ARTS, with the employment of equipment, the main forms of which are: Sword (劍), Spear (槍), Knife (刀), Stick (棍), Chia (戟), Tang (鐺), Forked Spear (叉), Pia (耙), Whip (鞭), Chin (鐧), Hammer (鎚), Axe (斧), Hook (鈎), Sickle (鐮), Goa (拐), Pa (抓), Bow and Arrow (弓箭), and Tan Pi (藤牌). The total amounts to eighteen types of equipment. With the addition of the techniques of the pressuring of targets and attacking of vital points, (點穴), as known in Acupuncture (針灸術), most of which were kept secret in ancient times, the martial art in China became almost encyclopedic in nature.

With the emergence of Tai Chi Ch'uan, which is synthetic in principles and in techniques of movement, what it most strongly and persistently stresses is the internal spiritual experience and training. It does attach great importance to the directive development of "intrinsic energy' in addition to the external physical movements. This is where Tai Chi Ch'uan pre-eminently distinguishes itself from other forms of martial art. The development of Tai Chi Ch'uan, however, may be viewed in the following three stages:

(A) First Stage

As Tai Chi Ch'uan has a very long historical background, to trace its primitive beginnings at the present time is by no means easy. The germs are no doubt in the doctrines and practices attributed to the various founders of the system in the T'ang Dynasty (A.D. 618-907). According to Hsu Yu-Sheng (1879-1945) (許禹生), one of the greatest authorities on the history of Tai Chi Ch'uan, the basic ideas of this system seem to have come from the four sects at the end of the T'ang Dynasty.

1. The sect of "Three-Generations-and-Seven" (三世七), created by Hsu Hsun-Ping (許宣平), the techniques of which were transmitted to Sung Yuan-Chao (宋遠橋),

2. The sect of "Shao Chiu-Tien (小九天), the art of which was taught by Cheng Ling-Si (程靈洗), who had it transmitted to Han Kung Yueh (韓拱月) and then to Cheng Mi (程泌).

3. A sect of "A Priori Ch'uan" (先天拳) was originated by Li Tao-Tzu (李道子), also known as Li Tao-Shan (李道山), who was also called the master of Wu Tang. His art was transmitted to the Yu Clan (俞氏), of which the most famous was Yu Ching-wei (俞清慧).

4. The Method of "A Posteriori" (後天法) was originated by Yin Li-Hsiang (殷利亨), who taught it to Hu Ching-Tzu (胡鏡子) and then to Sung Chung-Shu (宋仲殊).

(B) Second Stage

Tai Chi Ch'uan, according to popular beliefs, is undoubtedly the supreme achievement of Chang San-Feng (張三丰) who, at the end of the Sung Dynasty (South Sung A.D. 1127-1279), revolutionized and synthesized all the systems in existence and created the so-called "Esoteric system" (Nei Chia Ch'uan) (內家拳). What makes it unique as it is practiced now is its systemic training of the mind (spirit) as well as the body.[1]

Before looking into the future, we must turn back to the life of Chang San-Feng. It is, indeed, very difficult to determine when he was born and how long he lived. Firstly, in his *"Inscription for Wang Chien-Nan"* (王征南傳) in the *"Collection of Nan Lei"* (南雷文集), Huang Tsung-Hsi (黃宗羲) (1610-1695),[2] a most famous historian and thinker in Chinese philosophy of the early Ch'ing Dynasty (1644-1911) made the remarks that: "Shao-Lin is famous for courageous acts in the world because of its boxing system, the techniques of which are focused mainly on the attacking of the opponent. Hence, people can always take the advantage of defeating him. Besides, there is the so-called 'internal or Esoteric system,' the techniques of which are to overcome the opponent by neutralizing his

[1] Basing on the official record of the Ming Dynasty (1368-1643), William C.C. Hu tries to establish the historicity of Chang San-feng from 1391-1459. See *the Origin of Tai Chi Ch'uan*, Part I. Black Belt, Vol. 2, No. 5 (Sept. Oct. 1964).

[2] "Huang Tsung-Hsi Chuan" [*Ch'ing History*, "Biography of Huang Tsung Hsi".]

dynamic force through the power of tranquility in an instantaneous way. In contrast to the internal system, hence, the Shao-Lin has been named as the 'Exoteric system' (Wai Chia Ch'uan 外家拳). The source, on the main, can be traced to Chang San-Feng of the Sung Dynasty (960-1279)." Secondly, based upon the above *Inscription,* a biography of Chang Sung-Chi (張松溪), that appeared in the *Gazetteers of Ning Po Prefecture* (寧波府志), mentioned the fact that Chang San-Feng of the Sung Dynasty was an alchemist of Wu Tang. Having heard his name, Hui Tsung (徽宗) (c. 1101), an emperor of that dynasty, asked him for an interview, but owing to the difficulty of communication, his aim was unrealized. Thirdly, in the *Brief History of Tai Chi Ch'uan,* edited by Wu Tu-Nan (吳圖南), he says, "Chang San-Feng was born on the 9th day of the 4th moon, in the summer of the year of Ting Wei (丁未), in the era of Ting Tsung (定宗) of the Yuan Dynasty (1280-1368); (i.e., in the 7th year of Li Tsung (理宗) of the Sung Dynasty in A.D. 1247."

In the above records, we are assured that Chang San-Feng apparently lived in the period of Sung. If the last record is reliable, Chang was born at the end of Southern Sung when Yuan was still in its beginning stage. Nowadays, those who are practicing Tai Chi Ch'uan in China, usually consider that date mentioned above as the birthday of their eminent teacher.

From other sources and the evidence of internal criticism, there are many gaps in this story which require a great deal of verification. (for instance, the story that Chang San-Feng lived at the end of the Sung, and what was actually written in his *Biography* mentioned above by Huang Tsung-Hsi.) In the *Biography of Artisians* (方伎傳) of the official history of the Ming Dynasty (1362-1644), it says: "Tai Tso (太祖) (c. 1368), or the first emperor, having heard the name of Chang, sent a delegate, in the 4th year of Hung Wu (洪武) (A.D.

1381) to search for him, but was unable either to find or bring him to court." Furthermore, Lang Ying (郎瑛) in his book entitled. *Chih Shu Lui Kao* (七修類稿) of the Ming Dynasty, has this to say: "The Saint Chang Chun Shih (張君寶) came to pay a visit to the emperor during the third year of Tien Shun (天順) (A.D. 1459). I saw his appearance featuring a long beard and straight hair. A title of honor had been bestowed upon him by the emperor (Ying Tsung 英宗) as "The true spiritual man who has attained the Tao". Apparently, what has appeared in the two official historical records of the Ming Dynasty is different from what has been said by Huang Tsung Hsi. It seems that the time gap between the third year of Tien Shun and the 14th year of Hung Wu is 78 years, and, since the downfall of Sung in A.D. 1279, up to the 4th year of Hung Wu, there is a span of 130 years or more. If Huang Tsung Hsi's theory is correct, Chang San-Feng would have lived more than 200 years, for the Yuan Dynasty (1260-1368), following the Sung, has a history of 108 years. Physically speaking, this might be an absurdity. Besides, in spite of his alleged birth date at the Sung Dynasty, we find no evidence to support this theory in the official records of the Sung and Yuan or in the memoirs of the Literati of the two dynasties. Hence, it is believed that he must have been a man who lived in the beginning part of Ming.

But, in the *Biography of Artisans* in the Ming history, the record is as follows: "It is alleged that San-Feng is a man of the period of the Chin Dynasty (金) (1115-1234). During the earlier part of Yuan, he studied the Tao at the Tai Ching (太清) Palace of the Lu District under the same teacher with Liu Ping-Chung. However, all this cannot be verified." With what we know from fragmentary sources, his life, with careful reconstruction, would amount to the following description:

Chang San-Feng, a native of I Chow (懿州) at Liao-Tung (遼東), was styled "Ch'uan I (全一), alias Chun Shih (君實), although San-Feng is a name by which he is generally known. He devoted himself to Confucianism when he was only twelve. In the first year of Chung Tung (中統) (c. 1260), he was selected in examination as "Mao Ts'ai" (茂才) with honors. When visiting Yenching (Peking) in the summer of Chia-Tze (甲子). he became famous for his literary talent and was appointed as the District Magistrate of Chung Shan (中山). In his leisure time, he often visited K'o Hung Mountain (葛洪), the headquarters of the Taoists, and became deeply interested in the alchemy of the Taoists. As time went by, he built a cottage in the mountain of Wu Tang, where he concentrated his mind on the study of Tao, and finally attained the supreme achievement of creating the art known as Tai Chi Ch'uan. No doubt, he was a man of high character and had in his ability the gift of cultivating the creative potentialities in man.

In order to understand how he came to create this system of art for the conditioning of the body and mind, we ought to know his relationship with the art of Shao-Lin. Shao-Lin was the most famous Buddhistic Monastary built in the era of Taiho (太和) in the Later Wei Dynasty (後魏) (c. 386-534) in the T'ang Fung District, North China. In the period of Liang (梁) (A.D. 502-556) Buddhidarma, known as Ta-Mo, came to China in A.D. 527 from India. By emphasizing meditation (Ch'an or Zen), he was against book-learning, and with a view to helping the monks, who usually sat meditating for hours and days, to learn how to exercise properly and constantly and how to attain physical fitness, he wrote the three famous classics, namely *The Change of Sinews* (易筋經), *The Marrow-Washing* (洗髓經), and *The Eighteen Lo Han Shou* (十八羅漢手), from which arose the famous system of the Shao-Lin. This is usually considered the orthodoxy of Chinese martial art. As tradition has it, after spending ten years in the monastery, Chang San-Feng mastered all the techniques such as "Dragon Ch'uan", "Tiger Ch'uan", "Leopard Ch'uan", "Snake Ch'uan" and "Stork Ch'uan". Huang Pei-Chia (黃百家), the son of Huang Tsung-Hsi, in his book. *The Techniques of the Esoteric School* (內家拳法), has this to say: "With the introduction of Shao-Lin, the techniques of the 'Exoteric School' (外家) in pugilism have attained their climax, Chang San-Feng, with his proficient knowledge of this school, having achieved a revolutionary reconstitution of it — the result is the 'Esoteric School of Pugilism'."

The origin of the two names attributed to these two schools is not a matter of semantics, but a fact deduced from practice. As a matter of fact, the school of Shao-Lin focused on the training of the sinews and bones in the external part of the body, but Chang, on the other hand, in addition to what had been developed by the Shao-Lin, turned his attention to the art of inhalation and exhalation and the development of "intrinsic energy" (內勁), the awakening of the "recoiled energy" (Kundalini), as the Yogi would say. Besides, he received the credit for being the first one who accepted and incorporated into this school the "techniques of Acupuncture" (attacking vital points in the channels of the body), which he learned from Fung Yuan-Yi (馮元一), a Taoist. Hence, the name "Esoteric school" (Nei Chia). It is even claimed by some experts in the art that it is possible that the Shao-Lin is called the Exoteric school because of the fact that the monks who practiced it generally lived in the monastery following the transcendental teachings of Buddhism instead of living with the family. The system of Chang San-Feng is different from the Shao-Lin in principles and techniques. As a Confucianist-Taoist, what he did emphasize is the breathing system which

had been practiced in China increasingly since the days of Chuangtze
（莊子）　(C. 369-C. 286 B.C.), the greatest of the early Taoists
after Lao-Tzu.

(C)　Third Stage

The history of the transmission of Tai Chi Ch'uan after Chang
is the thrilling story of modern China's upward climb to civilization.
The search is so sincere, the need so great, and the discovery so important that nothing in the martial art history is more vital than this
historical quest.　But to reconstruct what had happened and to relate
how the art of Chang was transmitted to the contemporary world, is
by no means easy.　As legend has it, hundreds of years after the
death of Chang, his art was transmitted to Shensi Province （陝西）
where Wang Tsung （王宗）, was popularly known as the great master.[1]
Chen Chow-Tung （陳州同） of Wen Chow （温州） learned the art
from him.　Thereafter, Tai Chi Ch'uan became a very popular form
of pugilism in Chekiang Province（浙江）.　Based on what was said
by Huang Tsung-Hsi, he in the *Inscription* mentioned above, had
recorded that during the period of Shen Tsung （神宗） of the Ming
Dynasty (A.D. 1573-1620), Chang Sung Chi （張松溪） was considered a great master of this art.　And according to the *Gazetteers of
Ning-Po Prefecture* （寧波府志） — in the Biography of Chang Sung
Chi — we are assured that he learned this art from Sun, the Thirteenth
Elder （孫十三老）.　Among some of the famous disciples of Chang
Sung Chi, one was Yeh Chi-Mei （葉繼美）, who again had his tech-

[1] With regard to the lives of Chang San-fang, Wang Tsung or Wang
Tsung Yueh, see the latter part of this chapter, and particulary the Epiloque
written in Chinese that appears as an Appendix of this book.

niques transmitted to Wang Chêng-Nan (王征南), who was the teacher of Huang Pei-Chia (黃百家). Paying great respect to his eminent teacher for his outstanding achievements, Huang Pei-Chia wrote a book entitled *"The Techniques of the Esoteric School"* which is the most important reference book on the martial art history of China.

Every important culture develops characteristics which give it a continuity and a significance of its own. But, the southern school of Tai Chi Ch'uan, as represented by Huang Pai-Chia and, later, by Kan Fung-Chi (甘鳳池), actually had no successor. Until recently, many of our historians took it for granted that the techniques described by Huang Pai-Chia are virtually the same as those we know from the prevailing Yang system in Tai Chi Ch'uan. No one questions the differences between the two. But, as a matter of fact, the northern school, as represented by the Yang clan (楊家), originated by Yang Lu-Ch'an (1799-1872) of Peking, learned their art from Chen Chang-Hsing (陳長興) (1771-1853) of Chen Chia Kou (陳家溝) in Honan Province. Many teachers believe the art of the Chen clan was taught by Chiang Fa (蔣發) through Wang Tsung Yueh (王宗岳). Hence, many historians of great ability have interpreted the historical continuity of Tai Chi Ch'uan since Chang San-Feng at this level; and most of the best books on the history of this art have been written from this point of view.

Looking back over the past, one cannot but wonder at the many years it took for the various modes of thinking which developed among different writers in isolation, to raise the question of the validity of the creation of the present prevailing systems of Tai Chi Ch'uan — including the Tai Chi Ch'uan of the Chen clan (陳氏), Yang Clan (楊氏), and the Wu clan (吳氏) — by Chang San-Feng. Four hundred years have elapsed since Huang Pei-Chia wrote a first description of the techniques of Tai Chi Ch'uan in modern times, yet scholars still consider it worthwhile to study and compare the techniques of the southern and the northern schools.

Today the picture is somewhat changed. In the last thirty years, many writers have displayed some initiative in affirming that the prevailing system of Tai Chi Ch'uan is a product of the Chen clan in Chen Chia Kou, at the Wen District of Honan Province (河南), the originator being Chen Wang-Ting (陳王庭) living at the end of the Ming and the beginning of the Ch'ing Dynasty. This was first mentioned by Sun Fu-Chuan (孫福全) in his book entitled, *The Study of Pa Kua Techniques* (八卦拳學), although this theory was disputed by Li Yik-She (1832-1892) (李亦畬) in his *Introduction to Tai Chi Ch'uan* (太極拳小序), and Chuang Shen (莊申) in an article entitled *"The Ancient Exercise Movements in China,"* (中國古代運動談), in which the author declared that nothing regarding the original source of the present Tai Chi Ch'uan could ever be known.[5]

Being an expert in the history of Chinese martial art, and having studied the origin of the development of Tai Chi Ch'uan for more than twenty years, T'ang Hao (唐豪) has recently (January, 1932) visited and made a survey on the situation at Chen Chia Kou, which as we know, is the earliest site for the spreading of the present system of the art. As a result of his field survey, he says:

"According to the traditional story, Tai Chi Ch'uan was first created by Chang San-Feng in the latter part of the north Sung Dynasty (960-1279). Some books give the dates as the end of the Yuan Dynasty (1280-1368) or even the earliest part of the Ming Dynasty 1368-1644). This is, indeed, exaggeration. Based upon the results of my own field survey at Chen Chia Kou,

---

[5] Cf. *The Continent Magazine*, No. 3, Vol. 13, Taipei, Taiwan, China.

it has been discovered that a large part of its postures in the art were virtually adopted from the *Ch'uan Ching, a "Classic in Pugilism"* (拳經) written by Ch'i Che-Kwong (戚繼光) (1528-1587). The compilation of the book was based upon the methods of pugilism popular in the same region. It is, therefore, safe to conclude that Tai Chi Ch'uan actually had its source in the masses, and is also the synthetic result of a continuous development."[6]

In fact, as the story goes, during the last years of the emperor Ch'ung Ching (崇禎) (c. 1628) of the Ming, intellectuals were encouraged to pursue the study of military subjects. Among these intellectuals was Chen Wang-Ting (陳王庭) (c. 1597-1664) of Chen Chia Kou, who was well-versed in both literary and military arts and had created the Tai Chi Ch'uan, in which the techniques of breathing were emphasized. From this we know what the Chen clan had to offer in the Ch'ing periods, had powerfully molded the thinking and techniques of Tai Chi Ch'uan in modern China. With the emergence of Yang Lu Ch'an (楊露禪) (1799-1872), there appeared the famous Yang School of Tai Chi Ch'uan in Peking.[7]

Yang Lu-Ch'an (real name, Fu-K'uei) was a native of Hopei. As a young man he became greatly intrigued by this art called Tai Chi Ch'uan. Finally he went to Chen Chia Kou and studied it under Chen Chang-hsing, who was so overwhelmed by his remarkable ability that he kept nothing that was secret from him. After many years of study, Yang began to study the basic concepts and philosophy of Tai

6 T'ang Ho, *T'ai Chi Ch'uan and the Pugilism of the Esoteric School* (太極拳與內家拳) p. 30. (in Chinese).

7 Chen Chin's (Ping-San) "The *Pictorical Explanation of the Chan Clan's T'ai Chi Ch'uan*," a secret ancient text preserved at Chen Chia Kou, Honan, published by the Truth, Goodness and Beauty Publishing Co., at Taipei, Taiwan in 1954, has nothing to say about Chang San-Feng, whom we usually consider as the originator of this art. This is significant indeed!

Chi Ch'uan and went back probably to the original concepts of Chang San-feng and Wang Chung-Yueh.8

While teaching in Peking, Yang was popularly calledd "Yang Wu-ti" or "Yang, the Unsurpassed." By combining the early concepts of self-defense and the later concept of therapeutic exercise, Yang started a new school which was named after him, the Yang-P'ai or the Yang School.9

Yang Lu-Ch'an had three sons. Yang Chi, the first son, died in early youth. Upon the death of Yang Lu-Ch'an, Yang Pan-hou, the second one, was left to carry on the tradition with his brother Yang Chien, who is most popularly known as Yang Chien-hu, the "Mister Number Three." Chao-Ch'ing, the third son of Chien-hu, was styled Ch'eng-fu, spent much of his time perfecting the movements after the death of his eminent father. It was Wu Chien Ch'uan (1870-

8 A most critical study of the history of Tai Chi Ch'uan has been written by Hsu Chen (徐震). In his work, *Tai Chi Ch'uan Kou Hsin Luk,* first printed in 1936, reprinted by the Unicorn Press, Hongkong, 1965, he advanced the theory that it was Yang who first attributed the origin of this art to Chang San-feng on the one hand and believed that Chen Wang-ting learned this art from Wang Tsung-yueh. But according to the latest research, Wang lived in the reign of Chien-lung (1736-95) of the Ch'ing Dynasty, while Chen apparently lived a hundred years before him at the end of Ming and the beginning of Ch'ing (see Koo Liu-Ching, "How to Simplify Tai Chi Ch'uan", (in Chinese) Shanghai. 1963, p. 8). However, several treatises and works on Tai Chi Ch'uan are attributed to Wang although there is no definite proof of his authorship. See Appendices in this book. Wang Tsung-yueh has often been referred to as Wang Tsung, who is considered as the greatest theoretical authority on this art.

9. Originally, Tai Chi Ch'uan was intended to be an art of self defense. With the invention of modern weapons about 100 years ago, the Yang people began to emphasize Tai Chi Ch'uan as an art of rejuvenation and health. See Koo Liu Ching, op. cit. p. 8. For more details of the history of the Yang School, see William C. C. Hu, "Yang Lu-ch'an and the Emergence of the Yang School", Black Belt, January 1965.

1942) (吳鑑泉), who was dissatisfied with the instruction he had received from Yang Pan-hou that he started a new school styled after himself, called the Wu-p'ai or the Wu School. With improvement and revision, Sun Lu-tang (孫祿堂), (1861-1932), who learned the art from Hoa Wei-chen (1849-1920), also started an independent style known as the Sun-Pai, or Sun School.10 It may also be added that Tung Ying Chieh (董英傑), the famous pupil of Yang Cheng-fu, has also recently published his own creation known as Tung Pai — Tai Chi K'uai Ch'uan." However, it is not supposed to take the place of the Yang version of this art, but is a more advanced form for the benefit of those who have learned Tai Chi Ch'uan at least three years.11

As far as the postures are concerned, fresh possibilities can be

10 According to Chi Ching-chih. Chen Chang-hsing first got the secrets of Tai Chi Ch'uan from Wang Tsung-yueh. "The same form of exercise was taught to Yang Lu-chan by Chen. Yang taught his two sons Pan-hou and Chien-hou this art, and Chien-hou in turn taught his sons Shao-hou and Cheng-fu and some disciples. It is known as the Yang school of Tai Chi Ch'uan.

Wu Ju-jang got his instruction from Yang Lu-chan and started the Wu school. Li Chia-ju learned the exercise of Wu school and started the Li school. Hao Wei-chen learned the exercise of Li School and started the Hao school. Sun Lu-t'ang learned the exercise of Hao school and started the Sun school. Thus the art of Tai Chi Ch'uan has been handled down to the present from generation to generation. The schools generally known include the Hao school of Hopei, the Chen school of Honan, and the Yang school of Hopei, and each has its special merits. However, there are more people who have learned the Yang school of Tai Chi Ch'uan. In fact, this exercise was handed down by Yang Lu-chan. Thus we can say that the development of Tai Chi Ch'uan and the popularizing of its practice in society are the meritorious works of Wang Tsung-yueh and Yang Lu-chan." (Chi Ching-chih, "The Theory and Practice of Tai Chi Ch'uan," West & East, Vol. XI, No. 1, Taipei, Taiwan, January, 1966.)

11 See Tung Ying Chieh, Tai Chi Ch'uan Sai-i. Published by Ying Chieh Tai Chi Institute, Hong Kong, 5th ed. 1965.

explored or advanced in the future. But judging from the standpoint of principles, after a continuity of tradition several centuries long, they "had reached a zenith when the art was handed down to Yang Lu-Ch'an by Chen Chang-hsing. As Tai Chi Ch'uan was philosophically sound, practically speaking, no further change was necessary. Therefore, any change in philosophical concepts would only create a decline of basic principles and corrupt the integrity of this art into more schools of individual styles or caprices."12

This is a preliminary synthesis of what we know to be the origins and historical development of Tai Chi Ch'uan. Other interpretations, of course, can be worked out with further explorations.13 For the purpose of clarification, the tentative scheme of its development may be presented as follows:

Yang School of Tai Chi Ch'uan and its Transmission in Modern China — A Systematic Chart —

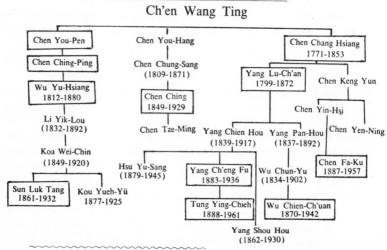

12 William C. C. Hu, op. cit. p. 34.

13 For further research on the historicity of Chang San-feng, please see the Epiloque in Chinese.

NOTES:

(1)   Chen Wang-Ting (c. 1597-1664), the 9th generation of the Chen Pu clan, locating in the Chen Chia-Kou, Honan Province, is the originator of the Chen style of Tai Chi Ch'uan.   During 1618-1621, he was a high official in the Ming Dynasty.   Chen Chang-Hsiang, the 14th generation of the Chen clan, had this art transmitted to Yang Lu-Ch'an, the founder of the Yang School.

(2)   The major representatives of the different schools or sects are indicated with the symbols thus: ┌──────────┐

(3)   Yang Ch'eng-fu, the grandson of Yang Lu-Ch'an, is the most eminent figure who held the responsibility of introducing this art all over China in the twenties and the thirties.   He had many famous pupils, among them are Tung Ying-chieh (1889-1962), Chen Wei-ming, Cheng Man-Ch'ing (1900-1975), Choy Hok-Peng (1886-1957), Wu Hui-Chun (-1937) and hundreds of others.   For a fuller list of the pupils of Yang Ch'eng-fu, see his book "The Application Method of Tai Chi Ch'uan" (in Chinese), Taipei, 1964, which was edited by Tung Ying Chieh, the teacher of the present author.   Tung's son Tung Fu-ling who has taught this art in Hong Kong, Macau and Singapore, is now teaching in Hawaii.

(4)   Sophia Delza, teacher of this art at The Tai Chi Ch'uan Club of the United Nations, New York, is a pupil of Ma Yueh-liang, son-in-law of Wu Chien-Ch'uan, the founder of the Wu School.

(5)   Kwok Ling-Yin (1895-   ), who has a school in San Francisco, is a pupil of Wang Chiao-yu of Peking, who learned the art from Yang Pan-hou.

(6)   *It may be added* Chen Wei-ming's (陳微明) chief disciple is Liang Ching Yu (梁勁予) teaching in Hong Kong since 1950.

CHAPTER III

TAI CHI CH'UAN AND I CHING,

OR THE BOOK OF CHANGES*

I. Introductory Remarks

The Chinese system of exercise has a long history dating back to the legendary emperor, Fu Hsi, China's first philosopher-king (the forty-sixth century B. C.), who was also the inventor of the Eight Trigrams (Pa Kua). It is also alleged that he ordered Yin Tang to perform the Grand Dance for the enhancement of the limbs and the curing of the diseases of the people. If this story is acceptable, the earliest system was not really an art of boxing but a therapeutic exercise. However, students in the later periods emphasized mainly the techniques, without paying any attention to the principles under-lying them. With the creation of the Shao Lin system of boxing by the Indian Bodhidharma (Ta-Mo) (菩提達摩), who died c. A.D. 475, there sprang up numerous schools known as Kung-fu, which still emphasize their interest in the self-defense aspects of the art, while academicians and philosophers, as a rule, shunned any associa-tion with them. It was not until Chang San-feng, (張三丰) (c. 1391-1459), the Confucian-Taoist scholar and alleged originator of Tai Chi Ch'uan, began to base his principles and conceptions of his famous system on the I Ching, or the Book of Changes, that the Nia Chia

* Reprinted from Chinese Culture, Volume X, Number 1, March 1969.

（內家） esoteric style of exercise, which is supposed to have differentiated itself from the Wai Chia (or exoteric style 外家), was finally established.

Why this type of exercise is called Tai Chi Ch'uan is the question that all historians and philosophers ask. According to Chen Hsing, （陳興）, the famous theoretician of the Chen school of Tai Chi Ch'uan in the contemporary era, in his illustrated treatise on Tai Chi Ch'uan, there is the following explanation: "In the 7th year of Hung Wu of the Ming Dynasty (1368-1644), by first ancestor by the name of Po (卜) taught his children in his leisure of farming and study, the method of expediting digestion through the idea of having the conjugate principles of Yin (陰) and Yang (陽) circulating all over in the human body. Since the idea is based upon the principle of Tai Chi or the Grand Ultimate (太極) (of I Ching), it is named Tai Chi Ch'uan."[1] Whether this name was originated by Chang San-feng or Chen Po is difficult to determine. What is certainly true is that the principles, and some of the main concepts, of this exercise have been derived from the *I Ching*. According to Chen Wei-ming (陳微明), an eminent pupil of Yang Cheng-fu (楊澄甫), "Tai Chi is originally circular in shape, and it is the combined entity of the Yin and Yang principles. Tai Chi Ch'uan seeks complete satisfaction in every place and its movements are divided into activating and conserving and insubstantial and substantial, so it is named Tai Chi." In discussing Tai Chi Ch'uan, Hu Pu-an (胡樸安) said: It is said in the Hsi Tzu (Appendix) (繫辭) of the *I Ching*: "There is behind the phenomenon of change the changeless absolute, or the Grand Ultimate (Tai Chi). This generates the two primary forces

---

[1] Chi Kiang-tao, Tai Chi Ch'uan, the *Physical Exercise for Maintaining Health and Preventing Sickness* (3), West and East, Vol. X. No. 10, October, 1965, p. 9.

which generate the four images. The four images generate the eight trigrams." In other words, the four images and eight trigrams are all indirectly generated from the Grand Ultimate.[2]

In addition to the above sources, Chi Kiang-tao (綦江濤) also pointed out: "This form of exercise is named Tai Chi Ch'uan because all its movements are in accordance with the idea of Tai Chi, that is, the movements from the central point (abdomen)." Evidently influenced by the Sung philosophers (the Neo-Confucianists), Wang Tsung-yueh (王宗岳) (in his Theory of Tai Chi Ch'uan) said: "Tai Chi is generated from Wu Chi (無極) or the Ultimate Nothingness. It is the moving power of dynamic and static states, and the source of the Yin and Yang principles. When they are in motion they separate, and when they remain static, they combine." With the above postulations, Chi Kiang-tao concludes: "We can understand that, the reason why the exercise is named Tai Chi Ch'uan, is because all its movements are in the pattern of the circular Tai Chi Diagram, and they are expressed with curves emphasizing the principles of Yin and Yang, insubstantial and substantial motions, opening and closing mood, and dynamic and static state."[3]

Although the historicity of the origin of the name Tai Chi Ch'uan cannot be established with certainty, the basic principles of this exercise are, no doubt, derived from I Ching. From the point of view of movements and postures, there are not great differences between this exercise and those of the other systems. However, it must be pointed out that this particular exercise, with its emphasis on spiritual value and the concern of morality itself, is not to be compared with

[2] ob. cit., p. 10.
[3] Chi Kiang-tao, ob. cit., p. 10.

those systems emphasizing only the training of sinews and muscles.4 Exercise, in all its branches, can bring the greatest benefit to mankind only if man recognizes a unifying principle for its creative ingenuity. Indeed, the highest dimension of human exercise concerns itself with the world view and moral and spiritual purposes of life. It is, in the true sense of the term, a science of living, and gives human existence a moral "raison d'etre". Above all, only when the Chinese system of exercise is integrated with a broad world view and a high moral purpose, as well as with spiritual value, can exercise become a blessing to man. Thus, with the emergence of Tai Chi Ch'uan, by basing itself on the cosmic and ethical principles of *I Ching,* the various exercise systems in China had their matrix.

II. The Nature and Origins of the *I Ching*

As a new "Approach to the *Book of Changes,* John Blofeld puts it quite well in this manner:

"It was not until fairly recently that Asian scholars began to interest themselves widely in the material sciences which-for better and for worse-have done so much to transform human life, especially in the West. Formerly, Asia's thinkers were chiefly occupied with the search for life's meaning (or, at any rate, man's true goal) and for ways of utilizing that vital knowledge for self-cultivation and self-conquest. One of the most valuable, though far from the most coherent, of the aids to understanding life's

---

4 See William C. C. Hu, *What Does 'Kung Fu' Mean?* Black Belt, January 1965, and *The Tiger, the Dragon and the Crane,* in the same issue.

rhythmic processes, with a view to bringing man back into harmony with them, is the Chinese Book of Changes."[5]

In fact, in the West, since Galileo, the father of the scientific method (who lived about four hundred years ago), western scientists have been continually searching for the natural laws or positive laws. The highest achievements are, of course, Newton's first, second, and third laws of motion and his law of universal gravitation. The Einstein equation for the relation between matter and energy is $E=MC^2$. The positive law such as this led finally to the understanding of the nature and the split of the atom. But no such law has been discovered in cultural or humanistic sciences. So far as we know, what we have arrived at are: Teleological laws, Statistical Laws, Near-Causal Laws, A Priorisms, and Methodological Presuppositions. Hence in the humanistic side, the West lags far behind what it has achieved in natural science.

As the *I Ching* represents the first struggle of the Chinese mind to discover the mysteries and secrets of the universe, as well as the nature of man and culture, it is a book of unified disciplines, including such studies as cosmology, sociology, culturology, and ethics. In a sense, the *I Ching* is a type of Synthetic Philosophy, the scope of which is similar to that of Herbert Spencer's. An interesting account of how the ancient sages arrived at their conclusions in using the Hexagrams as abstract types to express real facts is that they used formulae of changes in which multification phenomena are stripped of their variety, reduced to unity and harmony. In the Appendix of the Book, we find:

"In days of old when Fu Hsi was ruling over the world, he looked up to observe the phenomena of the planetary bodies in

[5] John Blofeld, *The Book of Change*, E. P. Dutton and Co., N.Y., 1966, p. 23.

the heavens, and gazed down to probe the laws of the myriad things on earth. He examined the markings of birds and beasts, and studied how they were adapted to their habitats. Some ideas he drew from the observations of his own being, while others he took from that of things scattering far and wide over the earth. Thus, he invented the Eight Trigrams, as a means of communicating the virtues of spiritual beings, and of signifying the features of the myriad things." (The Appendix, Part II.)

The above passage signifies the method with which the first sage formed his cosmic view and ethical principle. In The Appendix attributed to Confucius, we also read:

"The *I* (易) dovetails with Heaven and Earth, with the result that it completely interweaves the Tao of Heaven and Earth." (The Appendix, IV.)

"The *I* is a book vast and great, in which everything is completely contained. The Tao of Heaven is in it, the Tao of the earth is in it, and the Tao of man is in it. It combines these three primal powers and doubles them; that is why there are six lines. The six lines are nothing other than the Tao of the three primal powers." (The Appendix, Part II.)

Indeed, the author of the Appendix assumes that it could make "his knowledge comprehensive enough to embrace all things of the universe, and his philosophy useful enough to profit all people of the world." (The Appendix, Part I.)

The *I Ching*, which has been commented and interpreted by hundreds of books of various authors in China during the last 2,000 years, is, no doubt, a very complex and comprehensive system. With regard to the question on the origins of the *I Ching*, Wang Kuo-wei (王國維) (A.D. 1877-1927) wrote: "The text of this work proper—the EXPLANATORY NOTES ON THE HEXAGRAMS (Kua Tzu) and the EXPLANATORY NOTES ON THE DIAGRAMMATICAL LINES (Hsiao Tz'u) was composed in the early Chou dynasty. Its commentaries, THE TEN APPENDICES (Shih I; literally the TEN WINGS), were allegedly written by Confucius, or, at the latest, by his disciples according to his dictation."6 Instead of believing that the *I Ching* owes its remote origin to the Eight Trigrams of Fu Hsi, a modern critic, basing his speculation on anthropology, has advanced the theory that the Eight Trigrams had been drawn by the magicians of the preliterate society, and this magician might be the Magician-priest of the Yin Dynasty (c. 17th century B. C. to c. 11th century B. C.).7

In my own judgment, I would like to suggest that the original idea of *I Ching,* particularly the concept of Γao (also known as Tai Chi) was originated long ago, probably at the Totemic Age of the Paleolithic and Neolithic Periods. Both Confucianism and Taoism started their systems from Tao, which has been enunciated in the *I Ching.* According to this book, one Yin and one Yang is Tao, which was defined by Laotzu as undefinable-the beginning of the beginnings and it is the law of the universe. This conception of Tao is very similar to that of "Mana", or "Orenda", among the primitive peoples. The original idea was later further developed by Fu Hsi, King Wen and the Duke of Chou, both of the latter lived in the 12th century B. C. Some centuries later, it was brought to completion by Confucius

6 Wang Kuo-wei (王國維), *New Evidence of Ancient History,* Chap. 1, the Lai Hsun Ko Press, Peiping, 1935. Quoted from Chang Chi-yun (張其昀), THE BOOK OF CHANGES (*I Ching*), A Philosophical Master-piece Mirroring the Zeit-Geist of the Western Chou Dynasty, Chinese Culture, Vol. 4, No. 4, October 1965, pp. 12-13.

7 Ling Ting-an, *Approaching the Shih-li Shueh of the I from the View-point of Action Theory,* The Continent Magazine, Vol. XXXII, No. 1, January 15, 1966.

or his disciples who made it into an all-embracing philosophy, containing all the subtle principles of "sageliness inside and kingliness outside."[8]

III. The Cosmic Law of *I Ching*

The fundamental cosmic law of *I Ching* has been described in the Kua (trigrams) and the Hsio (lines). The Kua and Hsio represent the Symbols of *I* (Changes), which are actually devoid of mysticism. At first sight, they are very complex and difficult as well as not easy to understand. However, with the Appendices and Commentaries attributed to Confucius (551-479 B.C.), we encounter not much hardship in elucidating the laws and principles therein. In the Appendices, we read:

"One Yin and one Yang constitute what is the Tao." (The Appendix, I.)

"Therefore, there is in the *Changes,* the Tai Chi (the Great Ultimate or the Great Primal Beginnings). This generates the two primary forces. The two primary forces generate the four images. The four images generate the eight trigrams." (The Appendix, II.)

"The eight trigrams are arranged according to completeness. Thus the images are contained in them. Thereupon they are doubled: Thus the lines (hsiao) are contained in them. With the interplay of the firm and soft, the *Changes* are contained in

[8] Wen-shan Huang (黃文山), *The Origins of Chinese Culture, A Study of Totemism,* Extrait des Actes du Congres International des Sciences Anthropoligique et Ethnologiques, Paris 1960, Tome II ler volume).

them." (The Great Appendix, II.)

"The *I* (易) is a book vast and great, in which everything is completely contained. The Tao of heaven is in it, the Tao of the earth is in it, and the Tao of man is in it. It combines these three primal powers and doubles them: that is why there are six lines. The six lines are nothing other than the Tao of the three primal powers." (The Appendix, II.)

Judging from the above statements, it is manifestably true that the fundamental law of all the phenomena of the universe is Tai Chi, or Tao, which generates the two cosmic forces.9 The *I*, indeed, conceives that nothing that exists, either animate or inanimate, does so, except by virtue of ceaseless interplay of these two primray forces. Yin and Yang, Heaven and Earth, Matter and Energy are considered as essentially One, or as two co-existent poles of one indivisible whole. Thus, Wang Pi (王弼) (A. D. 226-249), who lived for cnly twenty-four years, in his *Chou I Luen Liue* (周易論畧), had developed the most brilliant metaphysical interpretation of the *I Ching* in the last 1,700 years. He treated comprehensively the essence of a given hexagram, and explained the 'dominant factor' from which it flows. He said:

"Motion cannot control motion. That which controls the motion of the world is absolutely one."10

The One is Tai Chi or Tao which is the Fundamental Law or the First Principle of the universe.

9 Liu Po-ming (劉百閔) in his famous book, *I Shih Li Shueh Hsu Luen* (*An Introduction to the "Eventology" of I*), considers T'ai Chi as the First Fundamental Principle of the Book of Changes, (in Chinese, published in Hongkong, 1964, pp. 45-117).

10 Apparently what he had in mind was the immanent Tao. This led to the interpretation of the *I Ching* basing on the system of Lao Tzu (老子) and Chuang Tzu (莊子).

The Yin and Yang, generated from Tai Chi or Tao, are no longer considered as mysticism.11   They are negative and positive forces. With the advent of atomic science, we know there is the "atomic sun", the atomic nucleus, the tiny point in which all the matter and weight of the atom are concentrated, as well as its atomic energy and the positive charge of electricity, which holds the negative electrons in their orbits.   Hence the Yin-Yang doctrine is sometimes considered as the Yin-Yang science.

According to the Yin and Yang School, the activity or movement of phenomena takes the form of cycles or circular.   "But the far more important aspect of the interaction of Yin and Yang is its progressive direction leading to the development of society, morality and civilization.   The Yin and Yang give rise to the four forms. These refer to major and minor Yin and Yang.   But the word of form (hsiang 象) also connotes symbols, patterns and ideas.   This means that out of the interaction of the two cosmic forces, all patterns, ideas, systems, and culture are evolved.   The earlier trigrams are now given an entirely new interpretation.   "The Yin and Yang lines are no longer considered elements of good and evil fortune, but cosmic forces. When the Eight Trigrams, each containing three lines, multiply themselves to become 64 hexagrams, they are taken to represent all possible forms of change, situations, possibilities, and institutions.   Thus a complex civilization is conceived of as a process of systematic and progressive development which can be traced to its simple beginning. The cosmology may be naive and crude, but the philosophical spirit is clear.   Instead of a universe controlled by spiritual beings whose pleasures can only be discovered through divination, we have natural operation of forces, or as one is tempted to say natural law.   It is

11 Chart 1. Diagram of T'ai Chi and Eight Trigrams.

interesting that things are even assigned numbers in an attempt to reduce existence to the simplest formula or laws."[12]   Furthermore, we may say the First Principle or law (Tao) of the *I* is "Change". Hence:

> "The Eight Trigrams are established for observing cosmic changes in the operation of the Principles of the Positive Force (Yang) and the Negative Force (Yin)." (Shuo Kua).

In the interpretation of this law or principle, The Great Appendix goes on to say: "The *Book of Change* is a work which we cannot keep aloof from.   Its principle consists in constant change, and in restless motion." (The Great Appendix, Part II.)   It also adds:

> "This principle roams circuitously about the six diagrammatical lines of every hexagram, now in the upper line, now in the lower, ever moving from one place to another.   It reveals itself alternatively in the positive force and the negative force. And yet, it cannot be taken as a rule with a fixed course of action. It follows change wherever change is due."

Causation is here represented as "immanent change."   It is not determined by sociological or culturological factors.   Change indeed is the constant interaction of Yin and Yang-the two bipolar powers of Nature, which is never at rest, the mutually sustaining opposition of two forces which are essentially one energy.[13]

We owe a great deal, in this aspect to Nyoiti Sakurazawa, who has formed the UNIQUE LAW, stating that the universe represents the oscillation of the two activities, powers or forces — Yin and Yang

---

[12] Wing-tsit Chan, *A Source Book in Chinese Philosophy*, Princeton University Press, 1963, pp. 262-263.

[13] See Eiel, *Fragmental Studies of Chinese Philosophy*, quoted by Joseph Needham, *Science and Civilization in China*, Cambridge University Press, Vol. II. pp. 232.

— and their vicissitudes. The law can be stated as follows:

1. That which produces and composes the universe is universe-ether, or inner nature or energy. (Cunyata in Sanskrit, Chi (氣) in Chinese).

2. Energy polarises: one pole becomes charged with Yang force, the other with Yin force.

3. Force Yang (constrictive, from whence heat, weight, centripetal) and force Yin (dilating, from whence cold), are opposites.

4. Beings and phenomena occuring in the universe are multiple and complex aggregate of energy substance charged with Yin and Yang forces in all proportions.

5. Beings and phenomena are diverse dynamic equilibra. Nothing in the universe is stable or finished, all is unceasing motion, because polarisation, the source of beings, is without beginning and without end.

6. Yin force and Yang force attract one another.

7. Nothing is wholly Yin nor wholly Yang. Yin and Yang are characterized only relatively: all is Yin and Yang aggregate.

8. Nothing is neutral. Polarisation is ceaseless and everywhere.

9. The force of attraction between two beings is a function of difference between their charges of opposite forces.

10. Like force repels one another. The repulsion between two beings of the same force is the greater the closer they are.

11. Yin produces Yang, Yang produces Yin.

12. All beings are charged: Yang exteriorly, Yin interiorly.

Besides, the cosmic view of *I Ching* is monistic, judging from its Fundamental Principle of Tai Chi (or Tao). At the same time we now know that the dualistic conception of the universe, as set forth in the works of Aristotle, Descartes and Newton, and on which the structure of the experimental science is based, was unknown to *I Ching*. While dualism sees the physical and the metaphysical as two separate entities, the Chinese view Yin and Yang as eternally complimentary and eternally changing. The dualistic philosophy reigned supreme in Western thought dominating the development of science. But with the advent of atomic physics, findings on demonstrable experiment were seen to negate the dualistic theory and the trend of modern thought then has led back towards th monistic theory of *I Ching* and the conception of the Taoists.14

14 Besides what we have pointed out on the Taoist philosophy expounded by Laotzu, the theory of Chuang Tzu, his main follower, "is an impressive testimony to the fascination of this ancient Chinese philosophy of living in accordance with the Tao (the course of nature, as one sails or tacks, with the course of the wind." "There is much in common between Chuang tzu's and Teilhard de Chardin's vision of the universe as an organic whole. Joseph Needham has also pointed out parallels between Taoist thought and the philosophy of Alfred Whitehead, as well as the "field" theories of nature in modern physics and biology. For the importance of Taoist thought to our technological civilization is twofold. On the one hand, it is an organic and relativistic view of nature far more consistent with 20th century science than Newton's essentially mechanical model of the universe as in interaction of atomic "billiard balls". Chuang Tzu's world is not composed of causal chains in which present events are helpless puppets of past events. In Taoism, all events-past, present and future-are mutually related; they "arise together" like back and front or buying and selling. "Separate" events are therefore no more than narrow and partial glimpses of that one and eternal event which is the Tao-the total organic pattern of the universe.

"On the other hand, man himself-as one of these 'mutually arising' events-is not seen as an isolated being to whom the rest of nature is alien and hostile. The universe 'peoples' as an apple-tree 'apples', so that human organisms are symptoms of the organism of the world. Thus a Taoist technology tendency — and Chuang Tzu has many passages on the right and wrong use of skills. — would not be a "conquest" of nature but a highly sensitive and intelligent "going with the grain" of nature processes." (Alan Watts, *The World of Spirit, a Review on the Way of Chuang Tzu,* by Thomas Merton, New York, New Direction, New York Times Sunday Book Review, April 12. 1966).

Indeed, the philosophy of Tai Chi and the theory of Yin-Yang have had a great deal of impact upon the development of Chinese culture, including science, art and medicine. As to what has been adopted as the basic principles of Tai Chi Ch'uan, as an exercise of the Confucian-Taoist type, these will be considered in more detail in the last section of the present chapter.

IV. The Ethical View of *I Ching*

By reading the *I Ching,* we seem to realize that in the universe there is an ever-active, ever-creative Life, and an inexhaustible source of Energy-Life and Energy which are made available to mankind when a fitting stage of development is achieved. It is particularly significant that it has a great reverence for Life. Thus, it says: "The cardinal virtue of the cosmos is Life." (The Great Appendix, Part II.) Based on the concept of Life in *I Ching,* Sun Yat-sen (孫中山) derived his Theory of Life-atom (生元說), in which he pointed out that Life-atom is a "conscious element".15 This "new" hypothesis has been almost completely neglected by scientists for the last four centuries. At the present, Teilhard de Chardin was forced to attribute some degree of mind consciousness even to inorganic matter.16 And Andrew A. Cochran has tried to show that the belief that atoms and the particles of matter are lifeless, while firmly entrenched in modern

15 *The Doctrine of Sun Yat-sen* (Sun Wen Hsueh Shuo) (孫文 學 說) , Chapter 1, included in *The Complete Works of San Yat-sen* (Kuo Fu Ch'uan Shu), p. 3, National War College Press, Taiwan, 1960.

16 Teilhard de Chardin. *The Phenomenon of Man,* Harper and Bros., New York, 1960.

thought, has no supporting evidence; it is a philosophical prejudice that was inherited from classical physics and retained without challenge. The new hypothesis is more consistent with the known facts of science than the present concept of lifeless atoms and fundamental particles.[17]

Because of its reverence for Life in the *I*, we find the seeds of the "naturalistic" line of thought of Taoism and the "humanistic" line of thought of Confucianism going hand in hand. And in the passage of Chapter II of the Shuo Kua (說卦), we realize that the Confucian principles of Jen (仁) (love) and Yi (義) (righteousness) have been brought into harmony with the Taoists' naturalness of Heaven and Earth.[18] Referring to this, the *I Ching* says:

"In ancient times, the sage formulated the Philosophy of Change in accordance with the laws of nature and life. And thus, he held that the basic elements of the Principle of Heaven (T'ien Tao) are Yin and Yang; those of the Principle of the Earth (Ti Tao) are hardness (Kang), and softness (Jou); those of the Principle of Man (Jen Tao) are kindness (Jen) and justice. (The Appendix I.)"

The Ethical Principle-the principle of Love and Righteousness-has thus been set forth in the *I Ching* as it has been set forth by Buddha, Jesus, Motzu, and nowadays by Sorokin and others. The *I Ching* says: "That, which is unfathomable in the movement of the Yin-Yang operations, is the presence of spiritual power." If all of us can have a vision of this spiritual power—the power of "love en-

[17] Andrews A. Cochran, *Mind, Matter, and Quanta, Main Currents in Modern Thought,* March-April, 1966, Vol. 22, No. 4.

[18] See Ch'u Chai (翟楚), *Introduction and Study Guide to I Ching, Book of Changes,* with James Legge's translation of the Yi King, University Books, New York, 1964.

ergy" — we can start the chain reaction to ignite man's love for humanity throughout the world. Indeed. in this catastrophic moment of human history, an increased "production, accumulation, and circulation of love-energy" (Sorokin) in the whole human universe is a necessary condition for the prevention of a new world war.

In summary, the ethical view of Life expressed in *I Ching* is considered by modern scholars to be the basic principle by which the Chinese personality has been molded in the last 2,500 years or more.

V. Tai Chi Ch'uan and the Tai Chi Diagram

From the foregoing, it is clear that Tai Chi Ch'uan derived its main principles from *I Ching,* the Bible of China, and embraced three aspects. Symbolically, it bases its movements on the eight trigrams （八卦）. In Ch'i （氣）(energy), it includes Yin and Yang, hardness and softness. In Li （理）, reason (or principle), it consists of the fundamental law, Tai Chi or Tao and the principles of change and of love and righteousness. Hence, for the mastering of Tai Chi Ch'uan, one has to learn the symbology (structure), then cultivate the Chi, (intrinsic energy),* and gradually one will come to understand the Li or principles.

But the most systematic explanation of cosmogony and the philosophy of life of *I Ching* was carried forward by the Neo-Confucianists in the Sung Dynasty （宋代）(A. D. 960-1279). In order to understand the philosophy of Tai Chi Ch'uan more deeply and thoroughly, we must return to the explanation of Chou Tun-Yi （周敦頤）(A.D. 1017-1073), the first logical philosopher, later known as the master

* Same as "Ching" p. 29.

of Lien-Chi (濂溪).

Neo-Confucianism is the continuation of the idealistic wing of ancient Confucianism, and, especially, of the mystic tendency of Mencius. Fung Yu-Lan (馮友蘭) is right in trying to trace the main sources of Neo-Confucianism to three lines of thought. The first is, of course, Confucianism itself. The second is Buddhism, together with Taoism, via the medium of Ch'anism (Zen) (禪). To the Neo-Confucianist, Ch'anism and Buddhism are synonymous terms, and, in one sense, Neo-Confucianism may be said to be the logical development of Ch'anism. Finally, the third is the Taoist religion, of which the cosmological views of the Yin-Yang School formed an important element. The cosmogony of the Neo-Confucianists is chiefly connected with this line of thought.

Neo-Confucianism formed a genuine system of thought—a homogeneous whole. It did not become clearly formed until the 11th century by Chou Tun-Yi. His main writings are the *Diagram of Tai Chi* (太極圖說) and *Tung Shu* (通書). Long before his time, the Taoists had prepared a number of mystic diagrams as graphic portrayals of the esoteric principles by which they believed a properly initiated individual could attain immortality. Chou is said to have come into possession of the diagram originated by Ho Shang Kun (何尚公) of the T'ang Dynasty (A. D. 618-907), which he thereupon reinterpreted into a diagram of his own by basing his philosophy on certain passages in the Appendices of *I Ching*. His resulting diagram is called "Tai Chi T'u" or "Diagram of the Supreme Ultimate", and his interpretation of it is called the "Tai Chi T'u Shuo or Explanation of the Diagram of the Supreme Ultimate." The result is a synthesis of the philosophical thoughts of Confucianism, Taoism, and Ch'an (Zen) Buddhism — the opening of a new era of the Li Shuh (理學) of the Sung and Ming (A.D. 1368-1644.).

In summary, the content and theory of Tai Chi T'u Shuo consists of the followings:[19]

1. The Tai Chi is absolute; it is the reality of the universe, or the first principle. It is universal, omnipresent and cannot be designated to one thing or one event. Hence, it is also called ultimateless (Wu Chi) (無極) by the Neo-Confucianists.

2. The Tai Chi produces the two forces — movement and quiescence — which produce the Yin and Yang. These two forms are the two attributes of Tai Chi, while movement and quiescence represent the opposite forces of these two attributes. This theory is roughly similar to the reality consisting of two main attributes, viz: thought and extension, as expounded by Spinoza.

3. Through the interaction of Yin and Yang, the five elements or ethers—metal, wood, water, fire and soil—are produced. With these, heaven and earth are organized. Each of the elements, of course, has its own nature.

4. Through the composition of the two Ch'i—Yin and Yang— and the five elements, are produced the myriad of phenomena, in which male and female human beings are included.

5. The human being is the most intelligent of all beings, for he is the crystallization of form and spirit, body and mind. This theory is practically identical with the dualism of Descartes.

6. The sage definitely established human-heartedness, righteousness, mean and correctness as the highest standard of moral behavior. This is the ultimate of man, but quiescence is essential for the establishment of the ultimate. With the deep realization of the Tao (道), the structure and function of

[19] See Chart II: The "Diagram of Supreme Ultimate" (T'ai Chi Tu).

the sage are identical with those of the heaven and earth, sun and moon, the four seasons and spirits. Hence the Teh (德), or morality of the sage, is practically identical with the whole universe.

7. The symbol of heaven is Yin and Yang. The nature of the earth is softness (柔) and hardness (剛). The morality of man is love (仁) and righteousness (義) — with the understanding of the beginning and the end, the sage knows the theory of birth and death. With the establishment of the conception of three cosmic factors (三才) (the Tao of heaven, earth and man), the philosophy of the unity of heaven (nature) and man has been completed. This is the traditional philosophy of organism of China, which is identical with the scientific conception of organism, an element in the formation of the perfected world view in natural science.[20]

In summary, the principles expressed in the diagram may be analyzed in modern terms as follows:

A. *The Monistic Theory of Cosmology*—Tai Chi contains movement and quiescence, which in turn produces Yin and Yang and the five elements as well as the myriad of things and human beings.

B. *The Theory of Materialistic Pluralism*—The heaven and earth and the myriad of things are formed by the five elements.

C. *The Theory of Bodily Dualism*—The human body consists of structure and spirit, in other words, it is constructed out of body and mind.

D. *The Theory of Moral Values*—The highest moral standards are

---

[20] See R. G. H. Sue, *The Tao of Science, an Essay on Western Knowledge and Eastern Wisdom*, The M. I. T. Press, Massachusetts, 1957.

love, righteousness, mean (中), and correctness (equilibrium).
The theory takes quiescence as the ultimate of man.

E. *The Theory of Ideal Personality*—The form and function of
the sage are practically identical with those of the heaven, earth,
sun, moon, four seasons and spirits, that is, the universe.

F. *The Theory of the Unity of Heaven and Man*—The Tao of
heaven, earth, and man is identical.

These are the essential principles expounded in the diagram of
Tai Chi, basing its theories on *I Ching,* or the *Book of Changes.*21

VI.   Tai Chi Ch'uan and Its Association With

The "Diagram of Supreme Ultimates" (Tai Chi Tu) 22

Historically speaking, there are two types of Tai Chi diagrams.
The one, that has two fish in it, was handed down from ancient
times and has no practical value, except that it represents the Yin
and Yang, substantiality and insubstantiality, expansion and contraction, advancement and retreat in "joint-hand operations" (推手). The
Chou's diagram, which embraces all the abstruse principles, is different
because of the fact that it can be used as a base in explaining all the
principles of Tai Chi Ch'uan.   The following tiers are essential:

TIER I: The diagram is divided into five tiers.   The first one
is a

---

21 See, Kant Woo (吳康) *Collection of Essays on Philosophy* (in
Chinese), Vol. I-II, 1961 Commercial Press, Taiwan, pp. 237-256.

22 See Chart 1, the "Diagram of Supreme Ultimate" (T'ai Chi Tu).
For the original Taoist Explanation of the Diagram (from below upwards),
see Wei Tat, An Exposition of the I Ching, Institute of Cultural Studies,
Taipei, 1970, pp. 66-67.

太極圖

THE T'AI CHI T'U

DIAGRAM OF THE SUPREME ULTIMATE

無極而太極

ABSOLUTE AND ULTIMATE REALITY

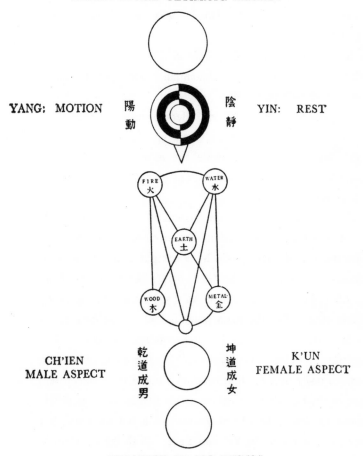

YANG: MOTION　陽　動　　陰　靜　YIN: REST

FIRE 火　　WATER 水

EARTH 土

WOOD 木　　METAL 金

CH'IEN
MALE ASPECT　乾道成男　　坤道成女　K'UN
FEMALE ASPECT

CREATION OF ALL THINGS

萬物化生

Cf "The Tai Chi T'u" and the "Explanation of Tai Chi T'u"
in Wei Tat' An Exposition of the I-Ching pp.62—67,
Institute of Cultural Studies, Taipei, 1970.

circle which is considered as the "ultimateless (無極). Yet the supreme ultimate" (太極). During the performance of the postures, the mind is in a state of quiescence embracing oneness, with the form of emptiness. This is called "ultimateless". All the movements stem from it. This is the mother of the myriads. This is the Tai Chi.

TIER II: In the middle, the circle is divided into two parts, in which the Yin and Yang, substantiality and insubstantiality, occupy half of each part. With movement, there appears Yang; while in quiescence, there is Yin. Hence, the establishment of the two modes. With expansion, there are the K'an (坎) and Li (離) trigrams which comprise the movements of softness with hardness hidden in it. The idea of quiescence is the underlying base of all.

TIER III: The five elements are associated with the five steps in Tai Chi Ch'uan. Everything is produced from the soil (土) or the center (中), which is compared to the idea of consciousness (mind). In the "joint-hand operations" the Peng (棚), Lu (攦), Chi (擠), and An (按), are inter-operating with each other. But the main point is that all the movements should be linked together by the consciousness, or mind. The diagram says: "These five elements (五行) become diffused in harmonious order and the four seasons proceed in their course." Because of the fact that the nature of the five elements is different from each other, the Chi of the seasons is not the same, but they are not external to the Yin and Yang. With the transformation of the position of Yin and Yang, the transformations of time, of movement, and of quiescence are followed, but all these cannot be isolated from the Tai Chi.

TIER IV: Illustrating the man. From the Tao of Chien

(乾), it gives to the male (Yang), and from the Tao of Kun
(坤), it gives to the female (Yin).

TIER V: Illustrating the things (matter). This is to say:
"When the two forms and five elements are consolidated, myriads
of things come into being. The real source is from "ultimateless
which is yet ultimate" (Tai Chi). In Tai Chi Ch'uan, movement and quiescence conform to a principle, and, in spite of all
the variations in technique, for the meeting of the challenges of
adversaries, the source is one. And, according to Chou: "The
sage regulates himself as the highest standard of mankind. In
action, he takes the mean...in living, he takes the correctness
...in doing, he stays with love...in decision, he judges with
righteousness. Movement (動) and quiescence (靜) are performed according to the Tao of Tai Chi. This is the way to
victory."

These are the original principles on which the Tai Chi Ch'uan is
based — spiritually, emotionally and physically.

VII. The General Principles of Tai Chi Ch'uan

With Reference to the *I Ching*

So far, we realize the fact that Tai Chi Ch'uan derives its main
principles from *I Ching,* or *the Book of Changes,* as well as the theory
developed by the Neo-Confucianists. According to tradition, Tai Chi
Ch'uan consists of·Thirteen Postures (Methods) (十三勢), which
again are associated with the Eight Trigrams (八卦) and the Five

Elements (五行). The Thirteen Postures (Methods) are: Firstly, the Five Steps: (五步): Advance (前進); Retreat (後退); Look to the Left (左顧); Look to the Right (右盼); and Central Equilibrium (中定), which are indissolubly connected with the Five Elements, namely, Metal (金), Wood (木), Water (水), Fire (火) and Soil (土). In addition, there are Eight Entrances (八門) (sometimes also known as Methods or Energies). Those that are operated at the Four Sides, South, West, East, and North are "Ward Off (掤)", "Pull Back (攦)", "Press Forward (擠)", and "Push (按)", while the others are the Four Corners (四隅) of the Eight Trigrams-Northwest, Southeast, Northeast and Southwest, are "Pull Down (探)", "Bend Backward (挒)", "Elbow Stroke (肘)", and "Shoulder Stroke (靠)". Morphologically, the scheme of correspondence can be represented as follows:[23]

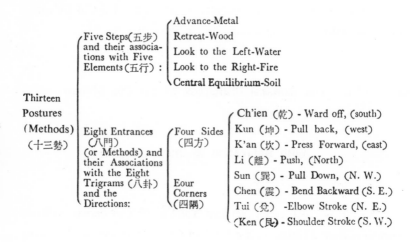

Thirteen Postures (Methods) (十三勢)

Five Steps(五步) and their associations with Five Elements(五行):
- Advance-Metal
- Retreat-Wood
- Look to the Left-Water
- Look to the Right-Fire
- Central Equilibrium-Soil

Eight Entrances (八門) (or Methods) and their Associations with the Eight Trigrams (八卦) and the Directions:

Four Sides (四方)
- Ch'ien (乾) - Ward off, (south)
- Kun (坤) - Pull back, (west)
- K'an (坎) - Press Forward, (east)
- Li (離) - Push, (North)

Four Corners (四隅)
- Sun (巽) - Pull Down, (N. W.)
- Chen (震) - Bend Backward (S. E.)
- Tui (兌) -Elbow Stroke (N. E.)
- (Ken (艮) - Shoulder Stroke (S. W.)

[23] See Chart III: Upper and Lower Diagrams.

Lu Chiu Yuan (陸九淵) (Hsiang Shan (象山)) (A.D.1139—1192), the great Sung philosopher, wrote: "The cosmic principle of change is simply of Yin (Negative Force) and Yang (Positive Force). The Yin and Yang are evidently two contrasting forces underlying all things of the universe, which contradict and complement each other." As the *I Ching* puts it:

"The Hard (剛) (unyielding) and the Soft (柔) (yielding) work against each other; the eight trigrams interact upon one another." (The Great Appendix, Part I.)

According to the traditional interpretation of Tai Chi Ch'uan masters, it is this main principle by which all the operations of the eight entrances or methods are based. With regard to the Five Elements theory, developed further by the Neo-Confucianists, as we are told by Needham, the conception itself was essentially a naturalistic, scientific one, but the theorists of this exercise had evidently associated it with the five steps, believing that each of the five steps is ruled only by virtue of one of the elements in the series. The mechanism of both was the unvarying uniformity which came to be known as Mutual Conquest, or Cyclical Conquest, wood overcoming earth, metal overcoming wood, fire overcoming metal, water overcoming fire, and earth overcoming water, at which point the cycle commenced all over again.[24] Although Cheng Man-ching (鄭曼青)[25] and most of the masters in China still believe this theory and its connection with the

---

[24] For the critical study of the Five Elements Theory, see Joseph Needham, *Science and Civilization in China,* Cambridge University Press, Vol. II, pp. 232—263.

[25] Cheng Man-Ching (鄭曼青), *The Thirteen Chapters on Tai Chi Ch'uan,* (十三篇) (in Chinese), Hong Kong Edition, 1955, Chapter 12, also Cheng Man-Ching and Robert W. Smith. *Tai-Chi-The "Supreme Ultimate" Exercise for Health, Sport, and Self-Defense,* Charles E. Tuttle Co, Rutland, Vermont, 1967.

five steps, modern sociologists such as Granet and Jablonski are skeptical about the value of this type of coordinative thinking.

According to them, "the idea of corespondence has great significance and replaces the idea of causality, for things are connected rather than caused."26 Hence, space was not absolutely uniform and extended in all directions, but was divided into regions, south, north, east, west and centre. And the theorists of Tai Chi Ch'uan also joined these together in the tables of correspondences, the East was indissolubly connected with Ch'ien and the "Ward Off", and the Kun with Pull Back and the South. These probably represent the morphological view of the universe of the ancient Chinese, although they are molded after the pattern of the eight trigrams.

In spite of the many strictures, we realize that the philosophy of organism which occupies such an important place in modern biological sciences is a product of *I Ching*. It was Leibnitz, a great German philosopher, who had it transmitted into the European thinking in the 18th century. On the study and practice of Tai Chi Ch'uan, it seems that the following principles are derived from the philosophy of organism—the "Unity of Heaven and Man" (天人合一) without which Tai Chi Ch'uan might become an exercise which has no meaningful value. To wit:

(1) Principle of the Circular Movement: The name Tai Chi Ch'uan, as we have shown, derived its terminology from Tai Chi,

26 Granet, M. La Pensee Chinois, Albin Michel, Paris, 1934; Jablonski, W. Marcel Granet and his Work, Yjss, 1939, 1, 242; and C. Wright Mills, Power, Politics and People (ed. by Irving Louis Horowitz, pp. 469-520. C. G. Jung has termed the method which the *I* used as "Synchronicity' An Acausal Connecting Principle' *Foreword to the *I Ching* or *Book of Changes,* translated by Wilhelm and Baynes, Bollingen Series XIX, Pantheon, N. Y. C. 1964. However, Chinese scholar such as Liu Po-Ming (劉百閔) argues that what the authors of the *I* used is Causal Method (因果法). Ibid, pp. 45-112.
* p. xxiv, lines 14-16, and footnote 2.

which, in symbolism, is a "circle", signifying generally eternity, the heaven. If it be thought of as a sphere rather than a flat circle, for instance, a one-cell living organism, it is suggestive of possible pulsation, evolution, and growth. If thought of as a spherical celestial body, its roundness suggests revolving movement and periodic renewal of life.

The eight trigrams can be arranged in a "Small Circle" and the 64 hexagrams can be arranged in a "Great Circle", although the latter can contain also a Great Square (方) (also 64 hexagrams) within the Circle (圓).27

Indeed, the circulative activity is associative with life, nature, culture and rhythm. This cyclic concept has been indicated by the four phases in the opening line of *I Ching:* "Heaven presents itself in four phases of operation, namely, Yuan (元), Heng (享), Li

---

27 A "Square" symbolizes a finite form, which is limited in every direction and therefore of a temporal nature. It is somewhat firmly engrained in the popular mind that an enclosing circle is symbolic of heavens, and that the Squareness is symbolic of earth. (See I. Mears and L. E. Mears, *Creative Energy*, Being an Introduction to the study of *Yih King,* or *Book of Changes,* with Translations from the original text, E. P. Dutton Co., New York, pp. 77-87.

It is significant that T'ai Chi Ch'uan theorist has this to say: "Probably the average practiser of T'ai Chi Ch'uan knows only that its circles are round (圓). and does not understand that they are also square (方). Thus it is said that the T'ai Chi is a circle; and that the interior and the exterior, the left and the right, are all included in the circle. It is also said that the T'ai Chi is a square; and that the interior and the exterior, the left and the right, are all included in the square. The going out and the going in of the circle, and the advance and the retreat of the square, follow the square and correspond to the circle. The square is for development and the circle for intensity. When one understands the circle and the square, the outer forms and the inner significance, of the Four Sides, one's technique is perfect and there is no need for the Four Corner Operation. See Learning K. Chen, T'ai Chi Ch'uan, Its Effects and Practical Applications, Hong Kong Edition, p. 169.

（利） **and** Chen（貞）." These terms can be defined as follows:

(a) Yuan — originativeness (birth) — always giving rise to something new.

(b) Heng—Growth—the growth of myriad things on earth.

(c) Li—Maturity—the myriad things are nourished, they develop, and in due time, they are productive.

(d) Chen—Ending or Declining—Everything which depends upon a beginning must have an end.28

These terms, instead of indicating the evolutionary process of nature and culture, actually signify their cyclic nature: "The phase of Yuan takes its rise from beneath that of Chen." (Ending). As the universe is circular chain revolution in macrocosmic scale, the human organism is its microcosmic scale. Thus the movements in Tai Chi Ch'uan usually known as "The Reeling of Silk" （抽絲）—fit completely to the physiological need of human beings. The principle of ceaseless chain revolution is evidently a principle that has been adopted from the cyclic concept of *I Ching*.

(2) The Principle of Dialectic: Among the basic laws underlying all phenomenal changes, the most fundamental is that "when a thing reaches one extreme, it reverts from it". And the Commentary on the Explanatory Notes on the Hexagram "Revival", (Fu) （復） says: "There are no ups not followed by downs; there is no recedence not followed by revival."29

This type of dialectic thinking is.emblematic of the "folding and alteration movements" of Tai Chi Ch'uan, in which every movement, when it comes to the extreme (end), has to be connected by the

28 See Chang Chi-yun （張其昀）, *Fifty Centuries of Chinese History*, Vol. I, *Ancient Times* (in Chinese), Taipei, p. 17.

29 The Hexagrams arranged by Houses.

technique known as "folding and alteration". (摺叠) As a matter of fact, this is the way for the linking up of the movements and energies in a continual series in the exercise and its basic idea has also been derived from *I Ching*.

(3) The Principle of Balance and Equilibrium: The Changeless Absolute of Tai Chi or Tao begets the two conjugate powers— Yin and Yang—which are in balance. According to the art of Chinese medicine, it was by the attainment of a real balance between the two equal forces that happiness, health or good order could be achieved. The concept of "Zen Microbiotic", that has been applied to food or diet by modern Japanese scholars derives its origin from this principle. "The movements of Tai Chi Ch'uan adopt this principle, and the ideal of the movements is to attain the balance of Yin and Yang energies in the organism." "The simultaneous movement of two hands is either in the same direction or in different directions by means of natural parity. The left hand is the Yin power and the right hand is the Yang power. The balanced motions induce mutual responses as if a line of inspiration ties the two together and pulls them to action naturally."[30] It might be added that the movements of substantiality and insubstantiality naturally come from the pattern of the changings of Yin and Yang. With the end result, balance is the original essence of the conjugate powers of Yin and Yang; equilibrium is the way to harmonize these two powers to the right conditions. The Book of *Chung Yung* (中庸) writes: "Ho (unity 和) is the great Harmony of the world." So in every movement in Tai Chi Ch'uan, what it seeks is balance and equilibrium.

(4) Principle of Mean or Central Equilibrium: The *I Ching*

30 Wang Chien-chiu, *Knowledge acquired from the Practice of T'ai Chi Ch'uan*, East and West, Vol. X, No. 11, November 1965, p. 2.

stresses the concept of the "Mean" (中) at the very beginning of the Book. The *Chung Yung* (中庸) also advises: "Chung (Centre) is the chief foundation of the world." Hence the *I Appendices* advances the theory that extremes produce opposite reactions and cautious men to choose a central cause, a golden mean between the extremes, which would not err either by excess or by defect. In this sense they attain what is called Chung ("mean" or "centre"), neither too much nor too little.31

In Tai Chi Ch'uan, among the five steps, the most important one

---

31 The Doctrine of the Mean has been emphasized as "weighting the two extremes of something, and holding it by the due mean." Thus the sixth Nine of the Chien (Heaven) Hexagram reads: "The dragon in extreme will have cause for repentance." The comment on this line says:

"The phrase 'in extreme' refers to one who knows progression but does not know regression; one who knows life, but does not know death; one who knows possession, but does not know loss. It is only the Sage who knows progression and regression, both life and death, both possession and loss, and thus attains to right way (Cheng). He only is the Sage." (Wen Yen, Sect. I, Chap. 6).

Accordingly, the present writer would like to advance the Law of Centre (中道法則) as follows:

1. The underlying principle in Nature's Unique Law between the pair of the opposite Yin and Yang is Harmony, Equilibrium and the Golden Mean.

2. Where one of the poles predominates, the Vital Centre is lacking. Extreme is not the right way, because there exists no axis around which the bipolar whole harmoniously revolves. The wrong form which lacks centre has no equilibrium.

3. "To embrace the Centre and guard the Unity or Oneness (抱中守一), the Heaven and Earth become an organic whole." As man is a microorganism, to regain awareness of this unity or Centre is precisely man's raison d'etre. The analysis and interpretation of this law have been brilliantly expounded in the Appendices of *I Ching*. See also my "System of Culturology," Taipei: Chung Hwa Book Co., 1968, Chap. 17, (黃文山，文化學體系，台北，中華書局印行).

is the "Central Equilibrium" (中定). Practically, every step, every movement starts and returns to the Central Equilibrium. Internally speaking, "the movements in Tai Chi Ch'uan require to start from this central point (abdomen) without the use of strength, and all parts of the whole body move with the initial movement." And because of the fact that the abdomen is the very center of the human body, the Chi is therefore required to sink to the Tan Tien (丹田)—the centre of the body.

I Ching, or the Book of Changes, is a masterpiece of metaphysics, as well as a science of human affairs. Tai Chi Ch'uan is the basic exercise for the seeking of health and longevity. If we can study it with due regard to the principles of *I Ching,* (and the *Tao Teh Ching* of Lao Tzu (老子道德經) as well as Hui Neng's *Platform Scripture* 慧能，六祖壇經),32 we will have no difficulty in understanding the most profound secret of the Oriental Art for rejuvenation.

---

32 See *Tao Teh Ching,* tr. by John C. H. Wu, New York: St. John's University Press, 1962, and his *The Golden Age of Zen,* Taipei: The National War College, 1967; Wing-tsit Chan's translation, (ed, Paul K. T. Sih), *The Platform Scripture,* New York: St. John's University Press, 1963; also *The Altar Sutra of the Sixth Patriarch,* tr. by Lu K'uen yu, in Ch'an or Zen Teaching: Series Three, London, 1963. Consult also Wei Tat, (韋達), *an Exposition of The I-Ching or Book of Changes* (周易義疏), Institute of Culture Studies, Taipei, 1970, Chap. I. pp. 9-21.

CHAPPTER 4

THE BASIC PRINCIPLES OF TAI CHI CH'UAN:

CONFUCIANISM, TAOISM AND ZEN BUDDHISM

Intellectual currents (or ideologies) of the great thinkers are the forces in the making of events. The Chinese cultural development in the matter of the mind in the last 2,500 years or more, no doubt has been greatly molded by Confucious, Laotzu and the Zen Buddhists. Their range of subjects is very vast; they are, in fact, the most comprehensive and profound schools of spiritual achievements known to culture history. In the earliest forms, they included the finest ethical system, with a range of mind-development and pioneer psychology, sociology, and culturology second to none. In their developed forms, they included philosophy, religion, ethics, mysticism, methaphysics, psychology, magic and ritual. These types of philosophy or religion — intellectual, devotional, and the way of life and action — produced the greatest of art, including the martial arts of China. Indeed, the martial arts of the Tang, Sung, Ming and Ching Dynasties were largely the product of Confucianism, Neo-Confucianism, Taoism and Zen Buddhism.

Let us review very briefly their unique contributions to the creation of one of the greatest arts of life — Tai Chi Ch'uan.

I. Confucianism and Neo-Confucianism.

Confucius (孔子) was born in -551 in the State of Lu in modern Shantung, and died in -479. Although his life might have seemed, at a time, somewhat a failure, his subsequent influence in China and the world was so far reaching as to justify the title often attributed to him of the "uncrowned emperor" of China.

He was living in a feudal age, an age of political disintegration and social unrest. There had been a long and gradual process of intellectual disorganization, decadence of beliefs and convictions, and relaxation of duties and relations. His problem was to establish by rational means a system of universally accepted truths, concerning man, society, and the world. The *Lun Yu* (論語), or Analects, the Bible of Confucianism, is a collection of moral maxims, put together in written form soon after his death by his disciples, and preserves the most reliable information about him and his principles. The most important philosophic concept of Confucius is his recognition that "the measure of man is man". The essence of his ethics is a high and fine concept of Jen (仁) or "true manhood". He once defined "true manhood" as the "love of man". This humanistic idea of the "love of man" naturally results in the discovery of the Golden Rule in inter-personal relations.

As philosophy of life, a system of moral codes, Confucianism shows its unwillingness to go beyond the empirical world and its phenomena. But traditional Chinese philosophy ascribes both Taoism and Confucianism to an earlier source, to a work which lies at the very foundation of Chinese culture and thought. This is the *I Ching,* or *Book of Changes,* which was originally a book of divination. Later the Confucianists gave the book its cosmological, metaphysical and ethical interpretations, which constitute the "Appendices" now found in the text. From this text, we find largely the main principles on which Tai Chi Ch'uan is based. These are:

A. The Principle of the Harmony of the Yin and Yang. In the exercise of Tai Chi Ch'uan, this very principle is usually considered as the essence of the whole movement. In Appendix III, it is said: "In the *I* (易), there is the 'Tai Chi', or Supreme Ultimate, which produces the Two Forms, the Two Forms produce the Four Emblems, and these Four Emblems produce the Trigrams." Beginning with the concept of the origin of all created things, there is the Tai Chi, or the Supreme Ultimate, (so-called First Principle or Unique Principle), represented by a circle with two segments. The Tai Chi is said to have produced the Yin and Yang, which came to be regarded as two cosmic principles, or forces, with the Yang representing masculinity, activity, heat, brightness, dryness, hardness, etc., and the Yin representing femininity, passivity, cold, darkness, weakness, softness, etc. Through the interacting or the interplaying of these two primary principles, all phenomena of the universe are produced. The concept has remained dominant in Chinese cosmological, philosophical, biological, psychological, ideological, sociological and culturological speculation down to recent times. These are the laws of nature, history, and culture.

In a modern sense, the universe, like an atom, is fundamentally composed of two elements: namely, Yin and Yang, or negative and positive. Anything that is not balanced Yin and Yang-wise, is apt to cause disharmony and eventual disintegration. To live in accordance with the doctrine of Yin and Yang is to live in harmony with Tao, the law of Nature. And the word of Confucianism is "The harmony is the universal path on which all human acting should proceed."

It has well been pointed out that "According to the Chinese, Life manifests as dynamic equilibria of Yin and Yang, the two polarities of a unitary Vital-Force, in ever-changing pattern complexities and complexes of patternings. The life and health of an organism depend upon the free flow of this force, and a proper balance between the two polarities. If the equilibrium is upset or the flow restricted, the organism is sick; balance and free flow must be restored. The re-establishment of balance is accomplished by discharging excess accumulations, by stimulation of polarity in deficiency, by dispersing obstructions, and by sealing the avenues of wasteful escape of Vital-Force."[1] In the system of Tai Chi Ch'uan, attention is particularly paid to the equilibrium of these two Vital-Forces in the human organism.

B. The Principle of Organism. The world view and life view of the *I Ching* is organismic. In this book, and particularly in the theory of the Neo-Confucianists, the Tao of Heaven, Earth, and Man is identical. This has been remarkably interpreted in the *"Exposition of the Tai Chi Diagram"* by Chou Tun I (1017-1073). The world view of the Confucian humanism is well expressed by Chou in the following statement:

"It is man alone, who receives the finest (substance), and is the most spiritual of beings. The sages ordered their lives by the Mean, by the Correct, by Love and Righteousness. They adopted Ataraxy as their dominant attitude, and set up the highest possible standards for mankind. Thus it was that the virtue of

[1] Denis Lawson-Wood, *Chinese System of Healing, an Introduction to Acupuncture*, Health Science Press, England, p. 17.

the Sages was in harmony with that of the Heaven and Earth, their brightness was one with that of the sun and moon, their actions were one with the Four Seasons, and their control over fortune and misfortune was one with that of the gods and spirits."

This significance of this type of the philosophy of organism to modern man is not easy to understand. We owe a great debt to Joseph Needham, who has, remarkably, pointed out that Greek atomism and mathematics are doubtlessly regarded as the foundation of the Cartesian and Newtonian Science, the European science in the 17th century. But science since that time, has become still more modern in order to assimilate the field of new physics and to take account of the parts of the universe, the enormously great, and the enormously small, which transcend the range and sizes for which the Newtonian world-picture stands. Deepening knowledge of biological phenomena, or biological science, has necessitated a reformulation of the scientific conception which the philosophy of organism has necessarily had to play. Leibniz, a great German philosopher, living at the beginning of the 18th century, may have been influenced by the systematic representations in the *I Ching* (or Book of Changes), and finally, by the presentations by the Neo-Confucianists in the Sung Dynasty of about A.D. 1,000. Needham also adds: "Perhaps the theoretical foundations of most European natural sciences owe more to men such as Chuang Chou, Chou Tun I, and Chu Hsi than the world has yet realized."[2]

If the philosophical concept of atom was an essential for the construction of modern science in the 19th century, the philosophy of

[2] Joseph Needham, *Science and Civilization in China*, Cambridge University Press, Vol. III, p. 505. See also the present writer's "Introductory Remarks by the Translator" to Needham's first volume that has been translated into Chinese, Commercial Press, Taipei, 1971.

Organism is essential for the construction of modern science in its present form, stemmed from the bureaucratic society of ancient and medieval China. The philosophy of Organism and elements in the formulation of the perfected world view in science as great mechanism and atomism to which it gave birth, actually stemmed from the *Book of Changes.* In recent times, the philosophy of organism has been expounded by Whitehead in England,[3] Sri Aurobindo[4] in India (known as "Integral Philosophy"), Sorokin[5] (the "integral methodology" in sociology), and Kroeber[6] (the importance of the concept of "Configuration" in the Science of Culture) in the United States.

According to the idea of the Chinese, the universe is a vast organism, and the human body is a small organism. As a logical consequence, in the system of Tai Chi Ch'uan, attention is paid not to the limbs or to a single organ, but to the integral whole — that is, the human organism.

Besides the above, there are two minor principles which may be described very briefly. The first is the Principle of Continuity, and the second is the Principle of Circle. Fundamentally speaking, the *I Ching* teaches that the movement of the universe is a matter of fluctuation, or cycles of fluctuation, or cycles of creation, which can be found in everything. This fluctuation, or cyclic process of time, all the periods of evolution, are manifestations of that one eternal fluctua-

---

[3] His notion of the Philosophy of Organism appeared first in *Science and the Modern World* (1925) and came to full fruition in *Process and Reality* (1929).

[4] See Haridas Chaudhuri and Frederic Spiegeberg (ed), *The Integral Philosophy of Sri Aurobindo,* Unwin Bros. London 1960.

[5] Pitram A. Sorokin, *The Socio-Cultural Causality, Space, Time,* Duke University Press, North Carolina, 1943.

[6] A. L. Kroeber, *The Configurations of Cultural Growth,* California University Press, 1944.

tion (or cycles) of creation in which and through which the universe exists. Following this theory, the movements of the postures in Tai Chi Ch'uan are cyclic in form. Hence the "Principle of Circle". Next, according to the Appendix of the *I Ching,* the action of Ch'ien, which symbolizes the Heaven, is continual. In observing this law of nature, a gentlemen therefore always devotes his energy to performing good deeds without cessation. Hence the Principle of Continuity.

Herein lies the glorious mission of the Tai Chi Ch'uanists who were in an excellent position to contribute towards the attainment of the goal through their art, the underlying principles of which are the views of the world and life of the Confucianists and Neo-Confucianists. Though transcendental, the pragmatic nature of the Confucian philosophy really appeals to the needs of the Chinese people. Furthermore, its insistence upon the Middle Way (中道) — balance, sanity, "nothing in excess" — was also well adopted to the traditional Chinese way of thinking and action.[1]

II. Taoism

The Taoist system of culture mentality and way of life of the Ideational type, which still today occupies at least as important a place in the Chinese thought as Confucianism, was not only a system of philosophy and way of life, but also a religion.

The most profound and beautiful work in the Chinese language written in the dawn of man's self-awareness is the *Tao Teh Ching* (道德

---

[1] For further exposition of the relationship between the principles of *I Ching* and Tai Chi Ch'uan, see Chapters III and VI.

經). Lao Tzu (老子) (born c. 604 B.C. and died c. 479 B.C.), the founder of Taoism, is said to have been the author, setting forth the principles of the Tao and its power, or virtue (Teh). According to traditional record, he was made a -6th century contemporary of Confucius. Modern scholars, for example, Fung Yu-lan, believes that the life of Lao Tzu should be placed within the -4th century, and that the *Tao Teh Ching* may be dated not long before -300. The next greatest Taoist book is *Chuang Tzu* (莊子), by Chuang Chou (莊周), (c. 369-286 B.C.). Both works and the figures of their reputed authors are essential to the philosophical and religious system of Taoism.

The starting point of the Taoist philosophy is, of course, the preservation of life and avoidance of injury. From this point of view, Tai Chi Ch'uan is often regarded as a Taoist system of exercise for the prolongation of life and eternal youth. Besides, in the development of this art, there are two significant phases that can be viewed as the product of the Taoist philosophers:

First, in the matter of training, the Tai Chi Ch'uan exercise can be divided into the following stages: (1) Concentration of the mind; (2) Practice of the Postures or Forms; (3) Control of Vital Breathing and the coordination of breathing with the movements; (4) Meditation on the Tan Tien (丹田), or Psychic Center, and the various nerve centres; (5) The development of "intrinsic energy" (Ching) (勁) through the control of psychic power; (6) the attainment of "emptiness" (虛) or superconciousness, when the little ego merges with the Cosmic Consciousness. From this point of view, Tai Chi Ch'uan is a unique system which is utterly different from the other systems of martial arts in China. By this, we mean that its emphasis is particularly on mental cultivation and spiritual training rather than pure physical culture training only.

Therefore, in order to understand the impact of the philosophy of Lao Tzu on Tai Chi Ch'uan, we must try to understand his meta-physical conception regarding the universe, for his view of life is based on his view of the universe, or the law of nature. The ideas expressed in the greater part of *Lao Tzu* represent an attempt to realize the laws underlying the change of things in the universe. Things change, but laws underlying the change remain unchanged. If one understands these laws, regulating one's action in conformity with them, one can then turn everything to one's advantage.

A. Lao Tzu's conception regarding the origin and growth of the universe.

What was the origin of the universe? To some of the Greek philosophers, it was represented by such elements as water, air, fire, and wind. But, according to Lao Tzu, it was expressed by an abstract totalistic conception — Tao. He said:

"There was something undefined and yet complete in itself,
Born before Heaven and Earth,
Silent and boundless,
Stands alone without change,
Yet pervading without failure,
It may be regarded as the Mother of the world,
I do not know its name;
I style it 'Tao',
And in the absence of a better word, call it 'the Great'."[7]

---

[7] *Tao Teh Ching*, Chap. 25, translated by John C. H. Wu, St. John's University Press, N.Y. 1961.

Although the word "Tao" was used to express the origin of the universe, the nature of "Tao" could by no means be described by a common language. Hence Lao Tzu said:

"Tao can be talked about,

but not the eternal Tao." (Chap. 1)

"Now what is the Tao?

It is something elusive and evasive." (Chap. 19)

Again, he considered Tao is the universal principle of existence. Thus he said:

"The great Tao is universal like a flood.

How can it be turned to the right or to the left?

All creatures depend on it,

And it denies nothing to anyone.

It does its work,

But it makes no claims for itself." (Chap. 4)

If the universe was originated from "Tao," all the phenomena must also come from "Tao." Lao Tzu's conception is apparently a Taoist monism. He said:

"Tao gave birth to One,

One gave birth to Two,

Two gave birth to Three,

Three gave birth to all the myriad things." (Chap. 42)

In this, Lao Tzu might have been influenced by *I Ching,* the Book of Changes. According to *I Ching*: "One Yang and one Yin: this is called Tao". This Tao is equivalent to Tai Chi or Supreme Ultimate, while the Yin and Yang correspond to two Forms. But, it has been pointed out that the most important metaphysical idea in the *I Ching* (Appendices) as in Taoism is that of the Tao. Yet it is quite different from the concept of Tao of the Taoists. For the authors of the *I Ching,* not only is Tao nameable, but, it is Tao and

Tao is nameable. For the Taoists, Tao is nameless, unnameable — the law of nature.

If, in the original stage, Tao was the "formless Form," the Imageless Image", or "Elusive and Evasive", how, in the process of development, did "myriad of things" stem from it? Lao Tzu pointed out:

"Now what is the Tao?

It is something elusive and evasive,

Evasive and elusive!

And yet It contains within Itself a Form.

Elusive and evasive!

and yet It contains within Itself a Substance:

Shadowy and dim!

And yet It contains within Itself a Core of Vitality.

The Core of Vitality is very real,

It contains within Itself an unfailing Sincerity.

Throughout the ages Its name has been preserved.

In order to recall the Beginning of all things.

How do I know the ways of all things at the Beginning?

By what is within me." (Chap. 21)

This seems to say that the "Tao," "evasive and elusive," gradually gave birth to the "Form," the "substance," the "Core of Vitality" and the "Sincerity," from which again stemmed all the myriad of things. In the stage of change, and yet unchanging, it is called the "Incorporeal" (Wu) (無), while in the stage of having been changed, and yet still changing, it is called the "Corporeal" (Yu) (有). Thus:

"As the origin of heaven-and-earth,

it is nameless;

As 'the mother' of all things, it is nameable". (Chap. 1)

"All things under heaven are born of the corporeal:

The corporeal is born of the Incorporeal." (Chap. 40)

Undoubtedly to Chuang Tzu: "The Tao has reality and evidence ...It existed before Heaven and Earth, and ended for all eternity ...Though older than the most ancient, it is not all." To modern scholars, the origin of the conception can be traced to "Totemistic Culture."[8] The basic notion does not differ from "Mana" or "Orenda" among the American Indians and other tribes. Yet it is Sinicism. It is the spirit of Chinese life since the Paleolithic and Neolithic periods. Its secret laws can be found in the rhythm of time and space on all occasions and sites. It is said to be the law of the universe. Socially speaking, it is the supreme emblem of social monism — the ultimate of man's oneness with nature.[9]

B. The Law of the Universe — Tao.

It is quite clear that Tao, in the conception of Lao Tzu, is not only the origin and growth of the universe, but also the law of nature. Thus he said:

"Man follows the ways of the Earth,

The Earth follows the ways of Heaven,

Heaven follows the ways of Tao,

Tao follows its own Way." (Chap. 25)

What is its own way? Its own way is the way of Nature, which consists of two aspects:

[8] See the author's "A Synthetic Study on the Origins of Culture in China", The Chu Hai Journal, No. 6, Chu Hai College, Hong Kong, January, 1973.

[9] Seee my article: "Totemism and the Origin of Chinese Philosophy" in the Bulletin of the Institute of Ethnology, Academia Sinica, No. 9, Spring, 1960.

"The movement of the Tao consists in Returning.

The use of the Tao consists in softness." (Chap. 40)

From this passage, we would say that Tao must move. Without its movement, there is no universe.10 With its movement, there must be change, and with change, there is Returning (Reversal). Hence Lao Tzu said:

"While all things are stirring together

I only contemplate the Return." (Chap. 16)

Apparently, "returning" or "reversal" is the law of Nature and Culture which had been advocated both by Lao Tzu and the *I Ching* as interpretated by Confucianists. When the development of anything brings it to one extreme, a returning to the other extreme takes place, that is, in the dialectic of Hegel, everything involves its own negation. In social life, as aptly pointed out by Derk Bodde, "This theory has had a great effect upon the Chinese people and has contributed much to their success in overcoming the many difficulties which they have encountered in their long history."10

In the second place, Lao Tzu seemed to emphasize another law — the law of softness. Lao Tzu said:

"When a man is living, he is soft and supple.

When he is dead, he becomes hard and rigid.

When a plant is living, it is soft and tender.

When it is dead, it becomes withered and dry.

Hence, the hard and rigid belongs to the company of the dead:

The soft and supple, belongs to the company of the living."

(Chap. 75)

Again, one of the sayings of Lao Tzu (which has been considered

10 Fung Yu-lan, *A Short History of Chinese Philosophy*, edited by Derk Bodde, Macmillan Co. 1960, p. 19.

as one of their mottoes by the Tai Chi Ch'uanists) is:

"The softest of all things

Overrides the hardest of all things." (Chap. 43)

Because the Taoists always appreciate the morality of "Yielding," they, therefore, as the followers of Lao Tzu, emphasize the symbols of "water" and the "feminine," because water is yielding, and feminine is receptive and passive. Lao Tzu said:

"The highest form of goodness is like water.

Water knows how to benefit all things without striving with them." (Chap. 8)

"Know the masculine,

Keep to the feminine." (Chap. 28)

The concept of "Yielding" (Jang, that is humility), as Granet pointed out, a custom of the "potlatch society" must have been of great importance in the most ancient Chinese society. This might have been the source of interpretation for Lao Tzu, who actually considered the law of softness is the law of survival. He said:

"Bend and you will be Whole,

Curl and you will be Straight.

Keep empty and you will be filled,

 Grow old and you will gain,

Have much and you will be confused." (Chap. 22)

C. The Theory of Immortality.

The aim of the individual in Taoism is the achievement of material immortality as a "Hsien" (仙). From the beginning, Taoist thought, under the influence of Lao Tzu (in such sayings as "The

Spirit of the Fountain dies not"), was captivated by the idea that it was possible to achieve a material immortality. They were fascinated by youth with its firmness of flesh and exquisite skin complexion, and they believed that techniques could be found out whereby it would be possible to arrest the processes of aging, or to return to the physical condition of the young organism. Lao Tzu said:

"The Sage is not sick, being sick of sickness;

This is the secret of health." (Chap. 70)

With this conception in view, the Taoist aspirant for "hsienship" was prepared to undergo a considerable amount of training. Their practices for material immortality, according to modern research, hence fall into several categories:

1. Respiratory techniques
2. Heliotherapeutic techniques
3. Gymnastic techniques
4. Sexual techniques
5. Alchemical and Pharmaceutical techniques
6. Dietary techniques

Taoism, as a Chinese individualistic religion of salvation, thus has a strong conviction that "The destiny of myself depends on me and not upon Heaven". And thus, the Taoists' problem lies mainly in how to preserve life and avoid harm and death.[11]

D. The Inspiration of Lao Tzu to the Tai Chi Ch'uanists.

The Taoists had no formal treatises on art, but the admiration

---

[11] Cf. Joseph Needham, op. cit. Vol. 11, pp. 23-156.

and practice of the techniques for longevity and their idealization of the mind and spirit, as well as the law of nature, gave profound inspiration to the great martial artists of China. This being the case, it is no wonder why most of the Tai Chi Ch'uanists took Taoism as their theoretical base. The following principles that had been expressed in the *Tao Teh Ching* may be considered as the methodological assumptions of Tai Chi Ch'uan:

1. The Principle for the Control of the Breath, or Chi.

In order to attain longevity, the Taoists usually practiced two kinds of techniques. The first is the training of the so-called "External Tan" (外丹) (Elixir for longevity by taking drugs or medicines), while the second is the training of the "Internal Tan" (內丹) (the nourishment of the Chi). In *Chuang Tzu,* we find the passage: "Man's life is due to the conglomeration of the Chi, and when it is dispersed, death occurs." Lao Tzu had definitely stated:

"In gathering your vital energy (Chi) to attain suppleness,
Have you reached the state of a new-born babe?" (Chap. 10)
"To control the breath by will is to overstrain it." (Chap. 55)
"Empty the heart of desires;
Fill the belly with food." (i.e. vital energy) (Chap. 3)

Tao Teh Ching, judging from the above passages, seems to recommend the respiratory method for the control of the breath. There are many books in the *Tao Ts'ang* (道藏) (A.D. 1190 and 1445) discussing the techniques, and all the techniques went under the collective name of 'nourishing the Chi", or the "nature", (inspiration and expiration, anoxaema, pi chi). The circulation and transformation of Nei Chi (內氣) (internal energy) had to be effected and accelerated by imagination, meditation, or psychic power. In order to develop the "intrinsic energy" (nei Ching) (內勁), the Tai Chi Ch'uanists apparently follow such principle and techniques of the Taoists.[12]

2. The Principle of Serenity and Emptiness.

According to Lao Tzu: "Tao follows its own way" which is natural (Tzu-jan) (自然), spontaneous, self-originating. Hence, in the matter of controlling and nourishing the Chi (energy), the fundamental prerequisites are "Serenity" or "Acquiescence". The principles expounded by Lao Tzu are thus:

"Serenity is the master of restlessness." (Chap. 26)

"Peaceful and Serene

Is the Norm of the World." (Chap. 45)

"Attain the utmost Emptiness

Cling single-heartedly to interior peace." (Chap. 16)

These could be considered as the guiding principles for the spiritual training by the Tai Chi Ch'uanists, for they emphasize the method of "Employing the mind or consciousness and not the exertion of strength," and the "lowering (sinking) down of the Chi to the "Tan Tien," or Psychic Center. In this kind of operation, serenity (or internal peace) is what is required.

3. The Principle of Softness.

Although in Joint Hands Operation and Self-Defense, the practitioners of Tai Chi Ch'uan are urged to employ the principle of the Interaction of Firmness and Softness, most of the theorists are of the

---

[12] Compare the theory of *"Tek Chi"* (得氣) in Modern Acupuncture, Cf. Y. Y. Yu, The Secrets of Acupuncture, The World Book Co., Singapore, 1972, pp. 97-102.

opinion that Tai Chi Ch'uan is an art of Softness (suppleness). In addition to what have been cited above from Tao Teh Ching, the following passages are self-explanatory:

"Herein is the subtle wisdom of life;

The soft and weak overcome the hard and the strong." (Chap. 76)

That the weak overcomes the strong, and the soft overcomes the hard,

This is something known by all, but practiced by none."

(Chap. 78)

4. The Principle of Non-Striving and Non-Aggression.

Lao Tzu seems to base this principle on the Tao of Heaven, for he said:

"The way of Heaven is to benefit, not to harm.

The way of the Sage is to do his duty, not to strive with anyone."

(Chap. 81)

"Just because he strives with nobody,

Nobody can ever strive with him." (Chap. 45)

"If you do not strive with others,

You will be free from blame." (Chap. 60)

Finally, the following passage is especially significant from the point of view of Tai Chi Ch'uanists, because it emphasizes the technique of "neutralizing", instead of "attacking," in self-defense:

"A good soldier is never aggressive.

A good fighter is never angry.

The best way of conquering an enemy

Is to win him over by not antagonizing him." (Chap. 68)

Thus, the so-called "virtue of non-striving" is fully understood by the Tai Chi Ch'uanists in the application of their strategy.

5. The Principle of Returning.

Lao Tzu warns us "not to know the invariable and to act blindly is to go to disaster." One should know the laws of nature and conduct one's activities in accordance with them. This, by Lao Tzu, is called "practicing enlightenment." The general rule for the man "practicing enlightenment" is that if he wants to achieve anything, he starts with its opposite. If one wants to be strong, he must start with a feeling that one is weak. In his book, we find the following:

"Therefore, the Sage wants to remain behind,

But finds himself at the head of others;

Reckons himself out,

But finds himself safe and secure." (Chap. 22)

"Indeed, as ever hidden, we should look at its inner essence:

As always manifest, we should look at outer aspects." (Chap. 23)

In the Tai Chi Ch'uan classics, particularly the "Theory" written by Wang Tsung Yueh (王宗岳), this principle becomes his guiding spirit. Wang said: "If the opponent attacks you on the left, your left side should change instantly to insubstantiality. The same technique is applicable to that of the right." And according to Wang: "A hero who is capable of attaining an invincible stage in all the directions and phases, does so by the application of this strategy."13 Indeed, the Tai Chi Ch'uanists seem to follow Lao Tzu very closely in the matter of strategy. Lao Tzu said:

"The strategists have a saying:

I dare not be host, but rather a guest;

I dare not advance an inch, but rather retreat a foot."

13 See the author's Translation of Wang's Text at the end of this book.

In self-defense, the Tai Chi Ch'uanists always emphasize the principle — "In making a move, know how to choose the right moment". (Lao Tzu) — and in the "Song of Fighting Hands," it says: "If I think the opponent is about to strike me, I should strike him first."

Here we have Taoism at its best. Indeed, many of the principles of Tai Chi Ch'uan are based on the philosophy of Taoism, without which the configuration of this martial art would be totally different from what it is now, and would be a tree without root itself. Finally, it may be added it is Needham's provocative suggestion that the character of Taoism, the "path" which sought not inaction but action in harmony with nature, amounted to a profession of faith in natural sciences. He also concludes that the "coordinative" inheritance of the Chinese mind is an essential tool in the organic universe of contemporary science. These are some of the reasons why Professor Needham says that the "Taoists had much to teach the world; perhaps the future belongs to their philosophy."

III. Zen (Ch'an) Buddhism

With regard to external factors, the most pervasive cultural influence in China is Buddhism. As India's contribution to China, this religion (or philosophy of life) has assumed forms congenial to its new environment. So rich and varied are its expressions in philosophy, art, architecture, and sculpture, that it is an inalienable part of Chinese cultural heritage.

Buddhism was originated in India 2,500 years ago by Buddha, Prince Siddhartha Gautama of the Sakya clan in the kingdom of

Magadha, who lived from 560 or 550 to 477 B.C. In India, its country of origin, Buddhism has disappeared almost entirely, but it has spread through Tibet, China, Korea, Japan, Ceylon, Thailand, and Burma, and is embraced by more than 500 million people. Buddhism, in a real sense, is not a religion, but a philosophy, because Buddha denied the existence of gods or a God. It is atheism. His teachings were entirely on the rational and moral level, rather than on that of divine revelation.

When Buddha was 35, immediately after his enlightenment, he expounded the fundamental principles of his philosophy. The first principle was "anicca" — the doctrine that all things are impermanent. The second principle was "sunyata" — the doctrine of void, that is, all manifested things when analysed and taken to pieces, are found to lack continuous form or unchanging substance. All things are compounds, and all compounds are void of ultimate content. The third principle is the doctrine of love or compassion. He believes hatred ceases only by love; this is an eternal law. The fourth principle is the doctrine of the conquest of instincts. He said: "If one man conquers in battle a thousand men, and if another conquers himself, the latter is the greater."

For the purpose of conquering oneself, he expounded the essence of his doctrine — The Four Noble Truths. His doctrine of causation applied to the individual character is expressed in the Four Noble Truths, viz: the omnipresence of suffering; its causes, selfish desire; its cure, the elimination of that separative desire, and the way to its removal. The Noble Eightfold Path of Buddhism, acknowledged by all schools, is the means of obtaining this destruction of desire and the noblest course of spiritual training yet presented to man. They are: Right Belief; Right Thought; Right Speech; Right Action; Right Means of Livelihood; Right Exertion; Right Remembrance; Right

Meditation.

The first Buddhists arrived in China at the beginning of the first century A.D. Obviously the Buddha's teaching, at the very outset, was rather alien to Confucianism and Taoism. Here and there were Chinese pessimists, but the majority, particularly the Taoists sought the indefinite prolongation of life. The Neo-Confucianists, for example, Chu Hsi (A.D. 1130-1200) also fought continually against Buddhism. To them, the universe, composed of matter-energy (Chi) and ordered by the universal principle of organization (Li), was entirely real. This kind of organic view of the universe was consonant with science, and could not but be deeply inimical to the world-denying metaphysics of Buddhism. Yet, Buddhism was to have some of its great triumphs in China, because it has always set great store on the inner powers of mind, knowing that its resources are infinite, and there is no instrument yet invented which can do more than the mind of man can do when its powers are fully developed. To the Buddhists, all weight and emphasis is on the mind. So, too, for the Tai Chi Ch'uanists.

In spite of all the opposition, the first characteristic product of Chinese Buddhism was the Zen (Chan) method or way, which is supposed to have been founded by the Indian Bodhidharma (Ta-Mo), who died c. A.D. 475[14] and who is also said to have been the founder of the famous martial art system known as Shao Lin Ch'uan, the predecessor of Tai Chi Ch'uan. Zen is the Japanese pronounciation of

---

[14] Bodhidharma (Japanese, Bodi-Da-ruma) did not "establish" Zen in its entirety as it is now; he did strike an original spark from the main body of Buddhism.

He is alleged to be the 28th patriarch of Indian Buddhism, and the first patriarch of Chinese Zen (Ch'an). According to Daisetz Suzuki, the patriarch came to China from India in the year A.D. 520.

the Chinese word "Ch'an", and Ch'an is the abbreviation of the
original phrase "Ch'an-Na" — a corruption of the pronounciation of
the Sanskrit word "Dhyana" or the Pali, "Jhana". But Zen Buddhism is so Chinese in style and in mentality that an Indian origin
seems improbable. It is a fact that the interaction of Buddhism with
Taoism resulted in the Chinese Ch'an or Zen school. In fact, Zen is
the Chinese form of Buddhism — a synthesis of Indian Buddhism
with Taoism.

In his study of the "The Indianization of China: A Case Study
in Cultural Borrowing," Hu Shih pointed out the original development of Zennism with remarkable historical insight in the following
passages:

"From the 7th century on there arose the Southern school of
Chinese Zennism, which was built on the central idea of Sudden
Enlightenment and discarded all the scholastic verbalism, the
slavish ritualism, and even the minute practices of meditation.
'Buddhahood is within you. Worship not the Buddha, for the
Buddha means the enlightened One, and the Enlightenment is
within you. Abide not by the Law, for the Law simply means
Righteousness, and Righteousness is within you. And abide not
by the Sangha (the brotherhood of the monks), for the brotherhood simply means purity in life, and purity is within you.' Thus
spoke Hui Neng (慧能) (A.D. 638-713), the founder of Southern Zennism."15

Zennism, a Chinese product, is no doubt an iconoclastic and revolutionary movement in the world history of thought. Suzuki, the
Japanese authority on Zen has remarked:

15 In Harvard Tercentenary Publications, *Independence, Convergence,
and Borrowing, in Institutions, Thought and Art,* Cambridge, 1937, pp. 220-
247.

"In the history of Zen, Yeno (Hui-neng or Wei-lang in Chinese) comes foremost, and it may be better in more than one sense to consider him the first patriarch of Zen in China. His message was really revolutionary. Though he is described as an illiterate son of a farmer, living in the Lingnan district far away from the center of T'ang culture and civilization, he had a great pioneer spirit and opened a new field in the study of Buddhism, upsetting all the traditions which preceded him. His message was: dhyana and prajna are one; where dhyana is, there is prajna, and where prajna is, there is dhyana; they are not to be separated from one another. Before Hui-neng the two were regarded as separate; otherwise, their identity was not clearly affirmed, which resulted in the practice of more or less emphasizing dhyana at the expense of prajna. Buddha's all-important enlightenment-experience came to be interpreted statically and dynamically, and the doctrine of sunyata (emptiness), which is really the cornerstone of Buddhist thought-structure, became a dead thing. Hui-neng revived the enlightenment experience."16

Indeed, in his introduction to Hui Neng, Suzuki refers to the *Platform Sermons of the Sixth Patriarch* (Lu-Tso T'an-Ching) (六祖壇經) as having created a sensation among the 8th century Buddhists for two reasons: In them Hui Neng appealed to the masses by his rejection of Shen-hsiu's conceptualism as a wrong interpretation of Supreme Wisdom (Prajna); he also warned against the danger of misrepresenting meditation (Dhyana) as the "tranquilizing drug" of a passive quietism.

Zen or Ch'an or Dhyana (Samadhi Dhyana meditation which

16 See Daisetz Teitaro Suzuki, *Zen: A Reply to Hu Shih*, in *Philosophy East and West*, Vol. III, No. 1, April 1953.

denotes a state of perfect mental concentration), committed to the process of enlightenment through meditation, seemed to meet some basic demands of the Chinese people for whom the Chinese philosophy, even Taoism, still offered no satisfaction. From the historical point of view, as according to Chang Chen-chi, there are at least seven types of meditation practices which are generally employed by the Zennists:

1. Meditation through breathing exercises;
2. Meditation by concentrating one's mind on a point;
3. Meditation through visualization;
4. Meditation through Mantram Yoga — the reciting or intoning of incantations or mystic words;
5. Meditation by absorbing one's mind in Good Will, or devotional thoughts;
6. Meditation by identifying the Mind Essence, and
7. Meditation through movement.

As a matter of fact, most of the Zen Buddhists always meditate for many hours throughout the day, attaching great importance to the correctness of the posture and the way of breathing in order to attain salvation and prajna-intuition. "But Hui Neng's conception of meditation . . . was not the art of tranquilizing the mind . . . One-sided meditation is sure to tend toward quietism and death . . . Meditation has nothing to do with mere sitting cross-legged in contemplation, as is generally supposed by outsiders . . . it is, rather, acting, moving, performing deeds, seeing, hearing, thinking, remembering . . . "17

If this is true, Tai Chi Ch'uan naturally offers an excellent method (or way) for a "Movement Type" of meditation for the Zen Buddhists. Thus Chang Chen-chi states:

17 See Clearence Burton Day, *The Philosophers of China*, The Citadel Press, 1962, p. 145.
18 Chang Chen-chi, *The Practice of Zen*, Harper, N.Y. p. 159-160.

"This Primordial Movement (i.e. Tai Chi Ch'uan) is a very gentle exercise, ingeniously devised to bring the negative and positive forces in the body into perfect harmony, thus automatically taming the mind, controlling the Prana, and even bringing one directly to the state of Samadhi. The Primordial Movement has now become one of the most popular gymnastic exercises widely practiced by the Chinese in all walks of life."[18]

Besides the above point, probably through the principle of meditation, the Zen Buddhists also contributed something which is basic in Tai Chi Ch'uan exercise, by which the practitioners can grasp intuitively a center of personality which ties in unity the warring opposites of reason and unreason, intellect and sense, morality and nature. In other words, there is a much deeper sense of harmony, more awareness of the central core of human existence, through the identity of dhyana and prana.[19]

[19] It might be interesting to quote the passages from Maurice Zalle who has admirably described the relations of Zen and Tai Chi Ch'uan in its defense aspect, as follows:

"Tai Chi Ch'uan is a Chinese system of controlled muscular movement that is both an exercise and a method of self-defense. Tai Chi Ch'uan is not an aggressive art: in this system self-protection always takes the form of a reaction to an attack by an aggressor, an attacker.

Yet the practitioner of this method uses no force in repelling his opponent. His every movement during the bout, the battle, the encounter, is light and soul-like, gentle as a falling leaf. In his riposte, his rebuttal to the attack, the Tai Chi Ch'uan practitioner uses no total body contact. Only a momentary flick of an isolated portion of his extremities, his legs and arms, is used, but to very potent effect...The student of this defensive art must practice these positions statically and dynamically until they become automatic.

Then he must enter into Zen if these exercises are to be adequate to protect him from a marauder's onslaught.

To enter into Zen, to become a true warrior of any oriental martial art, to obey unconsciously the code of the warrior in the true tradition, one must transcend the principle of body and enter into the world of consciousness.

There is an outer oriental martial art, and there is an inner spirit of that art. The outer aspect is the technical knowledge of the art of bodily encounter. The inner aspect of the art of preserving oneself from murderous or vicious attack is the control of the mind.

He who wishes to live in an oriental martial art, rather than just to practice it on the physical level, must so train his consciousness to attain a self-discipline that at last his conscious mind will merge into an identity with the very principle of life itself. Mind. and become the state of mind called in Japanese "mushin" and in Chinese "wu-hsin", that is, the state of "no-mind," what the science of psychiatry calls the unconscious.

When the practitioner of an oriental martial art attains this state of mind, he will find himself invincible, for he will be in a state of at-one-ment with the all-powerful state of being that is beyond the dualism of life and death.

When the oriental martial artist uses "wu-hsin," he becomes to all appearances an automaton, not employing ordinary caution in dealing with his adversaries. In this state he appears bereft of his ordinary consciousness. He displays to the onlooker and to his opponents a seeming contradiction of being at one and the same time unconsciously conscious and consciously unconscious. At this state he is at the highest level of his art.

Bodhidharma, called in Japanese "Daruma", named this highest state of consciousness the "Prajna Immovable." This term means wisdom that cannot be dislodged.

In this state of consciousness the mind of the warrior abides at no certain definite point but flows from one object to another. He is able to anticipate his opponent's next move instinctively and intuitively and to move his weapon, no matter what its nature, simultaneously to meet his opponent's move, both to block it and to retaliate at the identical point of the attack. This point of the blocking of an attack and its simultaneous reprisal or counter-attack is the stopping-point of the practitioner's mind, the place where his consciousness abides.

Eno, called Wei-Neng or Hui-Neng in Chinese, demanded the Zen follower to attain the stage of "Prajna and Dhyana" if he wished to achieve the summit of Zen. Every samurai, ancient warrior of Japan, strove to reach this level. the stage of "Activity through Meditation". This aspiration must be taken up also by practitioners and students of the various oriental martial arts if they are dedicated to the full development of their art.

An explanation of the compound term "Prajna and Dhyana" is in order here for the potential Zennist — for it is a natural progression from the oriental martial arts into Zen and from Zen back again into the specific martial art practiced.

"Dhyana" is meditation as Zen practices it. It is a process.

In this respect it is interesting to quote a passage from *Neo-Confucianism, etc.: Essays by Wing-tsit Chan,* in which he said:

"The Zen masters understood prajna not as rational knowledge but as intuition. In fact, it was Shen-hui's overrational interpretation of prajna that led to the decline of his influence on the historical development of Chinese Zen...In short, according to Suzuki, Zen is not explanable by mere intellectual analysis. Historical handling of Zen cannot go further than the objective relationship with other so-called historical factors. Zen is to be grasped within and "Hu Shih seems to neglect this." (*Hu Shih and Chinese Philosophy,* in *Chan's Essays,* p. 294. Compiled by K. H. Chen, Oriental Society, 1969)

CHAPTER V

TAI CHI CH'UAN AND HEALTH

It has been pointed out that there are two kinds of health, artificial and natural. A marvelous gift has been given by modern medicine to man for protection against most infectious diseases. But man is not satisfied with artificial health that depends on special diets, chemicals, vitamins, endocrine products, and periodic medical examinations. He wants natural health, which comes from resistance to infectious and degenerative diseases, and which offers equilibrium of energy (Chi), and the nervous systems. In creating modern human beings, we must attempt to give them the freedom and the happiness engendered by the perfect soundness of organic and mental activities. Tai Chi Ch'uan is composed of calm, relaxed movements designed to establish the equilibrium of vital forces in the organism (the union of the polarity of the Yin and Yang forces). It helps the whole body to perform its function efficiently rather than intervening in the work of each organ. Through these gentle movements, we have learned the secret of an immunity to degenerative diseases. With the knowledge of how to exercise properly and with the determination to discipline ourselves consistently, we acquire the possession of natural health, which would enormously increase our freedom and happiness or bliss.

The Chinese, as a people, paid much attention to natural health in earlier historic periods. One of the oldest classics on medicine is

Huang-ti, or the Yellow Emperor's Nei Ching or Internal Classic (內 經), which possibly were written in the Han Dynasty, (206 B.C.- A.D. 220). It offers the theory that the art of massage should be used for the curing of paralysis. Indeed, scientific theories had long been advanced by ancient Chinese to explain the fact that exercise or movement could lead to health and happiness, and even might be used to cure or prevent disease. Five of the Ch'uan, or exercises, were in existence: namely, Dragon Ch'uan, Tiger Ch'uan, Leopard Ch'uan, Snake Ch'uan and Crane Ch'uan. These were presumably exercises featuring the animal's postures and stances in order to strengthen man's physique, and to attain the aim of longevity. Hence, Hua T'o (b. A.D. 190), the first Chinese physician as pointed out previously, had the theory that the human body, which moves often, would eliminate the "grain gas" and enhance the circulation of the blood, thus preventing the occurrence of sickness. Man is "similar to the axis of the door whose hinges will work smoother and last longer because of its constant rotation." This is what his creed was. It has been the experience of many people, of course, that with exercise they feel better and will enjoy greater longevity. This explains the theory of therapeutic exercise and its value to natural health.

In this respect, Tai Chi Ch'uan has made its extraordinary contribution to the natural health of man, on the one hand, and has nothing in common with the strenuous exercises as practiced in Western countries, on the other. It makes good impact upon the central nervous system and builds a fine base for the improvement of the other nine organic systems of the human body, namely (1) Skeletal, (2) Muscular, (3) Circulatory, (4) Lymph, (5) Execretory Organs, (Lungs and Kidneys), (6) Digestive, (() Endocrine Glands, (8) Nervous System, (9) Sensory Organs. Let us discuss its effects upon the main systems as follows:

1. Central Nervous System

Through recent developments in the science of Physiology, particularly Pavlov's research on the central nervous system, we are in a better position to realize that this system holds a most important role in the human body. The central nervous system consists of the brain, the cerebellum and the spinal cord. It acts directly on the nerves of the muscles, and indirectly on those of the organs. An immense number of nervous fibers intersect the organism in every direction. One of the principal functions of the nervous system is to respond in an appropriate manner to stimuli coming from the environment, or to produce reflex actions. Some of the movements are influenced by the mind or consciousness. For example, when we think about our respiratory motion, its rhythm is at once modified. Although the muscles that perform standing, walking, and running, receive their orders from the spinal cord, they depend for their coordination upon the cerebellum.

Relying on the order of the nervous system, the activity of any particular organ can be regulated according to its need. Thus, any method which strengthens the function of the central nervous system will have a good result on the whole body from the point of view of health. The contribution of the art of Tai Chi Ch'uan to health lies exactly at this point. Its flowing technique helps to: (1) concentrate the mind; (2) calm the disposition; (3) use the mind or consciousness to move the body without using awkward strength; (4) make the muscles pliant; (5) quicken reflexes; (6) improve the circulation; (7) make one alert and easy; and (8) accelerate the activities of other systems or organs.

Besides, the practice of this art and movement, as a matter of fact, arouses a great deal of interest. Performing the movements which are done in a slow continuous sequence, will develop a sense of joyfulness and well-being. In the "Joint Hand Operations," one feels a sense of spiritual inspiration. The enhancement of emotion in this way, according to modern physiological research, will certainly activate the functions of the body. According to experimental evidence, we deeply realize that in any exercise, prior to the employment of physical force, the impact of the Spirit alone will accelerate the process of blood circulation and metabolism. All these facts thoroughly explain why the movement — even flowing, sustained and light in the process of practicing — creates a good effect on the central nervous system.

2. Circulatory System and Respiratory System

It has been pointed out, particularly, that the impact of disciplined movement of Tai Chi Ch'uan upon the circulatory system, (the blood, the heart, blood vessels, veins and arteries), and the respiratory system, (the lungs, the mechanism of breathing), stems mostly from the activities of the central nervous system. In a living body, blood is present everywhere. It pulsates in the arteries, glides through the veins, fills the capillary vessels, and bathes all tissues in transparent lymph.

The entire sequence and the composition of the movements of Tai Chi Ch'uan flows smoothly into each other and brings every muscle and joint, as well as the breathing system, particularly the diaphragm, into play. Hence, it can accelerate the circulation of the blood and the lymph, and reduces the impure blood from the organ. This is evidently the best method for the elimination of waste products from the blood.

In the process of practicing, the mind or consciousness is utilized to coordinate the breathing and the movement. The result is that the breathing attains a state of naturalness, so that the effect of breathing is strengthened and the circulation of the blood and lymph is simultaneously activated. The blood is also refreshed and revitalized because of the large intake of oxygen through complete and deep breathing. The properly oxygenated bloodstream, in turn, promotes the health of the nervous system, and the endocrine system (the glands of the internal secretion: thyroid, adrenal, pancreas and pituitary).

In Oriental philosophy, it considers the psychic center as located about three inches under the navel. Therefore, in the Tai Chi Ch'uan breathing system, deep breathing is required with the using of the mind (or consciousness) to direct the Chi down to this center, which the Chinese Taoists call the "Tan Tien" (丹田) , or field of elixir. This is actually a type of diaphragmatic breathing, which exerts gentle pressure upon the stomach and other organs in that region. Through the pressure on the abdomen, the arteries transfer the blood up to the heart and improve the condition of the blood circulation itself[1]

---

[1] It is no longer true that heart disease is automatically associated with advanced age; a Commonwealth Statistician's report makes it clear that in the years 1950 to 1962, the age group 35 to 39 yielded an appalling 78% increase in fatal heart attacks on a percentage of total population.

"Good muscle tone in the arms and particularly in the legs, resulting from regular exercise, maintains an improved circulation of blood in the veins," says Dr. White. "Since the veins have valves which, when in good condition, prevent the blood from going the wrong way, the compression of the veins by the skeletal muscles helps to pump the blood back to the heart. Soft, unused muscles do not accomplish this as well."

"Exercise also improves the tone of the diaphragm," Dr. White continues. "This results in its better function as the piston of a pump, not only for bringing oxygen to the lungs with the removal of carbon dioxide, but also for the suction of blood into the heart."

Furthermore, through the movements of the diaphragm, the internal massage helps the liver to eliminate the impure blood, and also aids in the improvement of the liver itself. While performing the exercise, every organ in the body, particularly the heart, can be greatly benefited leading to the prevention of arteriosclerosis and the innumerable misfortunes caused by nervous and mental diseases. In addition, the movement of the muscle also enables the function of the heart to attain a most satisfactory adjustment. Intellectuals, and others who do not know the art of relaxation, will get much benefit out of it after even a short practice period.

3. Digestive System

When a disorder of the nervous system occurs, it frequently affects the digestive system adversely. The natural process of digestion is interferred with and this becomes the forerunner of many digestive troubles. Tai Chi Ch'uan tends to prevent and cure these disorders as its continued practice increases deep breathing, which in turn, improves the circulation and stimulates the activity of the intestines. This increased mobility will improve the whole digestive system and prevent constipation.

4. Metabolism

Metabolism is usually measured by the quantity of oxygen absorbed and the carbonic acid produced, when the body is in a state of complete repose. This is called basal metabolism by scientists. To improve this basal metabolism is an important task of Tai Chi

Ch'uan. Senior prople, who are frequently troubled by illness stemming from a low metabolic rate, such as arteriosclerosis, find Tai Chi Ch'uan helpful in clearing the system of the end products of improper metabolism. Hence, for mature people, the practice of this art and exercise often leads to most satisfying results.

In synthesis, Tai Chi Ch'uan is an art whose movement toward health, has its basis in physiology. It rebuilds one's spirit and body. It can definitely change the weight of the body and take off the burden of fat that affects not only the individual's physical mobility but also his character. Mr. Yearning K. Chen, in his *Tai Chi Ch'uan: Its Effects and Practical Applications,* states: "People suffering from neurasthenia, high blood pressure, tuberculosis, gastric and enteric diseases, paralysis, kidney diseases, etc., can all be profitted by the practice. Extraordinary results will come to even those with incurable diseases. However, people having serious cardiac diseases, or being in the second or third stage of tuberculosis, must prolong the spells of practice gradually, instead of trying too hard at the start."[2] With

[2] Y. T. Liu, in *Tai Chi Ch'uan (T.C.C.) Health Exercises For Advanced Pupils,* has this to say in this regard: "The writer has had 42 years of service with the government postal service in China and, after retirement from his position of Postal Commissioner on reaching 60, lived happily in Shanghai until, when 69, he was medically found to be suffering somewhat incipient heart ailments — enlargement of heart, hardening of arteries and irregular pulsations. Only then, he began to learn and practice the T.C.C. Health exercise daily under a Grand Master — Mr. Wu Kuei-Ching. After the first year, the ailments were found to have been arrested and, after another year, his heart condition was medically found to have become normal. Ever since, he has performed his daily exercise without letup and his health has continually improved. Now he has reached 83 and has not had a single day of indisposition or ailment during the last few years residing in this country; and his health is much better than that in his younger age. It is his desire to interest others in this Chinese ancient system of exercise in order to share its benefits and, while living in California and now in New York (Flushing), he has been tutoring a number of the middle-aged and oldsters."

regard to conditions of the body after a long practice, "the cheeks will have a healthy red color; the temples will be full and swelling; the ears will be crimson; mentality will be alert, the eyeballs will be brilliant and full of spirit. The voice will be loud and reach far. Breathing will be regular, with no panting and hastiness. The teeth, the gums, and the jaw will be strong. The shoulders and chest will be sturdy and sleek. The abdomen will be solid and elastic like drum leather. When one is standing, the two feet will be as firm as if stuck to the ground, and capable of changing from substantiality to insubstantiality and vice versa. The step will be light. The muscles will be as soft as cotton when the intrinsic energy is active. Besides, the skin will be smooth and rosy, and sensitively auditive".3

Hence, from the therapeutic point of view, Tai Chi Ch'uan is beneficial to the young and old, women and men, particularly to those elderly people who are not able to participate in the more strenuous exercises or sports of the West.

---

3 Yearning K. Chen, *Tai Chi Ch'uan, Its Effects and Practical Applications*, Shanghai 1948, pp. 10-12. See also Sophia Delza, *Body and Mind in Harmony, Tai Chi Ch'uan — An Ancient Chinese Way of Exercise to Achieve Health and Tranquility*, David McKay Co., New York, 1961, Chaps. 1-11; also Edward Maisel, *Tai Chi for Health*, Prentice Hall, New York, 1964.

CHAPTER VI

TAI CHI CH'UAN
IN THE LIGHT OF MODERN PHILOSOPHY
AND SCIENCE

Tai Chi Ch'uan is not only a Chinese system of art or exercise, it is but also a view of life; the major aspects of this art have diminished into the shade, while only a small part remains known. Still less known is its philosophic and scientific aspects. For the reasons previously given, Tai Chi Ch'uan appears to be a system of philosophic and scientific exercise, inexhaustible qualitatively and quantitatively. Of its many aspects of being, the following can be differentiated: philosophical, physical, biological, psychological, and ethical.

A. The Philosophical Aspects of Tai Chi Ch'uan

On the philosophic plane Tai Chi Ch'uan is based on the philosophy of the *I Ching* and the view of the world of Neo-Confucianism. According to modern research (particularly that of Joseph Needham), modern science is now being obliged to incorporate it into its own structure; that is, the philosophy of organism.

The idea of organism first springs to the Chinese mind closely connected with the Eight-Trigrams of the *I Ching,* Yang and Yin, Chien and Kun acting as the positive and negative poles respectively of a cosmic field of force. Tung Chung-shu (董仲舒) (c. 179-c. 104 B.C.) of the Han Dynasty and Chu Hsi (朱熹) (1130-1200) of the Sung Dynasty further developed this line of thought and the implication was that the universe itself is a vast organism, and that the human body is but a small organism. It has only recently been pointed out by a distinguished scientist such as Needham that the philosophy of organism in Europe owes a great deal to Leibniz, whose mind was stimulated by the Neo-Confucianist version of Chinese correlativism. The contributions made by Leibniz, radically new to European thought, was Chinese in inspiration.

At present, with the interaction not only of all philosophical systems both Occidental and Oriental, but also of all cultures in which these systems have developed, philosophy is in a state of flux. However, its main stream and tendency are clear. In the light of dialectic, the Hegelian form of idealism found its antithesis in the 19th century in a wholesome revolt stemming from many directions: e.g., from various Naturalistic philosophies such as Dialectic Materialism and Evolutionary Naturalism, from Neorealism, and finally from those contemporary types of philosophy such as Pragmatism, Logical Positivism, and Existentialism.

Here, is it not possible that a new synthesis in philosophy is now in the ascendency, and this points toward some kind of organism. The trend, which is undoubtedly represented by Whitehead, runs in various ways through all modern research in methodology and the world picture of the natural and social sciences — the development of field physics, the biological, psychological, sociological, culturological, and anthropological formulations. While there are still many mechanistic biologists, there is far more emphasis on emergent evolution, holism, configurationalism, integralism, and last, but by no means least, the philosophy of organism.

There is no reason to suppose that the new synthesis will mark the end of the dialectical process of human thought. What is significant is that the philosophy on which Tai Chi Ch'uan is based, is a theoretical organism which Leibniz and Whitehead applied to Nature, and which had originated in China.

B. The Physical Aspects of Tai Chi Ch'uan

Tai Chi Ch'uan, besides being helpful for the achievement of health and tranquility, contributes a way of meeting "a great force with a small one" in self-defense. This is due to the application of the laws of dynamics in physics. A few fundamental points can be explained in the following principles:

A. In accordance with the laws of force, its effect, time and changes of velocity: In self-defense or wrestling, those who practice the techniques of the Exoteric School, (Wai Chia) (外家), are versed in the act of striking the opponent with high speed and the greatest strength possible, and the result lies in an infliction of pain or injury on the enemy. Except with powerful strength, it is not easy to cause the opponent's downfall, or lead him to a change of position on account of the speed of force. Although the striking techniques of Tai Chi Ch'uan, particularly in regard to the use of force and the retarded speed of the movements of the hands, are employed in different ways according to different circumstances, the striking hand, after its contact with the body of the opponent, does not retreat at once. On the contrary, additional force is consciously and continually made felt on the body of the opponent, in order to prolong its effects and time. In this way, the body of the opponent will follow the direction of the force and change its original position. This is performed in accordance with Newton's Second Law of Motion, which states: "The change of motion is proportional to the motive force impressed; and is made in the direction of the straight line in which that force is impressed," or "the acceleration is proportional to the resultant force and is in the same direction as this force." The use of the so-called "intrinsic energy" (內勁) in the techniques of Tai Chi Ch'uan is very much identical with the implication of Newton's Second Law: it is not the problem of the nature of force, but the problem of the effect and time of force.

B. In accordance with the Law of the Inertia of the Physical Body: Newton's first Law of Motion states: "A body at rest or in uniform motion will remain at rest or in uniform motion unless some external force is applied to it." We realize that the physical body has the characteristic of maintaining its tranquility, or the mood of motion, and these characteristics are known as "inertia" in dynamics. Again Newton's Third Law of Motion tells us: "To every action force there is an equal and opposite reaction force." For example, when you fire a gun, you will experience its recoil, which is the result of the physical body's reaction force. With regard to the example of inertia, the sudden stop of a bus will cause the man standing to be thrown forward or even thrown down on the floor. This is an expression of inertia in the physical body. In the striking technique of Tai Chi Ch'uan, the less force you use the better, the aim being to avoid reaction force of falling on one's own body. Next, after the use of force on the opponent's body, where he resists you with tremendous strength, you should reduce your own force, or loose your own hand, in order to control him by the law of inertia in the physical body. In this case, he will go forward involuntarily and continually, and might eventually lose his equilibrium. If an added force is extended on his body in the same direction of his falling, he will be thrown down immediately.

C. In accordance with the Principle of Resultant Force: In the techniques of Tai Chi Ch'uan, what is important is to apply the law of non-resistance ("yielding") and not to use force or strength to resist the force or strength of the opponent. On the contrary, one should add force to the opponent's force in accordance with its direction, in order to effect the loss of his equilbrium. This is, of course, performed on the basis of the resultant force. It is known that the chief characteristic of the technique of Tai Chi Ch'uan is its emphasis on "softness" and on taking favorable opportunity and situation in self-defense. Hence, there is a great difference between any method that emphasizes the use of "abrupt force" and "abrupt going forward" and those that emphasize the use of "feint energy" and neutralizing energy". By the former, the result is to defeat the slowness with greater speed, and the lesser force with greater force. By the latter, which is, of course, Tai Chi Ch'uan, its strategy in self defense is to wait for suitable opportunity with tranquility, and to use the energy to neutralize rather than to strike or resist.

D. In accordance with the Principle of Equilibrium of the Physical Body: The physical body has three kinds of equilibrium, namely: stable equilibrium, instable equilibrium and indifferent equilibrium. Where instable and indifferent equilibriums are concerned, it is necessary to attain the stability of the central equilibrium: otherwise the bodies are liable to fall flat easily. For the first kind, that is stable equilibrium, it is necessary, in order to stabilize its equilibrium to a greater degree, to lower its center of gravity on the one hand, and extend its base on the other. In a standing position the center of gravity of the human body is located at the Naval psychic center (a vital point known as "Tan Tien"). One is not able to attain a high degree of stability, in this case, without the aid of external body or force. The practitioner of the martial arts, for the purpose of stabilizing himself, has to lower his "breathing" (energy) down to the psychic center, to "breathe with the abdomen", so to speak. This is one of the first requisites, although he also pays attention to the base, that is the standing of the two feet. Hence in Tai Chi Ch'uan movements, one's own feet always change from insubstantiality (emptiness) to substantiality (solidity) and vice versa, so that when one foot is not firm, the weight of the body is supported by the other foot, and the posture becomes stabilized again. In other words, the base alters according to the shifting of the center of gravity, and this is one way to attain stable equilibrium or balance.

To sum up, every movement in Tai Chi Ch'uan is closely related to dynamics, which is not a mystic one as some people believe. That the circle neutralizes the forces of a coming attack is also a technique, the principle of which is closely related to Newton's Laws of Motion. Manifestly, the direction or route of any matter in motion is straight. If one intends to get control of the coming attacking force at an angle and change its direction and shift the opponent's center of gravity out of the base, the best technique is to adopt a circular formation. It does not only neutralize the attacking force, but also borrows it for one's own use: for the aid of a slight returning force usually leads to remarkable results in counter attack. If one dodges the coming force, a return hit following the opponent's retreating direction is likely to attain the maximum efficiency. Hence, the "neutralizing", "attacking" and "borrowing" techniques or "energies" in Tai Chi Ch'uan are based directly or indirectly on the principles and laws of physics.

C. The Biological Aspects of Tai Chi Ch'uan

The biological counterpart of "intrinsic energy" manifests itself in the very nature and basic processes of life. The energy, (the Chinese word "Chi" implies "energy plus matter"), still less known but often known as the "intrinsic energy" (內勁) or "vital energy", that mysteriously unites various inorganic energies into a startling unity of a living organism and directs the processes of organic evolution and improvement, is the first biological manifestation of the energy of love.[1]

Modern researchers in biology and bio-sociology have pointed out: "all inorganic matter as we see it within the stars, planets, rocks, sand and mountains is losing its energy through the disintegrating processes explained in the second law of thermodynamics. Now, the vital processes of organization in all organic life are functioning in the opposite direction by building up and constructively organizing the energies within the universe. It is the newly discovered law of the universe with its directiveness that will make us understand the unusual powers that exist in all of us as human beings."[2]   Although biological scientists are still unable to find the factors which determine directed expressions in the unfolding of the patterns of organs, nerves, muscles and blood vessels, laboratory experiments show that the encapsulated energy is released whenever we move a muscle. The

[1] Chi is similar to Prana in Yoga which is sometimes considered as "absolute energy", "cosmic energy", "vital energy" and "electronic energy".

[2] Quoted from Louis Allen Selzer, *A New Conception of the Universe*, a lecture given on July 15, 1960 at the Institute of Aeronautical Sciences.

biologist refers to the A.T.P. adenosine triphosphate which holds the potential energy of expression in the muscles, but he does not yet understand the organized vital forces which release the energy of this phosphate bonds.

The practitioners of Tai Chi Ch'uan believe that the directiveness in the organism is a "fundamental characteristic of life-phenomena" as basic and universal as the traits of "mutual aid" (Kropotkin's theory) and "struggle for existence" (Darwin's theory). Without the operation of a biological counterpart of intrinsic energy, life itself is not possible, nor its continuity, its evolution, the improvement of health, or the coordination of muscular and mental control.

It is on this level that the art of Tai Chi Ch'uan becomes interesting. It is interested in psychic spiritual processes, phenomena of internal concentration, meditation, consciousness, great inner control of mastering the mind within time and space, as well as the development of "intrinsic energy". Without the vital directive processes, integrating and coordinating functions of biological intrinsic energy, the world of life could hardly have emerged, the will could hardly have concentrated, and health could certainly not have improved.

D. The Psychological Aspects of Tai Chi Ch'uan

Psychologically, the experience of mind is a complex consisting of emotional, affective, volitional, and intellectual elements. Health is soundness of body and mind. In the East, health problems have always centered upon the psychological, spiritual and biological orientation. The West, in turn, has come to recognize that the health problem involves psychic health, tensions, psychic patterns, in the life of the individual by which his health is impaired. Thus the once neglected subject has become one of the principal studies of psychological, biological, and, even sociological and culturological scientists.[1]

First, there is the field of biochemistry, which in the past two dozen years has raised our understanding of life and the human machine to a new level. Scientists have told us that the human nervous system is a vast complex and highly integrated assembly of a trillion nerve cells or neurons. Nearly all of them are located in the brain and spinal cord, the central nervous system, with only fibers from these cells extending into the remotest parts of the body. In these nerve cells, "throbs the essential energy of life." Through them the body and mind alike are controlled, and the sense-motor mechanism is coordinated and integrated in such a way that conscious thought and direction of human activity become possible.

In the "breathing system", or "the internal exercise" of Tai Chi Ch'uan, the focal point is the central nervous system — including the brain and spinal cord. With the directive force of the mind or the psychic power, and proper breathing, it develops an "intrinsic energy" which tunes up the body, slows down the aging processes and lengthens the life span. It is the "intrinsic energy" which finally energizes the trillion cells or neurons, the key-note of life activity.

Secondly with the discovery of psychobiology, we understand that the human body harbors a host of "clocks" in the joints, brain, and other organs, that keep time in units ranging from twelve months to several years. When all the clocks in a given system are put in motion, the inherent cyclic characteristic of the organ is revealed. Indeed, the cyclic changes in almost every organ of the body, and in

---

1 For my theory of Culturology, see Pitram A. Sorokin, *Sociological theories of Today,* Harper & Row, New York & London, 1966, pp. 205 n. 389-391.

almost every mental and emotional function, have been found by scientists.

It is significant that all the movements in Tai Chi Ch'uan contain circles. All movements, both with and without forms, are composed of circles. When used, the circle should be distinguished as Yin and Yang, softness or firmness, substantiality and insubstantiality. That all these cyclic movements have their selective significance in the life of the human body is now known to scientists in the psychobiological field.

Thirdly, in this twentieth century, there is the new theory of matter being reducible to energy-signifying the mysterious power suggestive of the psychic. Likewise, in psychology, where behaviorism and other forms of mechanism are under criticism from many points of view, we come to appreciate the "holistic character" in the functioning of the human mind. As Harris reminds us, "in mind and in mind alone, we have the miracle of a fragment of the Universe, a fragment of the whole, with the capacity of thinking in the terms of the Whole."[3]

These lines give an idea of the importance of the mind in the Universe. Although many psychologists have acknowledged the fact that many external environmental factors affect behavior, recognition of the importance of many internal stimuli, — such as hunger and thirst, is one of the reasons why earlier "naive conceptions" of behavior, in which the human organism was regarded "as a ball pushed here and there before forces in the outside world, proved unsatisfactory." The known techniques of Tai Chi Ch'uan range widely in complexity from a single point to the most subtle circle. From the

[3] Errol E. Harris, *Nature, Mind and Modern Science*, New York: The Macmillian Co., 1945, p. 45.

training in postures to the control of the autonomic nervous system, what the Tai Chi Ch'uan classics did emphasize is the principle of "Mind over Matter". Our present conception of the effect of prayer or meditation upon pathological lesions is based upon observation of patients who have been cured almost instantaneously of various affections. Concentration, meditation, spiritual enlightenment, self-examination, and especially, the complex methods of Yoga, of Zen Buddhism, of the founders of the religions of love such as Confucianism, Taoism, Zoroastrianism, Hinduism, Jainism, Buddhism, Moism, Judaism, Christianity and other ethico-religious movements, all prove the objective importance of the spiritual activities which hygienicists, physicians, educators and sociologists have almost always neglected to study and to follow. They open the way to a new world, — the world of the mind.[1]

In the classics of Tai Chi Ch'uan, there is shown a very important principle, namely, "to use the mind, or ideas, to activate the Chi", (breathing or energy), and "to use the Chi (energy) to operate the body". And, in another context, it mentions the importance of "consciousness" or "idea," and the principle of employing "consciousness(idea) instead of force or strength." There is nothing that is metaphysical in these techniques. The secret of the power lies in the dedication and the cultivation of the spiritual, or psychic power in the human organism. After all, "man's freedom lies in his ability to cultivate his greatest source of creative and regenerative power." (Pitrim A. Sorokin)

[1] Teilard de Chardin considers 'love-energy' as the highest form of human-energy. Cf. His book — *Human Energy,* Collins, London, 1969, pp. 145-162. Sorokin comes to the same conclusion when he says: "Perish by your own hands, or rise to a higher moral level through the grace of Creative Love." Cf. "The Mysterious Energy of Love," in *Main Currents in Modern Thought,* Sept. 1958.

Finally, in Tai Chi Ch'uan, besides a requirement of the tranquil state of mind and full devotion or spiritual concentration on the movements during the exercise, special attention is given to deep breathing sinking down to the psychic center or the "Tan Tien" (naval or psychic center), and the movement of the transverse diaphragm. In so doing, the central nervous system and the "Abdominal Brain" are given the training due, and are consequently improved within days as the exercise goes on.

Some writers who are familiar with Oriental and Occidental philosophy consider that man has four brains, and not merely one as is commonly believed to be the case. Man's four brains, each having its separate characteristics and distinctive offices and functions, are as follows: (1) the Cerebrum, (2) the Cerebellum, (3) the Medulla Oblongata, and (4) the Solar Plexus, or Abdominal Brain. The Cerebrum is the highest and front portion of the "brains" located in the cranium or skull. The cerebellum is situated beneath the posterior lobes of the Cerebrum. The Medulla Oblongata is the upper and enlarged end of the spinal cord — the extension and prolongation of the latter into the cranium or skull. The Solar Plexus, or Abdominal Brain, is the great plexus, i.e., network of nerve-fibers, mass of nerve substance, etc., of the great Sympathetic Nervous System. "Its name, 'solar', was bestowed upon it by reason of (1) its central position; (2) the fact that its filaments extend in all directions to the important abdominal organs, like the rays of the sun; and (3) the fact that it is recognized as being the power-house, and great reservoir of 'life force', just as the sun is the great power-house and reservoir of material energy of our solar system."[4]

4 Theron Q. Dumont, *The Solar Plexus or Abdominal Brain*, 1918, p. 1-5.

Advanced modern psychologists are now making the same discovery, and bestowing new names upon the process. Although they give the old philosophers no credit, the facts remain the same. Here are the facts: the Cerebro-Spinal Nervous System, controlled by the Cerebrum — the seat of thoughts and ideas, is directly connected with the Sympathetic Nervous System, controlled by the Solar Plexus, or Abdominal Brain, — the seat of feelings and vital processes; they are connected by means of many delicate nervous filaments, or "connected nerves." This gives us the key to the "mind over body" methods, "mental healing," "suggestion," etc. The practitioners of Tai Chi Ch'uan simply follow the methods which were perceived, discovered and adopted by ancient Taoists, and which gave the latter the key to the practical methods of influencing, directing and controlling the the activities of the Sympathetic Nervous System.[5]

E. The Ethical Aspects of Tai Chi Ch'uan

Ethically, the view of life of the practitioners of Tai Chi Ch'uan is a synthesis of Confucianism, Taoism, and Zen Buddhism, and is the most profound achievement of the Chinese people. It may eventually become the foundation of a united movement for health of mind and body in the future.

First, according to the philosophy of organism, the Chinese philosophers (whether they are Confucianists, Taoists or Zen Buddhists), in reaching the ideas of Social Monism and Cosmic Consciousness, found that Tao is the Way of Life, and the Way of Life is Love. Love (or Jen) (仁) is, along with Truth and Beauty, one of the

---

[5] Figure 1, p. 190, Form 1, p. 189.

three highest forms of goodness. Chuang-tzu (莊子), (c. 369-286 B.C.) an eminent Taoist of the Pre-Chin period in China stated: "Heaven and Earth and I came into existence together, and all things with me are one." Hui Shih (惠施), (c. 370-310 B.C.) also said, "Love all things equally, Heaven and Earth are one body." In the hands of the Neo-Confucianists, scholars such as Luk Chiu-yuan (陸九淵) (1139-1193), reechoed the same theme by saying: "The universe is my mind, my mind is the universe." He also experienced an instantaneous enlightenment and said: "All affairs within the universe come within the scope of my duty; the scope of my duty includes all affairs within the universe." In this way, the ancient philosophers tended to make the whole universe one harmonious cosmos in which each particle is not fighting all the other but harmoniously working with the rest of the world.

In Tai Chi Ch'uan, the postures or forms were composed for the purpose of struggling with the inimical environment, in self-defense against the pressure of all inimical forces. But, in principle, what it emphasizes is non-aggression, non-violence, non-resistance, or non-opposition, and the overcoming of firmness with softness. It believes conflict of any kind inevitably leads to destruction of each creature. The fruit of conflict is only death. Love tends to destroy death itself, and replaces it with eternal immortality. Hence in the system of Tai Chi Ch'uan, its spiritual dedication, dedication to a noble humanitarian cause, to the Cosmic Love, in the view of modern sociologists and psychologists, is one of the most important factors for the prolongation of life.

Secondly, the view of life of the Tai Chi Ch'uanists is also derived from the philosophy of Laotze. The original problem of Laotze, and of the Taoists, was how to preserve life and avoid harm and danger in the human world. In order to live prudently, one must live according to Natural Law. Hence, Laotze warns us: "Not to know the invariables and to act blindly is to go to disasters." What he called the invariable or law of life is that: "The man who lives prudently must be meek, humble, and easily content." "To be meek is the way to preserve your strength and so be strong."

Accordingly, in Tai Chi Ch'uan, we intend to overcome activity with inactivity, firmness with softness, and to make use of the opponent's attacking force to strike back at him. This is equivalent to receiving any inimical force calmly, and creating suitable situations to take action. This is the way to punish a man by the laws made by himself. Thus, with "softness", "humility" and "sacrifice", we are far from being divorced from the laws of nature. On the contrary, we are within the continuum of the natural law. A revival of Taoism, — "the philosophy of the Future", as Needham, a famous scientist calls it, — will reveal the great ethical value of Tai Chi Ch'uan — the highway to eternal youth.

Thirdly, there is the gigantic power of love manifested in the undying influence of Buddha upon the countless millions of human beings, and on the course of history. His great compassion, his love for all creatures in the universe and his devotion to peace are indispensable for the physical, moral and mental growth of all human beings. Here is the heart and soul of freedom and of all moral values. In following Zen Buddhism, the secret of longevity of those who practice Tai Chi Ch'uan lies not only in their daily exercises, but also in their dedication to the altruistic education of mankind and to the cultivation of the peace of mind in human fellows. The "sudden enlightenment" (Satori) and the "liberation of the mind," as practiced by the Zen Buddhists, have certainly incalculably increased the understanding of "Super-consciousness" and the moral output of the practitioners of Tai Chi Ch'uan.

　　While we may not pretend that our data suffice to admit of widespread generalizations in a topic of such vast importance for the health of human beings, they nevertheless should suffice to show that meaningful relationships between modern philosophy, science and Tai Chi Ch'uan are manifestly significant. We therefore sincerely hope that our "Theory of the Integral Tai Chi" (整合太極論) would give the world a new creative idea, and a fresh dynamic approach to the basic problems of Health as well as civilization. This philosophy of life is, after all, an all-embracing synthesis in world thought such as integrates the highest cultural values of East and West. it lays the foundation of the art of integrated living which aims at the unity of mankind — the collective community of Tatung "The Great Harmony" (大同) in the sense of Confucius.

PART II:

METHODOLOGICAL AND THEORETICAL

CHAPTER VII

FUNDAMENTAL POSTURES OF TAI CHI CH'UAN

Although in the movements of Tai Chi Ch'uan emphasis is laid on the "spirit" or "mind" rather than on the "forms" themselves, the learning of the forms must be accomplished. Please bear in mind that the "mind" runs the 'Chi' or energy, which in turn exercises the body, but we do need to master the forms as a proper foundation for further development in Tai Chi Ch'uan.

For this purpose we will attempt here to describe some of the important methods as well as patterns of the fundamental postures of Tai Chi Ch'uan. The descriptions are divided into two parts as follows:

The Method of Torso (Shen Fa 身法)

A. Straightening the Head: With regard to the posture of the head, one should always remember the following points: (1) The head should be erect and natural. (2) Except for a few postures which require a slight raising of the back, it is necessary to maintain a straight line from the coccyx to the neck. (3) Do not lower the head or look upward frequently or persistantly.

B. Normalization of the Face: Always maintain a good appearance and avoid tension. The following points are important: (1) Keep your eyes on a level base and avoid any angry gaze. The eyes, unless directed to move with the hands, look levelly forward with a quiet, comfortable but steady gaze. (2) The mouth must be kept slightly shut. The tip of the tongue should touch the upper palate. Always swallow the saliva, which is the treasure of the body. (3) Breathe naturally, deeply and slowly and through the nose. (See rules in the following chapter)

C. Relaxing of the Neck: While in movement, the neck should be relaxed, following the posture to right or to left, or vice versa. Do not exert strength and avoid tension.

D. Relaxing or hollowing of the Chest: To "relax the chest" is a 'must' in all the postures.

E. Raising of the Back: During the 'relaxing of the chest' the back naturally has to be slightly raised. This posture is to be accompanied by the 'lowering of the shoulders'. Avoid hunchback.

F. Tucking in the Buttocks: The buttocks must be tucked in, so that a straight line is maintained with the spinal cord.

G. Centralization of the Coccyx: This is a position that should always be maintained, so that the coccyx is in a central position.

H. Lowering of the Shoulders: The shoulders are low and loose and they are not to be pulled up.

I. 'Sinking' of the Elbows: The points of the elbows 'sink downward'. When they are pointed outward, the shoulders are pulled forward.

J. Loosening of the Waist: The waist is in an important key position, similar to the axis of the wheel. It must remain loose and moveable.

Method of The Fists (Ch'uan Fa 拳法)

The closing of the fingers into a fist in Tai Chi Ch'uan does not differ too much from that of other martial arts. In the beginning stage, one may close the fingers a little tighter, (the so-called 'solid fist') while in the last stage, following the differentiation of the posture into insubstantiality and substantiality, the closing of the fingers should follow the same pattern. While the solid fist is closed tightly, the empty fist remains loose. Generally speaking, the types of fist may be described as follows:

A. Normal Fist: The holding of the fist with the "Hu Kow" (虎口) facing upward, when expanding forward, or reversing backward. This is known as 'Normal Fist'.

B. Reversed Fist: This is the fist that has the "Hu Kow" facing downward. This is applied to fists that are raised higher than the head.

C. Standing Fist: The fist that has its knuckles facing upward is called "Standing Fist."

D. Punching Downward Fist: The type of fist that has its "Hu Kow' facing the front and the knuckles facing downward is called 'Punching Downward Fist'.

E. Facing Upward Fist: The type of fist that has its knuckles facing downward and the fingers facing upward is called 'Facing Upward Fist'.

F. Facing Downward Fist: The fist that has its knuckles facing upwards and the fingers facing downward is called the 'Facing Downward Fist'.

G. Paw Fist: There is one special type, the Paw (Chau 爪) Fist or

'Hooked Hand', where finger tips are closed, grasping the thumb. The tip of the thumb joins the fingers at their base. In this type, the fingers always move and point downward to the floor with bending wrist.

Method of Palms (Chang Fa 掌法)

In the beginning stage, the pushing outward and reversing backward of the palms should be done naturally and comfortably without using any strenuous force. When one is in the advanced stage, and knows the difference between insubstantiality (empty) and substantiality (solid) of posture, one should try to express this mood in the palms. In pushing forward, open the fingers slightly, the strength residing at the root of the palm. This is called a 'Solid Palm'. When reversing, the palm gradually loosens, and this is called 'Empty Palm'. In the Theory of Tai Chi Ch'uan, Wang Tsung Yueh said: "The root (of energy) is embraced in the feet. It springs from the legs, commands the waist, and expresses itself in the fingers." This implies that the direction of the energy to the hands should be adjustable to the whole movement of waist, legs and feet. The various palm methods, based upon the directions and symbols of the palms are as follows:

A. Normal Palm: The finger tips pointing upward, the middle of the palm facing the front, and the wrist forming a ninety-degree angle upward. This is called 'Normal Palm'.

B. Standing Palm: The fingers point upward, the middle of the palm facing other directions than the front. This is called 'Standing Palm'.

C. Hanging Palm: The fingers point downward, regardless of the direction which the palm is facing. This is called 'Hanging Palm'.

D. Facing Upward Palm: The middle of the palm faces upward, or upward diagonally, regardless of the direction the finger tips are pointing. This is called 'Facing Upward Palm'.

E. Facing Downward Palm: The middle of the palm faces downward or diagonally downward, regardless of the directions to which the finger tips are pointing. This is called 'Facing Downward Palm'.

F. Side-Standing Palm: The tip of the thumb points upward and the palm stands sideward, regardless of the direction that the middle of the palm is facing. This is called 'Side-Standing Palm'.

G. Reserved Palm: The palm stands sideward, and the thumb faces downward. This is called 'Reversed Palm'.

Method of The Legs (Tui Fa 腿法)

In the postures of Tai Chi Ch'uan, with the exception of the 'Riding Horse' step, in which the two legs are used to hold the weight of the torso, the weight of the torso is usually held by one leg. In movement, the leg which holds the weight of the body is used to train the strength of the muscle of the leg. Based on definite standards, the methods of the legs may be classified as follows:

A. Raised Leg: While the leg holding the weight of the body is slightly bent, raise the other leg with knee thigh high. When the raised leg is straightened, the tip of the toes point upward. Furthermore, the whole body, while performing this posture, should be kept loose and stabilized. This is an important point which should be emphasized in the various styles of the leg method.

B. Kicking Leg: After raising the leg, kick to the front, or to the left or the right. During the kicking, the whole leg is straightened, thigh high. The using of the sole to kick out is called 'kick with sole', and the using of the tip of the toes to kick is called 'kicking upward'.

C. Leg Kicking Horizontally (Pei Lien Chiao 擺蓮脚): In this style, only the right leg is used. Raise it, with the tip of the toes pointing upward, and circle it upward from the left to the right, hip high, and kick to the right.

D. Bowing Leg: This is the method which is generally used in the solid step. While one leg, either right or left, is bowing, the knee of which is in a vertical straight line with the toes at the front, the hind leg remains natural and relatively straight without using strength. The sole touches the ground, and the whole weight of the body is on the bowing leg.

E. Sitting Leg: This is the method used in the 'empty step'. While drawing on the bowing leg backward half a step with toes touching the ground, (empty step), shift the weight of the body to the other leg with knee bending. This is called 'Sitting Leg'.

F. Seated Leg: There are two styles in this position. One is the 'Horse Riding Step', (Ch'i Ma Pu 騎馬步). According to this style one should separate one's feet by a space equal to double the length of the foot, (about two feet, or two feet and a half). Place the toes slightly outward, with knees and tips of toes in the same direction. The other is the "Creeping Down" style, (Hsia Shih 下式). Draw the upper part of the body backward and lower it. The center of gravity is shifted to the right foot, and the right leg is bent, while the toes of the left foot turn to the right with the toes raised. Sit down on the right foot as far as possible. As the right foot stands still, the left leg is straightened.

Method of The Feet (Chiao Fa 脚法)

The movements of the feet are actually parts of the movements of the legs. However, for the sake of clarity, this section is added and may be considered as a supplement to the former.

A. Kicking With Sole (Teng Chiao 蹬脚): Stand still with one leg bending, kick with the sole of the other leg slowly in front. The tips of the toes of the kicking foot point upward and inward, while the energy is to be concentrated and exerted downward.

B. Kicking With Tip of Toes: Stand still with one leg, knee bending, raise the other and kick with the tip of the toes slowly, hip high. As to directions: the right foot kicks to the right front, while the left to the left front.

C. Separation of Foot: In the styles of the "Separation of the Right or Left Foot", their postures are the same as stated in "Kicking With Tip of Toes". No kicking is involved in these postures, however.

D. Turning of Foot: In order to turn the body, one must turn the foot first. To turn the left foot, the heel is generally used, while the other part of the foot (tip of toes) is raised above the floor. To turn the right foot, the tip of the same foot is generally employed, while the other part of the foot (sole) is raised above the floor. If the two legs have to turn simultaneously, one foot must remain on the 'solid step', while the other is on the 'empty' step.

E. Putting Down the Foot: To put the foot in front, the heel reaches the ground first and then stabilizes the foot slowly. To put the foot down in back (in the retreating backward step, the tip of the toes reach the ground first). In some 'empty steps', it must be pointed out, the tip of the toes, at the front, also reaches the ground first.

F. Shifting of the Leg: In the shifting of weight from one leg to the other, stabilize the body first on the 'solid leg', which is slightly bent, then raise the other leg to take a forward or backward step slowly. This is done by controlling the knee bends. Do not shift a step without stabilizing on the 'solid leg'.

Method of The Steps (Pu Fa 步法)

The postures of steps in Tai Chi Ch'uan are differentiated into two catagories: The Yin, (insubstantial, or empty), and Yang, (substantial, or solid). In other words, when the left leg step is 'solid', it is also the one which holds the weight of the body, and vice versa. The types of step may be described as follows:

A. Front Bowing Step: This is a 'solid step', in which the front knee is bent supporting the weight of the body. While the hind leg is relatively straightened, the sole of the two legs are not in one straight line. The rear sole may stay diagonally, and the distance between the two feet is approximately equal to the double width of the shoulders. The front leg and the hind leg are parallel, though the tip of the front foot may turn slightly inward. If the bending leg is on the left side, it is the "Left Front Bowing Leg," and vice versa. This type of step is used in the forms such as: 'Grasping the Bird's Tail', 'Single Whip', 'Brush Knee and Twist Step', 'Flying Slantingly', 'Fan Through the Back', 'Chop Opponent With Fist', 'Strike, Parry and Punch', 'Hit Tiger at Left and Right', 'Separation of Wild Horse's Mane', 'Fair Lady at Shuttles' and 'Shoot Tiger With Bow'.

B. Rear Sitting Step: This type of step is also called 'empty step' and is generally formed by reversing the solid step in half a step backward. Draw the front bowing foot close to the hind foot, which is holding the weight of the body, and let the left front foot hang loosely with toes touching lightly on the ground. The torso is erect, and must not bend forward. The distance between the front and rear foot is about the length of the solid step. If you are sitting on the left leg, this is called 'Left Leg Sitting Step', and vice versa. This type of step is used in the forms such as 'Pulling Back', 'Apparent Close Up', and 'Repulse Monkey'.

Parallel Step: The two feet stand parallel, approximately five to seven inches apart toes pointing to the front. This type of step is used mostly in the 'Commencement' and 'Conclusion'.

Riding Horse Step: With the two feet standing parallel, knees bent, the distance between the two feet is about double the length between the two shoulders. The weight of the body is equally supported by the two feet. Technically speaking, this might lead to the error that is known as 'double weightedness', but, actually, the two legs should be differentiated into insubstantiality and substantiality in the transition of the movement. This type of step is used in the forms such as the 'Waving Hands Like Clouds' and 'Cross Hands'.

Fishing Horse Step: This type of step is similar to that of the 'Rear Sitting Step', the front leg of which hangs backward loosely with heel raised and the toes touching the ground slightly. The distance of the two feet is approximately one or two inches between that of the front and the hind foot, or the left and right one. If the leg is in the front, it is called the 'Left Fishing Horse Step', and vice versa. In the forms such as the 'Stork Spreads Its Wings' 'Needle at Sea Bottom', 'High Pat on Horse', 'Step Up to Form Seven Stars', 'Retreat to Ride Tiger', this type of step is used.

F. T-Shaped Step (Ting-Tzu Pu 丁字步): This type of step is similar to that of the 'Sitting Backward Step', except that the front leg is slightly raised with heel touching the ground and the rear leg is at right with the front leg in the front. It is called the 'Left T-Shaped Step', and vice versa. This is the type of step used in the following forms: 'Play the Fiddle', 'Raise Hands and Step Up', and 'Fist Under Elbow'.

G. Creep-Down Step: This type of step has been described in the above section on Method of the Legs, (the second style of the 'Sitting Leg'). Those who have high blood pressure, however, are not encouraged to creep down too low at the beginning stage. It is used only in the form known as 'Creep Down', also called 'Snake Creeps Down'.

It is necessary to familiarize oneself with the above fundamental postures that are part of the techniques of Tai Chi Ch'uan. Remember to practice them well as this will facilitate the process of performing the forms as a whole.

CHAPTER VIII

A SUMMARY OF THE PRINCIPLES AND

METHODS OF TAI CHI CH'UAN

I. Introductory Remarks:

Tai Chi Ch'uan is a very ancient Chinese art of exercise for Health and Science of Meditation through Movement, the study or training of which involves six steps:

1. The study or training in the 'form' or structure (task framework).
2. The study or training in the "Reeling of Silk" (circular movements).
3. The study or training in the differentiation of "Intrinsic Energy" (Tenacious strength).
4. The study or training of Chi Kung (breathing system).
5. The study and training of the Shen (spirit).
6. The study and training in the coordination of the internal and external movements.

There are five orders to be completed:

1. Training the body in movements in order to generate more intrinsic energy.
2. Controlling the intrinsic energy by the mind or consciousness in harmony with sustained rhythms.

3. Combining intrinsic energy (精), breathing (氣) and spirit (神) to achieve Unity or Harmony.

4. Transmuting the Spirit into Void (虛) (Emptiness).

5. Transmuting the Void into Tao (道)[1]. (Spiritual Enlightenment).

Speaking of the Form or Structure or Team Framework, there are at least three or four different schools existing in China which have drawn their origins from the Chen Clan or school. In spite of the differences in their structures through revisions by different masters of the different schools, the principles are basically the same. The original documents which are respected faithfully and adopted consistently up to the present are no other than Chang San-feng's "Theory of Tai Chi Ch'uan", Wu Yu Hsiang's "Treatise on the Thirteen Postures," and Wang Tsung Yueh's "Theory of Tai Chi Ch'uan". (See Texts at the end of this book). However, due to the emphasis either on the principle of the unyielding (yang, hardness, rigidity), a great number of controversies have emerged. In order to dispose of the misunderstandings, the present summary aims at a synthetic study — the combining of the yielding and unyielding principles.

As we know, the basic principle of Tai Chi Ch'uan comes from the *I Ching,* it would be a right way to behave oneself in accordance with its principle — the "Mean"; that is balancing the complementary nature of Yin and Yang, instead of emphasizing one aspect of these forces.

---

[1] Laotzu said: "Being in accord with Tao is to be eternal. Although his body may die and decay, he shall live forever." The Book of Tao, translated by Frank J. MacHovec, The Peter Pauper Press, N.Y. 1962. page 25.

II. Outline of The Principles and Methods of
Practising Tai Chi Ch'uan

I. In posture, the trunk is upright, erect, comfortable. Body and mind: relaxed and calm.[1]

"The trunk must be kept standing perfectly erect, centrally balanced, comfortable and relaxed so that it can deal with the impacts from the eight directions." This is the instruction handed down to us by Wang Tsung Yueh in regard to the training of the body The trunk, first of all, should be upright, no inclining to either side. Let the body be relaxed to the state of complete comfort and the mind remain calm. No abrupt strength is to be used. It is of utmost importance

[1] Yang Cheng-fu, the   master of the Yang Style of Tai Chi Ch'uan, in his "Outlines of the Art of Tai Chi Ch'uan", had laid down the principles of Tai Chi Ch'uan as follows:
(1) Keep your head clear and alert;
(2) Chest in and back straight;
(3) Loins relaxed and legs spread out in sitting posture;
(4) Distinguish between the substantial (solid) and insubstantial (empty movements);
(5) Shoulders lowered down and arms hanging;
(6) Using idea (mind) but not force;
(7) Coordination between the upper and lower parts of the body;
(8) Keep the internal organs in harmony with the external body;
(9) Keep the movements continuous without a break; and
(10) Keep motion in calm posture.[1]
[1] Quoted from Han Cheng-Shen and Lu Chung-Shau, *The Defense-Offensive and Defensive-Offensive Types of Tai Chi Ch'uan*, East and West, Volume X, Number 8, August, 1965, p. 7. (Taipei, Taiwan).

to adjust breathing, and use the mind to cause the movement of the Chi (energy or breathing), and the Chi to move the body. In this way, one can change with alertness and all the movements will fit completely with the physiological needs of the human body.

The methods are:

.1   The head: To keep the head "hanging straight up", and let the spirit go directly to the crown, this is called: "the intrinsic energy at the crown is insubstantial and alert."   If one's head is erect, his spirit will be stirred up and the upright erection of the trunk of the body will be maintained.   Hence in Wang's "Theory" it has this to say: "If the Shen (spirit) can be roused, then there is no reason for anxiety about the clumsiness and heaviness.   To achieve this, one should feel that the top of the head is suspended from above."   With the erection of the head, one's tongue should touch the palate.   Breathing should come through the nostrils, and the gaze to be at the front.

2.   The coccyx: The coccyx should be centrally balanced in order that the spinal column is upright.   In this way, the central nervous system will receive remarkable benefits through the proper circulation of the Chi in the whole body.

3.   Relaxing the chest (chest in) and drawing the shoulder blades together.   A preface to this exercise involves seeing how close one can draw one's shoulder blades together and how far one can relax one's chest.   As a rule, the relaxing of the chest and the drawing of the blades together immediately open the chest cavity.   The Chi sinks naturally to the Tan T'ien, and the body will be light and freemoving with the head standing upright and erect.

4.   Sinking the shoulders and keeping the elbows downward. To sink the shoulders is to loosen the two shoulders and let them hang downward in order for the intrinsic energy to sink to the tips of the elbows and through them to the fingers.   In pushing the hands for-

ward, consciousness should be placed at the middle of the palms. However, to use the "mind" (idea) or consciousness is to avoid the asserting of muscular strength.

5.   Relaxing the waist and keeping the buttocks round. Relaxing the waist leads to the sinking down of the Chi, thus enabling the legs to be stabilized. The suitable changes of substantiality and insubstantiality of the limbs depend mostly upon the suitable movements of the waist and legs. It is said in the "Theory": "Constant care must be taken about the waist and the spinal column". Again: "The Chi is similar to the wheel, and the waist the axis." In the application of this exercise, either in the structure (team framework) or in Joint Hands Operations (Tui Shou), it seems that the pulling or pushing of the opponent should be accomplished by the hand movement. In fact, it is the intrinsic energy coming from the legs and waist and carried by the mind that takes the Chi circulation to the fingers. The waist is the main pivot of the body. If the waist moves, the Chi a priori (primal energy) will revolve like the wheel, reaching the whole body without the slightest hinderance. Hence, the relaxation of the waist is of utmost importance. The change from one posture to another must be preceded by the loosening of the waist. In order to do this, one must avoid the error of closing the buttocks. And to activate the steps, the buttocks have to be round shaped. How can this be done? The way to do this is to maintain the elasticity of the two legs and the loosening of the intrinsic energy of the buttocks. With the round shape of the buttocks, one's steps in retreat, turn, and change can therefore be alert and nimble.

6.   The relaxing of the whole body. Tension leads to the strain of body, and impairs natural circulation. Relaxation, which is a mood and movement, relieves tension. A relaxed body is a normal body. Relaxation of the eyes and mind brings relaxation of the whole

body. The general relaxation, physical and mental, increases circulation, sinks the Chi downward, and brings about improved physical and mental health. With the complete relaxation of the body, there will be no abrupt force that remains in the body. With proper understanding and good technique, one allows relaxation to permeate the mind and body. Then, and only then, will dynamic coordination and function take place.

7. Calmness of the mind. "Calmness means no reckless use of the mind: tranquil repose means keeping oneself in harmony of feelings." ("Great Learning" 大學). When one concentrates the mind, the Chi can be sunk downward to the Tan T'ien, and the movements will attain a state of comfort.

8. Appearance: With regard to the aspect of the body, the appearance should always be normal. In any action, keep the posture exact, and the trunk centralized, i.e. the central equilibrium must be maintained. Cultivate the Chi and nourish the Spirit (shen) by harmonizing the breath. With regard to dynamics, "The appearance should always be alert as a falcon ready to pounce on a rabbit, the spirit, as a cat seizing a mouse." "In quietitude, one resembles the mountain; in motion, a river." (Wang's Theory). All such aspects come from the mind or consciousness of the body, not from the outside.1

---

[1] In Yang Cheng-fu's *"Method of Application of Tai Chi Ch'uan,"* there is a song which reads:
"How can one have no training in the body trunk, appearance, waist and head?
A lack of one item is simply a waste of time.
Assiduously learning the practice of the waist and head motions will develop many changes.
One will find himself relaxed and comfortable by keeping his trunk and appearance natural.
There are no other true principles than these.
Not understanding them will make one more muddles even when he has practiced for many years."
Quoted from Li Peng-fan, *The Initial Tasks in Learning Tai Chi Ch'uan,* East and West Monthly, Vol. X. No. 11, Nov. 1965, p. 6, Taipei, Taiwan.

II. All Actions should be light, nimble and alert, emphasizing continuity, flexibility, circling and unity.

In the training method of Tai Chi Ch'uan, "using the mind to move the Chi (breath, energy or prana) with quiet effort, the Chi may, therefore, be 'occluded' (gathered or stored) into the bones." "Using the Chi to mobilize the body without hinderance, the body may, therefore, be serviceable and at the desire of the will." (Wang's Theory). Any action, whether the hands or legs, must be conducted or directed by the mind, coordinated with the breathing. The slow and light motions, starting from the Commencement up to the Conclusion must be continual. In the changing of postures, methods, Chi and momentum, the motions are similar to the "Reeling of Silk" (circling), the aim consisting of "CONTINUITY, FLEXABILITY, CIRCLING AND UNITY", the methods of which are:

1. Continuity (Lien): one posture leads to another posture; one posture connects with another posture. They are like "a string of pearls strung together", and similar to "a grand river flowing endlessly." This is what is called Continuity — the MOMENTUM of Tai Chi.

2. Flexibility (Mien): To be flexible is soft, to be soft is loose, to be loose is nimble. Relaxing the whole body, one uses the mind to move the Chi, and uses the Chi to operate the body. Every motion in the first stage is adjusted to natural breath, the slower the better. It is again similar to the "reeling of silk." This is what is called flexibility — the IDEAL of Tai Chi.

3. Circling (Yuan): In movements, whether they are curving

or stretching, rising or falling, advancing or retreating, the developmental processes are circular. Circular-chain-revolution is a physical phenomenon as well as a physiological phenomenon. The universe is circular revolution in large scale and the atom is its miniature. The human body is an organism which repeats the same series of circular movements again and again in order to fulfill its natural function. Concerning the circular movement applying to Tai Chi Ch'uan, we find Wang Tsung Yueh's Theory has this to say: "In the direction of the Chi, it should be done as if it were circling the 'nine-curved string of beads', reaching the tiny cells." (Wang's Theory). This is what is called the CONFIGURATION of Tai Chi.

4. Harmony (Ho): In internal movements, the consciousness is identified with Chi, and the Chi with intrinsic energy. In external movement, the hands, eyes, trunk and steps are coordinated with each other. The Chi is "like the wheel, while the waist is like the axis." All the actions — up or down, out or in, to and fro, dynamic or static, insubstantial or substantial, curving or stretching — are united as a whole. This is what is called Harmony — the TECHNIQUE of Tai Chi.

III. Actions are adjusted to breathing, the unity of the internal and the external.

Deep breathing is necessary for health. In fact, we can breathe our way to better health and better living. In the exercise of Tai Chi Ch'uan, all actions are adjusted to breathing, using consciousness, not force. However, the training for proper breathing may be divided into three stages: (1) The inhaling and exhaling should be done through the nose; not the mouth.   Natural breath is encouraged for the beginners.   (2) After having acquired the skill of the movements, of each posture—inhale, while rising or extending; exhale while sinking—each posture should be coordinated with breathing.   In the operating or withdrawing, exhale while extending the fist, and inhale while withdrawing the fist.   In this stage one should breathe evenly, lightly, slowly, deeply and in longer intervals.   In this way, the eyes, brain, and internal organs can be enhanced.   (3) If striving for perfection, "one should attempt gradually to direct the Chi to be collected or gathered into the marrow, expressed in the spirit, harmonized with the breath, congealed in the ears, activated in the waist, alerted in the crown, reached toward the back, pulled by the heels, stemmed through the legs, operated by the hands, and functioning in the fingers," (quoted from the "Song of Tai Chi Ch'uan"). This type of exercise, actually, is rooted in the soles, leading to the spine and fingers.   It is technically called "urged by the roots". Besides, one must use the fingers to lead the forearms, the forearms to lead the elbows, the elbows to lead the shoulders, and the shoulders to lead the trunk.   This type of "running momentum" starts from the external to the internal, using the hands as "ends", and the waist as "axis".   It is technically called, "Fingers Leading".   In brief the methods for the practicing of breathing are:

1.   Natural Breath: Do the best one can and try to understand that one is required to learn slowness in posture and in motion. Continued practice will make breathing natural, deeper and more regular.

2.   Motions coordinated with breath: "To bend is to inhale, to expand is to exhale; to "receive" is to inhale, to release (discharge) is to exhale and sink the Chi downward."   All these have to be done without exhaustion.

3. The Unity of the External and the Internal: In order to realize this objective, one must harmonize the Chi with the motions of the body. To operate the Ching or intrinsic energy, momentum must be started from the root (sole or heel), and the "running momentum" is to be led by the fingers. In this way, the internal and external motions will be integrated as a whole.

IV. The breath is deep and natural — the Chi is directed by the mind to sink downward to the Tan T'ien (丹田).

In order to attain deep and natural breath, the abdominal type of breathing is used, that is, the Chi should be directed mentally to the Tan T'ien. (According to the practitioners of this art, the breath should originate from the Tan T'ien and return to it.") Its position in a person of average height may be detetrmined as follows. Divide the horizontal line joining the navel and the spine in the ratio of 3:7, measuring from the former. The Tan T'ien is then situated at about 1-1/3 inches below the point of intersection."[1] This type of breathing can achieve results such as: rid the lungs of accumulated impurities, restore the lungs to full use, and one feels better, has more energy (or oxygen), suffers less from fatigue, sleeps better, and wakes up faster. Furthermore, in order to realize the full benefit of abdominal breathing, one should utilize the inhalation and exhalation to excite the motions of the internal organs. The glands will thus be greatly strengthened. It also possesses the merits of expediting blood cir-

[1] Chi Kiang-tao, *Tai Chi Ch'uan, the Physical Exercise for Maintaining Health and Preventing Sickness,* West and East Monthly, Volume No. 7, July, 1965, p. 9.

culation, improving the cardiac muscle, nutrition, and liver function, and promoting the metabolism of the whole body. These come from the working of the Harmonizing of the Breath "Nei Kung" (Internal Functioning), the methods of which are:

1. Natural and deep Breathing: In breathing, avoid the use of force. Use the mind or consciousness to direct the Chi to drop to the abdomen and harmonize the breath quietly — this is a type of abdominal breathing.

2. The Chi has to be sunk to the "Tan T'ien": Using the abdominal type of breathing, one should breathe deeply, slowly and quietly and let the Chi (breath) sink to, and abide in, the Tan T'ien. Again, the Chi in the Tan T'ien is to be excited in order to move the internal organs, to increase the secretion of the glands, and the nutritional process — this is the function of mobilizing the Chi. (It is to be added, in order to sink the Chi to the Tan T'ien, one should relax the chest and draw the blades of the shoulders together, for the Chi can only sink freely when the chest is relaxed.)

V. Cultivating the Chi, harmonizing the breath, and the controlling of the mind and spirit inwardly.

In the exercise, to cultivate or nourish the Chi is of utmost importance. "There is no harm in cultivating the Chi", said Menicus. Again, in order to cultivate the Chi, one should harmonize the breath as quietly as possible, the methods of which are:

1. Harmonizing the Breath: The Chi has to be cultivated calmly and smoothly without any compulsion. This is the Taoist principle of non-action, yet full of action." When the mind moves,

the Chi follows. If the consciousness is calm, the Chi sinks right down to the Tan T'ien. Hence, in order to harmonize the breath, the mind and Chi must be in a state of quietitude.

2. The mind and Spirit should be controlled inwardly. In order to do this, one has to concentrate the mind first. After the controlling of the mind, as well as the spirit, they both should abide with the Chi in the "Tan T'ien." With the condensing of the vitality into Chi, the latter will be condensed into intrinsic energy. This is the technique of cultivating the Chi.

VI. Exciting of the Chi in its circulation in the body.

Besides the cultivating of the Chi, this exercise also emphasizes the operating (or mobilizing) of the Chi.1 The technique for the operating of the Chi is to use the mind-consciousness to direct or lead the Chi in the Tan T'ien to circulate in the whole body. When the Chi has been sunk to the Tan T'ien, it should be excited. The main result is this: with the arriving of the Chi, the intrinsic energy emerges. It is important to understand that the "intrinsic energy"

---

1 "Tai Chi Ch'uan theoreticians speak of "the Chi as sinking to, and abiding in, the Tan Tien or circulating throughout the body." They speak of the mind's "mobilizing the Chi, or the Chi's 'mobilizing the body,' or of the Chi's 'being gathered into the bones'. At the highest level, they inquire if one's concentration of Chi has brought one to the pliability of an infant. All these expressions refer to the derivation of power from Chi through mass integration. The power thus derived is, like that of massed wind or water, simply immense." Quoted from Cheng Man-ching, *Tai Chi Ch'uan, A Simplified Method of Calisthenics for Health and Self-Defense.* Taipei, 1961, p. 31.

(sometimes rendered as tenacious strength) is acquired through gradual practice, leading to perfect skill, and the final stage of "supernatural power" can only thus be realized.2 Their methods are as follows:

1. Excitement of the Chi has to be accomplished gradually: Using the mind-consciousness in the Tan T'ien to excite the Chi and to circulate it in the whole body without using force. (This is a "propelled movement", aiming also at exercising the internal organs.)

2. The leading of the Chi in the Tan T'ien should be adjusted or accompanied with the movements of the postures circulating within the whole body. Whenever the consciousness arrives, the Chi also arrives. The mind-consciousness goes together with the Chi.

2 Cheng Man Ching also said: "When the Chi has reached a certain stage of fullness as it accumulates in the Tan Tien, it begins to overflow. This overflowing Chi is physiological, commonly known in China as "hsueh Chi", literally, the Chi of the blood. Overflowing the Tan Tien, this sanguinary Chi, under the joint influence of the mind and the Chi itself, accumulates and generates 'heat' in the neighborhood of the lower extremity of the spine (Cf. Indian tantrism). As a result, more Chi is generated. When this stage is reached, the sanguinary Chi may be directed to propel the 'tsing Chi' (meaning the essence of life), causing the softer tendons and sinews, etc. to conduct the heat through the bone sheaths into the bones. The lower spinal vertebrae being thus heated up. the humour in them begins to 'sweat', just as the walls of a test tube filled with warm water sweats on cooling. On cooling, the sweat congeals as marrow, tightly adhering to the inner pores of the bones. In time, the bones will be filled up with the kind of marrow, which on repeated heating and cooling will be consolidated into something hard, tough, and indestructible (like resilient steel). When the Chi has entered, and rendered the bones consolidated and indestructible, the learner has reached the highest level at which the 'body' and 'function' of Tai Chi Ch'uan can no longer be separated; they have attained unity, (meaning the unity of the Tai Chi, i.e., of the Supreme Undifferentiated Absolute from which the name of Tai Chi Ch'uan was derived). The bones are now indestructible, tough, and resilient, not brittle or weak, but (strangely) as supple as in an infant's. This is rejuvenation; at least the possibility of it. Ibid, pp. 33-34.

After prolonged practice, the brute force and brute "Chi posteriori" will be totally eliminated and the intrinsic energy "à priori" (primal energy) will naturally increase. Once the habit becomes natural action, all the 'ideal-thought' force will control the physiological function. When one has achieved this advanced stage of maturity in training, one will go beyond the point of propelling the process of metabolism, attaining the objective of prolonging life and warding off disease.[1]

VII. In the practicing of the exercise the spirit should be absolutely integrated — the coordination of the hands and eyes.

What the exercise mostly needs is the absolute integration of the spirit — demanding what the practitioners used to call "mind arriving, eyes-arriving, and hands-arriving", in order that all parts of the body be kept as an integral whole. In the movements, use the consciousness to operate the hands, the hands to lead the elbows and the shoulders and the trunk. With the nose as boundary, the trunk is divided into left and right. The left hand takes care of the left side, while the right hand handles the right side. The two feet follow the two hands in coordinated motions. For the differentiation in the use of the intrinsic energy (Ching), the hands are again divided into principal and secondary. The upper and front is the prin-

---

[1] For those who are serious about the Taoist art of breathing may consult the Appendix — "The Art of Glowing Health". The Taoist breathing system, as described there, may be practiced with advantages in conjunction with the movements of Tai Chi Ch'uan.

cipal, while the lower and back is the secondary — adapted
to the changes in substantiality and insubstantiality, expanding and
closing. The vision represents the "mind-consciousness". When the
the consciousness arrives at a certain point of the moving hand, the
eyes come with it, and the Chi follows. In other words, if the eyes
gaze straight at the fingers while moving, the body and the Chi must
go forward accordingly. This is the technique known as "the coordination of the Hands and Eyes". The methods may be reviewed
briefly as follows:

1. Spirit absolutely integrated: During the exercise, the mind-
spirit has its focus. In practicing, the spirit must be centralized in
every posture with "eyes-arriving and hands arriving" without distur-
bance and severance.

2. The coordination of the hands and eyes: As a rule, the
eyes follow the movements of the middle fingers to and fro. With
prolonged practice, the hand will follow the eyes while discharging
the intrinsic energy, and the intrinsic energy is discharged with the
movement of the hands. This is what is called "the Coordination of
the Hands and Eyes".

VIII. The function of the waist-spine: The chief controller of bodily movements.

This exercise makes use of the waist-spine as the pivot of bodily
movements, just as the axle of a wheel, the turning of which causes
the motions of all parts of the car. The Theory says: "It is rooted
in the feet, stems in the legs, is commanded or directed by the waist-
spine, and functions through the fingers." If one keeps the waist-spine

as the chief controller of all the movements, there will be no difficulty in going forward and backward as well as turning in all directions. However, the following methods should be observed:

1. Using the waist-spine as the chief controller, one action leads to another without severance. It is through the waist-spine — the central axis of the body — all the "nine key kinetic joints" are linked together, these being: the neck, spine, waist, hips, knees, ankles, shoulders, elbows, and wrists.

2. In order to keep the continuity of the movements, it is necessary to insert the technique of "Folding and Alteration" in the movements of the hands (forward, backward, upper or lower), while in the legs, to insert that of "Turning and Changes" in advancing and retreating.

3. One of the chief principles in this exercise is the distinction or differentiation of the substantiality (solidness) and insubstantiality (emptiness). This applies to hands, legs and everywhere in the body. When the right leg in the front is substantial (carrying 80 or 70% of the weight of the body), the hind leg is insubstantial (carrying 20 or 30% of the weight). Simultaneously, when the left hand in the back is substantial, the right hand in front is insubstantial. The aim of this distinction is to keep one's self in a free-moving mood in addition to imposing stability. Following this distinction, if the step is divided into three parts of one third each, the center of gravity of the body should be maintained at the dividing line of the first one-third. This is known technically as "central equilibrium" (or center of gravity).

IX.   The method of step mainly emphasizing lightness, nimbleness, circling and stability.

The chief task in the practicing of the structure (team framework) is aiming at stability.   Hence the change of the steps has to follow the change of the trunk, and the movement of the leg follows that of the hand.   With the distinction of the substantiality and insubstantiality of the legs, as stated above, the following methods are in order:

1.   In moving forward, the steps are similar to those of the walking of the cats.   They are light, subtle, stable, and nimble.

2.   The movements of the legs take circular forms as those of the hands.   When standing, the toes and heels have to cleave to the ground with strength, the middle of the sole, however, is insubstantial.

3.   It is necessary to sink the Chi to the Tan Tien, and keep the knees and buttocks as if they were bound, in order that the center of gravity may sink downward and be stabilized.

X.   The interaction of the conjugate powers of Yin and Yang; The harmonizing of the dynamic and static with the direction of the mind, and the complimentary nature of yielding (pliability) and unyielding (hardness).

The exercise is based on the principle of Tai Chi in *I Ching*, or Book of Changes, and its conjugate powers of Yin (Negative Force) and the Yang (Positive Force).   The changes and the interaction of these two powers are endless. As the mind and body of a man is a universe in miniature, these powers do exist in the human body, and the basic spirit of this exercise aims at the cultivation of the mind and body by tacit understanding of the principle of Tai Chi and its begetting powers. The methods are as follows:

1. The Dynamic or Static states are directed by the Mind. In this exercise one uses the mind to mobilize the Chi, and the Chi to propel the body, and the main purpose is to enable one to conquer the "unyielding" with the "yielding". Hence, one must learn how to discharge the Chi (energy) in addition to storing it. This exercise emphasizes the complimentary nature of the Yin and Yang in quietude, its interaction in dynamics. Following the direction of the mind, there may be sudden dynamics and sudden statics, but the changes are endless, and its Ching (Intrinsic energy), infinitive.

2. As it has been pointed out, the Tai Chi Ch'uan theoreticians generally follow Laotze, who said, "Can you concentrate your Chi and bring about a pliability like that of an infant?" According to this concept, the Taoists also speak of "the most pliable galloping the most powerful and unyielding as a horseman gallops his steed".[1] This type of supernatural power can be acquired through the concentration of the Chi, the methods of which have been outlined above. In fact, in the first stage of training, one must, however, try to get rid of the rigidity and stiffness of the brutal force through the process of "thousands of fistings and hundreds of trainings," in the practicing of the team-framework. By emphasing the Chi without using the force, one may get rid of the petrified hard strength and return to natural pliability. When the body is entirely emptied of force, the intrinsic energy (tenacious strength) will emerge from the soles and

[1] Cheng Man-Ch'ing, ibid, pp. 45-46.

heels.

3. Because of the emphasis on the complimentary nature of Yin and Yang, the Chen school theoreticians in Tai Chi Ch'uan, although paying due attention to the principle of yielding (Yin), do not lose sight of "unyielding" (Yang). Hence, they advocate the theory that the "excellent hands" lies in the unifying of the Yin and Yang, i.e. 50 to 50 on each side.[2] The second stage, therefore, may be termed as the training of softness in hardness.[3] It should proceed in accordance with what is said in the Theory: "In order to practice Ch'uan, one should have the mind to seek softness, but with no idea in attaining hardness." In fact, what one seeks is tenacity and not force, for tenacity is active, while force is inert. To start: one should relax the body completely and consciously. The relaxation implies a sense of the elongation of the body and limbs, as well as the capacity of elasticity (flexibility). This type of strength is what is called "Ward off Intrinsic Energy". (Peng Ching). This is exactly the tenacious energy that is needed in Tai Chi Ch'uan in its seeking for "unyielding" (Kang). In essence, the strengthening of the capacity of unyielding depends upon the realization of the continuity of the "inner Chi" (internal energy). For increasing its capacity, it again depends upon the continual repetitions in the training of the 'reeling of silk' movements. Hence, the operation of the 'intrinsic energy' and the

[2] For instance, the Chen School from Chen Chia Kou. Cf. Shen Chia Chin and Kuo Liu Ching, *The Chen Style of Tai Chi Ch'uan*, Peking, 1936. and Kuo Ling Ying's *Tai Chi Ch'uan Pu Taipei, Taiwan, 1964*.

[3] "In days of old, the sage formulated the Philosophy of Changes in accord with the laws of nature and life. And thus, he held that the basic elements of the Principles of Heaven are positiveness (Yang) and negativeness (Yin), those of the Principle of the Earth are hardness (Kang) and softness (Jou)." "An Exposition of the Eight Trigrams" (Shuao Kua). (*I Ching*, or Book of Changes).

"elongation of the body and limbs"[1] are the keys for the attaining of the highest degree of both softness (pliability) and hardness (rigidity). This is the technique which should be followed in the exercise. The ideal of such a technique is 'instantaneous-softness' and 'instantaneous-hardness'; it is softness, yet it is hardness.[2]

XI. The Thirteen Postures (Methods).

The Thirteen Postures (Methods), forming the basic components in this exercise, consist of five steps — advancing (進), retreating (退), look to the left (左顧) (step), look to the right (右盼) (step) and central equilibrium (chung ting 中定),—and the "eight entrances" (八門) (also known as intrinsic energies), which are: Ward Off (掤), (peng), Pull Back (擺) (lu), Press Forward (擠) (chi), Push (按) (an), Pull Down (採) (chai), Bend Backward (挒) (li), Elbow-Stroke (肘) (chou) and Shoulder-Stroke (靠) (kou). The methods to be observed in the movements are:

A. Central Equilibrium:

While all the steps have to be changed or altered according to

---

[1] According to Chen Family's *Ch'uan Pu*: in order to elongate the torso, one has to attain insubstantiality, alertness and nimbleness in the top of the head accompanied with intrinsic energy: the sinking of the Chi to the Tan Tien and the relaxing of the chest and the drawing of the back. The elongation of the hands and legs has to be realized by the sinking of the shoulders, the loosening of the waist and the roundness of the buttock and the revolving of the knees.

[2] The author firmly believes that this is the only way through which we can finally solve the historical controversy between the so-called 'Soft School' and the 'Hard School' in methodology that has continued for so long a time in China.

the movements of the trunk, all the motions in the postures have to be changed into insubstantiality or substantiality, stemming from the central equilibrium, (hara, in Japanese). These apply to the above named five steps and eight entrances.

B. Central Equilibrium as a Principal Movement:

Within the Thirteen Postures (Methods), the central equilibrium is considered a principal step (for instance in the postures of left and right 'Playing the Fiddle'), whereas the others are 'sides' only. All the above postures, in fact, start from the Central Equilibrium, and cannot be independent of it. Hence every posture has its substantiality and insubstantiality as well as its Central Equilibrium. Central Equilibrium is the center of gravity. If one keeps the center, he is in a favorable situation, otherwise, an awkward one.[1]

XII. The operations of Ward off, Pull back, Press Forward and Push.

In the Joint Hands Operation (or Pushing Hands Practice, T'ui Shou 推手), the basic movements are "Ward Off," "Pull Back," "Press Forward," and "Push" — all included in the "Grasping of the Bird's Tail." Although the "Pull Back" is considered as the most critical "intrinsic energy" (ching), the "Ward Off" is really the basic

---

[1] The practitioners often say: ' If one practices the art with head lowered and loins bent he has not been properly instructed. Each boxing movement should be originated from the Tan Tien." See Chi Kiang-tao, *Tai Chi Ch'uan, the Physical Exercise to Maintaining Health and Preventing Sickness* (2), West and East, Vol. X, No. 7, July, 1965, p. 9.

one. However, in the practicing of T'ui Shou, no resistance is used. One must relax and yield to the opponent. In order that one can be guided by the "Sensate Energy" (Chiao Ching 覺勁), and "Listening Energy (Ting Ching 聽勁) so as to detect the opponent's move before he begins, the practitioner has to practice diligently on how to operate the "Ward Off", "Pull Back", "Press Forward" and "Push" energies (Ching), the methods of which are:

A. Ward Off (Peng): Ward off is used to uphold the attacking force of the opponent either slantingly upward or on the front level. However, it is not to be used to attack the opponent, but rather is guided by the "Sensate Energy" which senses the opponent's move so that one may turn the waist and neutralize the coming force.

B. PULL BACK (LU): Pull back is used to "capture" the opponent's hand and lead his force into 'voidness.' This is what is called "Neutralizing Energy". (Hua Ching 化勁).

C. PRESS FORWARD (CHI): Press forward is the method which is used with the momentum of the waist to press forward against the opponent's chest. Or if one is pulled back to the limit, he should take the advantage to "adhere and lift" and even "press forward" to uproot the opponent.

D. PUSH (AN): When one is "pressed forward", he must stop the "Press" and then loose his waist in order to "neutralize" the coming "Press" momentum before "pushing" the opponent either forward or downward. In this case, the technique of "uprooting" is being used.

XIII. The operation of the Pull down, Bend backward, Elbow-stroke and Shoulder-stroke.

After the practicing of Joint Hands Operation, one has to learn the "corner operations," which are termed as the "Great Pulling" (Ta Lu). The Ta Lu employs the eight methods and the five steps to pull the opponent to revolve in all the directions. When one has mastered these techniques, he, so to speak, is capable "to turn the square into the circle and turn the circle into the square," and comprehends all the alterations of Yin and Yang. The methods of these are:

A. Pull Down. Hold the opponent's wrist with one hand, on which is placed the other, and pull his wrist abruptly downward and outward in order to overcome his center of gravity and thus control him.

B. Bend Backward. Use one hand to pull down the opponent's forearm, and at the same time use the other one to bend his elbow so as to pull the upper part of his body downward and throw him away.[1]

---

[1] It should be noted that Yearning K. Chen makes a distinction between Bend Backward and Arm-twist. For the former method, he says; "In case "Pull Down" or "Pull Back" is disused, or, after one of your hands wards off the opponent's arm downward to the side, place one foot behind the opponent and put the forearm against his neck to bend the upper part of his body backward by exerting the motivation, the instrinsic energy, and the momentum of your waist and legs." And for the latter method he adds: "In 'Pull Back', hold the opponent's wrist with one hand, twist his arm, and place the forearm of your other hand on his elbow with the motivation, the intrinsic energy, and the momentum of the waist and legs, while stepping towards the front and bringing him down." Yearning K. Chen, *Tai Chi Ch'uan, Its Effects and Practical Applications*. Hong Kong, 1966, pp. 171-172.

C. Elbow-Stroke. When the opponent's arm or elbow is being pushed down, take the advantage by striking his chest with your elbow.

D. Shoulder-Stroke. When the opponent's arm is being pulled down or twisted downward, one should take the advantage in striking his chest with the shoulder. If this technique is employed, be sure the opponent is not too far from or too near to yourself. In the applying of the above technique, it should be done with the motivation, the intrinsic energy, and the momentum of the waist and legs.

XIV. The circular movements or the "Reeling of Silk".

The style of "circular movement", sometimes known as "spiral movement", is a special exercise of the Chinese, not to be found in the West, the methods of which may be described as follows:

A. Circular Movement: The opening, closing, turning and changing in the trunk, hands, waist and steps always take the shape or form of a circle. In each motion, there may be the grand circle, involving the whole body, or the partial circle involving the hands or legs. Irrespective of advancing or retreating, the function of circular movement must be observed. The spiral shaped movement is similar to what is technically known as the "Reeling of Silk".[1]

B. The Intrinsic Energy and the "Reeling of Silk":

---

[1] In the *Ch uan Pu*, it has the following axioms: "The operation of the intrinsic energy is similar to the "reeling of silk". Whether you are opening or closing, never separate youself from Tai Chi (i.e., the circle)". "The delicate hands combine one Tai Chi in each action." See Shen Chia Ching and Koo Liu Ching, *The Chen Style of Tai Chi Ch'uan*, Peking, 1936. 17-27.

(a)   The technique of the "Reeling of Silk":   In action, the palm, facing the eyes, revolves from the inner and then turns round facing the external with the aim of constructing a configuration of Tai Chi (circle).   During the move of the hand, right or left, first, revolve the wrist and turn the shoulder and the leg, then revolve the ankle and turn the leg; and finally, when one comes to the torso, revolve the waist and turn the spine.

(b)   The function of spiraling exercise: Firstly, it helps one to avoid the pitfall of 'resistance' in the act of self defense.   If the hands are moving in straight lines — forward and backward — without revolving the wrists, and the legs bowing forward and retiring backward without revolving ankles and knees, the net result will be resistance, rather than neutralizing.   Secondly, it must be remembered the method of 'Neutralized Intrinsic Energy', which is basic in this exercise, actually comes from the spiral movement in three dimensions.

(c)   The types of "Reeling of Silk":   These can be classified into two fundamental types: Firstly, the active type.   During the movement the palm generally faces the eyes.   The majority of the so-called "Ward Off" energies fall into this category.   Secondly, the passive or reversed type.   After the revolving of the wrist, the back of the palm begins to face the eyes.   The majority of the so-called "Pulling Back" energies fall into this category.   These two types of energies seem to be contraditory, but they end in a unity . . . (Tai Chi).

   In addition, owing to the differences of positions and variations, the type of "Reeling of Silk" can be further divided into: 1. Advance-Retreat; 2. Left-Right; 3. Internal-External; 4. Big-Small; and 5. Upper-Lower.   It should be noted: The Left-Right and Upper-Lower of "Reeling of Silk" constitute a whole circle in movement.   If the Internal-and-External is added, it changes into a cubic circle.   This is a special aspect of the spiral movement.   And on account of the 'holiness' of the body, there naturally arise the Big-Small, Advance-Retreat style of positional — structural — developmental Reeling of Silk.1

XV. In the Joint Hands Operation (Tui Shou), attention has to be paid to the techniques known as: "To adhere and lift", "To joint", "To adhere horizontally", "To attach from the rear", and "Neither let go nor resist".

In the learning of the Joint Hand Operations for application, it must be guided by 'Sensate Energy' (feeling or touching). If this energy can be mastered, one will have no difficulty in understanding the "Interpretative Energy" (Tung Ching 懂勁). However, in order to learn the Operations, one has to start with five techniques or energies listed above, the details of which may be described as follows:

    a. "To adhere and lift" — (chan 沾): This is to adhere your hand on the opponent's lightly. Your body and leg should go forward with your hand simultaneously. The object of this technique is to adhere the opponent's body and hand, keeping in contact with them.

---

1 The 'Reeling Silk" intrinsic energy has been particularly emphasized and developed as a theory by the Chen type of Tai Chi Ch'uan. According to its theory, without the 'Reeling of Silk" (circular movement) one cannot direct the intrinsic energy to wind round the body, the legs, and the hands, escalating and constituting a unity. Again, linking together without interruption in the operation of the postures enables the intrinsic energy to go through the joints and muscles — this also is considered as one of the real functions of the spiral movement. Shen Chia Ching and Koo Liu Ching, ib. cit.

b. "To join" (lien 連): With the adherence, join the opponent without letting him get away.

c. "To adhere horizontally" (t'ieh 貼): With joining, you have to take the initiative, then, try to control the opponent completely.

d. "To attach from the rear" (sui 隨): Coming to this point, if the opponent attacks you swiftly, you should respond as swiftly as possible. On the other hand, if he moves slowly, attach (follow) him slowly. The aim of this technique is to take away the initiative from the opponent.

e. "Neither let go nor resist": When attacking your opponent you should not stand far away from his body, neither should you resist force with force. The aim is to neutralize the coming force by withdrawing yourself backward. This is known as the "withdraw (yield) and attack technique".

XVI. The stages of comprehension and application of the intrinsic energies.

In addition to the value of maintaining health, the function for self-defense in this exercise should not be over-looked. The Joint Hands Operation is to learn not only how to use the waist and the legs, but also how to comprehend and apply the "intrinsic energies" (tenacious strength). The stages of learning and applying these energies may be described as follows:

a. First Stage — "The adhering energy". When one begins to learn the Joint Hands Operation, one should first of all pay attention to how to keep the effectiveness and alertness of the waist and legs in turning and changing. Regarding the technique of the hands, one has to follow the methods as described above, i.e. — "to adhere and lift", "to join", "to adhere horizontally", "to attach from the rear", and "neither let go nor resist".

b. Second Stage — "The listening energy" (t'ing ching). The listening to opponent's strength is not done by ear but through the sense of touching, so it is also called 'Chio Ching', meaning 'sensate energy'. When this technique is mastered and practised for a long time, one will find his nerves have the super-sensitive power, which are capable of warding off or neutralizing the attacking forces without thinking or reflection.

c. Third Stage — "The interpretative energy" (tung ching). Having mastered the listening energy, one will be able to take suitable advantage and position to "lift and discharge". Technically, this is known as "interpretative energy".

d. Fourth Stage — "The discharging energy (放勁)". If one can interpret and comprehend the attacking forces of the opponent, the next step is to withdraw your body first. Then, push your hands forward toward the opponent, and discharge your energy as to "lift up" or "up-root" him as far away as possible. As soon as it is discharged, withdraw your hands and body immediately. Technically this is known as the "discharging energy".1

---

1 Chi Kiang-tao, on his experience of several decades and material collected has summarized the steps of discharging as: (1) to adhere (chan); (2) to listen (ting); (3) to lift (tih); (4) to discharge (fong). And the important points of discharging have been listed as: 1. Distance; 2. Angle; 3. Time; 4. Chance and Situation; 5. Unity; 6. Distinction between the Sub-

stantial and Unsubstantial points in one's body; 7. Calm and relaxing attitude; 8. The hand is not to be moved by itself — The sending out of tenacious energy is to be originated from the waist and leg in coordination with the practitioner's thought, 'Chi' and spirit. 9. To feel intentively for the reaction, 10. Store up energy before discharging. See Chi Kiang-tao, *Tai Chi Ch'uan, the Physical Exercise for Maintaining Health and Preventing Sickness* (3), West and East, Vol. X. No. 10, Oct. 1965, pp. 7-8.

CHAPTER IX
THE BREATHING SYSTEM OF TAI CHI CH'UAN

In the course of movements in Tai Chi Ch'uan, it is essential to have regular or rhythmic breathing in coordination with all the forms or postures. This is one of the chief characteristics of this art of exercise. In fact, this system in China is known as "Nei Kung" (內功) or the "Art of Internal Functioning," because of its emphasis on breathing.

Breathing is the most important function of living organisms. The slightest movement requires an expenditure of energy and this energy is derived in a great part from the combination of oxygen and carbon. One can readily see that an adequate supply of oxygen is necessary in order to maintain life. Should the process of respiration be interfered with, the bodily tissues would soon stop functioning and result in death.

One complete respiration includes both an inspiration and an expiration of air. The normal number of respirations in a healthy adult human being is about fourteen to eighteen per minute; in children this number is much higher. The respiratory rate varies with age, the amount of activity and the state of health of the individual.

We cannot overstate the importance of the habit of deep breathing for the health of the body, mind and spirit. Modern man's life is grossly abnormal. Our days are spent in continuous tension and our senses are in constant stimulation, so much so that we have neither time nor opportunity for the practice of the art of breathing. We need to explore our own lives, our motives, our plans as we need to cultivate the habit of deep breathing, which is definitely one of the ways of reducing tension and the causes of longevity.

The breathing exercises of Tai Chi Ch'uan undoubtedly go back to the Taoists in China. Before describing the breathing system of this art in terms of modern science, it is advisable to analyze the respiratory techniques of the Taoists and the derivations of "Nei Kung," in Tai Chi Ch'uan.

Breathing exercises were known in ancient China as far back as to the Chou Dynasty (1027-256 B.C.). H. Wilhelm had drawn attention to an inscription on twelve pieces of jade of that Dynasty, which says:

"In breathing one must proceed (as follows). One holds (the breath) and it is collected together. If it is collected it expands. When it expands it goes down. When it goes down it becomes quiet. When it becomes quiet it will solidify. When it becomes solidified it will begin to sprout. After it has sprouted it will grow. As it grows it will be pulled back again (to the upper regions). When it has been pulled back it will reach the crown of the head. Above, it will press against the crown of the head. Below, it will press downwards.

"Whoever follows this will live; whoever acts contrary to it will die."

What was the connection of the Taoist respiratory techniques with this sixth century B.C. inscription is hard to say. As pointed out by Needham, the great aim of the breathing exercises was to try to return to the manner of respiration of the embryo in the womb. There are many books in the Tao Tsang which discuss the techniques and an important source is Ko Hung's (葛洪) *Pao P'o Tsu*

1. (as cited Joseph Needam, Science and Civilization in China. Vol. II, pp. 143-144)

(抱朴子) (early fourth century A.D.). There are considerable discussions concerning the relation, if any, between these practices and those of the Indian Yogis. Maspero, the French sinologist, pointed out that the Buddhist technique sought for regularity and slowness of inspiration and expiration; unlike the Taoist, which sought to retain air in the "Tan Tien" as long as possible. Yogistic training for meditation and rapt contemplation seems to have included suggestion, hypnotism, auto-hypnotism, and especially an extension of conscious control over the functions of the autonomic nervous system[1]. Maspero's considered opinion was that the Taoist techniques were an indigenous development of ancient pheumatic physiology, and not derived from contacts with Indian Yogism. But we would like to agree with Needham in that to what extent Taoist techniques paralleled with the rather well authenticated phenomena of Yogism remained to be determined.

Historically speaking, the existence of Tai Chi Ch'uan, which is also known as the art of the "Nei Chia" (內家) (esoteric school), is due to three reasons. First, it is the art of the Tao Chia (道家), which is different from what has been practiced by the Buddhists (Fang Wai) (方外). Secondly, the techniques of acupuncture such as stressing (Chieh) (節), grasping (Na) (拿), clutching (Chua) (抓), and closing (Pi) (閉) have to be carried out in the internal organism. They are formless. Furthermore, it employs the techniques for circulating and transforming breathing. In later times the names "Kung Fu" (martial arts) (功夫) and "Nei-Kung" (internal functioning) (內功), implying work or inwardly-directed work, came to be used.

---

[1] See Rammurti Mishra Fundamentals of Yoga, A Handbook of Theory, Practice and Application, The Julian Press, Inc. 1959, New York.

Because the Taoist aspires towards "Hsienship" (仙) — material immortality — people usually consider "Nei-Kung" as mystic or ununderstandable. In reality, the so-called "Nei-Kung" is nothing but respiratory exercises. In practice, they emphasize particularly deep breathing. As we have pointed out, the normal number of respirations in a human being is about fourteen to eighteen per minute, but what the Taoists did was to slow down the process of breathing by limiting the number from fourteen to twenty, or even more per minute. The objective of deep breathing is to attain what is technically known as "Ch'i Kung" (氣功) (circulation of breathing), and the attainment of nourishing the "Nei Tan" (內丹) (internal pills). The so-called "Nei Tan" of the Taoist is actually the mental process of sublimation, which frees the body from the impurities of the earth and makes it fit for immortality. The so-called "Tan" (丹) or sometimes "Gold Pill" (金丹) (or elixir of Gold), is a decoction that confers immortality.

In the normal adult, according to the theory of the Taoists, the air which fills his lungs and stomach can be differentiated into two parts; that is, the upper level and the lower level. The air staying in the upper level is called the "Air a Posteriori" (後天氣), inhaled from the external world. The air staying in the lower part, that is the "Tan Tien" (psychic center), is called the "Air ā Priori" (先天氣) stemming out from the mother's body giving birth to it. In the act of respiratory exercises, the "Air à Posteriori" can be exhaled, while the "Air ā Priori" at the lower level has to be lowered down to the pubic region or "Air Sea" (氣海) (abdominal region). During the act of inhalation, the "Air à Posteriori" inhaled can be fused into the "Air ā Priori" accelerating from the abdominal region. When this stage is attained or finally achieved in the exercises, it is called "Ch'i Tung" or the "circulation of breathing."

As Buddha said: "When you fix your heart on one point, then nothing is impossible for you." To the Taoists, the rhythm of breathing may be consciously or voluntarily directed from the "Tan Tien" downwards to the vital point known as "Hui Yin" (會陰), and thus passed on to the coccyx (the Posteriori). Following the spinal cord upwards, it is directed to the base of the cerebellum and the skull, and from the forehead to the philtrum the Adam's Apple, the solar plexus, and the navel and again returned to the "Tan Tien." It may also be directed from the "Tan Tien" upwards to the "Shan Kin" (山根), from where it reaches the skull (Bregma) and then circles backwards to the "Tan Tien".1 The earlier theories had envisaged the inspired air as nutritive as well as respiratory, while the new ones developed the idea of a special inner breath, or "Nei Ch'i" (內氣), the circulation and transmutation of which had to be effected and accelerated by imaginative meditation.

---

1 According to the science of acupuncture, the flow of vital force is mapped out and represented by "twelve "organ" meridians (Tsings) on each side of the body, and eight 'vessel" meridians (Mei). Two of the vessel of meridians, one of the vertical midline in front (the so-called "Jen-Mei" (任脈), and one on the vertical midline at the back ("Tu-Mei" 督脈), have distinguishing features which bring them into such close resemblence to the twelve "organ-meridians". (Cf. Denis Lawson-Wood, *Chinese System of Healing*, pp. 17-18). In the "circulation of breathing", the air is supposed to go through the Jen-Mei and Tu-Mei and vice versa. For amplification, see my little book on *The Art of Glowing Health* (see Appendices) in which the methods of "Long Breathing", "Microcosmic Orbit — The Small Yin-Yang Cyclic Breathing", "Macrocosmic Orbit — The Great Yin-Yang Cyclic Breathing", and the "Immanent Breathing", have been demonstrated by different charts that can be followed with benefits. Students of Tai Chi Ch'uan should make themselves familiar with the theory of Acupuncture. See Han Suyin. *Acupuncture — The Scientific Evidence*, Eastern Horizon, Vol. III No. 4, April 1964. Or Wu Wei-p'ing, *Chinese Acupuncture*, English translation by Philip M. Chancellor, Health Science Press, Rustington, Sussex, England, 1962.

The so-called technique of "immortality" of the Taoists really depends upon this kind of deep breathing. To meditate and to cultivate the Ch'i is to train a "Diamond Body" — the "indestructable health-body", so to speak. The fact can best be expressed in the words: "It is not I who live, it is it that lives me." To put it in plain words, after a long period for the training of the breathing and with the impact of deep breathing on the human internal organism, the blood will be full of oxygen and the circulation of the blood will be strengthened with great vigor. With the air on both levels communicating, it nourishes or cultivates a sort of "Chin-Li" (勁力) (energy plus strength) in the internal organism. With the acts of inhalation and exhalation, it will accelerate or sink downwards inside the body as if there were a "pill" revolving continually. This is again what the Taoists called the "Nei Tan" (內丹) (internal elixir of life). Actually it is the "Ch'i-Ching (inner energy or elan vital) nourished in the body itself. In other words, it is the crystallization of "Ching" (精) (the seminal essence), "Ch'i (氣) (energy, or breathing) and "Shen (神) (the divine element or spirit), all of which are known as the three treasures of the Taoists and the Tai Chi Ch'uanists as well. Once the crystallization has come into actuality, it has, so to speak, a mysterious or undefeatable life of its own. If we understand the Taoists' conception of rejuvenation and longevity in this manner, there is nothing that is mysterious about it. Ko Hung (葛洪) said: "Everybody can attain Hsienship." That is what he meant.1

As the Taoists mainly emphasize meditation, their technique naturally has its own limitations — the lack of external dynamism.

---

1 See Chang Chung-yuan, *Creativity and Taoism, a Study of Chinese Philosophy, Art, and Poetry*. The Julian Press Inc. New York, 1963.

This has been added by the originators of Tai Chi Ch'uan, whoever they were. In the "Nei-Kung," or "internal functioning," pursued by the Tai Chi Ch'uanists, their objective is not very different from that of the Taoists, but their methods are utterly different. In order to crystalize the Ching, Ch'i and Shen into a single entity which would ultimately produce the "Kung-Ching" (功勁) (intrinsic energy), they originated the art of movements for that purpose. In Taoism, the expression: "To produce emptiness" contains the whole work of "completing life and essence." To the Tai Chi Ch'uanists, the aim of training the "Ching" is to transfor it into "Ch'i," and the training of the "Ch'i" is to transmute it into "Shen," and finally to train the "Shen" so that it may return to "emptiness" (making the heart empty). Hence, the "Nei-Kung" of the former is more or less negative, while that of the latter is more or less positive. What the Tai Chi Ch'uanists try to attain is dynamism with tranquility. Their final aim is undoubtedly therapeutic, an art of mild gymnastics with rules different from those of the West, and embodying a certain element of "Kung-Fu" (martial arts) (功夫), probably originated as a department of Taoist physical exercise.

According to the theories of the Tai Chi Ch'uanists, beginners in the first phase of study can hardly comprehend the "Ch'i," not to say the training of the "Ch'i." With the mastering of the techniques and team-framework, one may, in the second phase, realize the importance of "Ching-Li" (勁力) (energy and strength). Hence, what he really needs, arriving at this phase, is to train the "Ch'i," through the method of "Nei Kung" in order that the "Ching-Li" (energy and strength) of the whole body may become the "Kung-Ching" (功勁) (the achieved intrinsic energy) to the highest degree.[1]

1 For the Taoist and Buddhist methods of Breathing, see Charles Luk. *The Secrets of Chinese Meditation*, Rider & Company, London, 1964.

CHAPTER X

SCIENTIFIC INTERPRETATION OF

THE BREATHING SYSTEM OF TAI CHI CH'UAN

1. The general rule governing the coordination of the breathing system.

In the course of exercising, all the movements should be coordinated with a rhythm of breathing. This is one of the chief characteristics of Tai Chi Ch'uan. Normally, breathing is involuntary. The carbon dioxide in the blood stimulates the respiratory center in the brain, which in turn causes the diaphragm to move. Thus, breathing continues during sleep and is not ordinarily a conscious act, even during waking hours. However, in Tai Chi Ch'uan, a person can consciously change at will the rate of respiration, and can even slow down the breathing process during the movements.

The coordination of movements with the breathing in Tai Chi Ch'uan is actually based on the changes of the motion. In the process of movement, the rhythm of inhalation and exhalation follows some definite principles. For the purpose of grasping the vital points, the following describes the general rules:

A.   Inhalation:

During the rising of the body, the bending of the arms, the kicking of the legs.

B.   Exhalation:

During the lowering of the body, the extending of the arms, the falling steps, etc.

For Example,

Inhalation:

In general, when rising and standing, one should inhale; as, for instance, after the performance of "The Needle at Sea Bottom", "Step Up and Punch" and Golden Cock Stands on One Leg" — or, when one arm contracts inwards after the performance of the "Grasp Bird's Tail" or the return of the two arms after the "Apparently Close Up."   Furthermore, during the "Rising and Kicking up of the Legs", the "Separation of the Left and Right Feet", the "Kicking with the Sole", "Turn and Kick with Sole", "Cross Legs", and "Turn Around and Kick Horizontally", inhalation is indispensable.

Exhalation:

Exhalation takes place during the sitting-down motion of the body, as in "Needle at Sea Bottom" and "Snake Creep Down", the stretching of the single arm or both arms in the "Grasp of the Bird's Tail" and the stretching of the left hand in the "Single Whip", "Step Up, Strike, Parry and Punch" and "Step Up and Punch Downwards". During the stepping-down of the legs, exhalation is required, as for instance, during the completion of the step-down in the "Brush Knee and Twist Step", "The Separation of the Left and Right Feet" and the "Kicking of the Sole in Right or Left."

Such are the general rules.   In some united movements, there may be some changes which cannot be strictly defined during some transitory movements, such as in the "Fan through the Back", slow inhalation and exhalation may take place. To summarize, all breathing must take place consciously and naturally. Panting is to be avoided; relaxation is dynamic.

2. The benefits derived from this breathing system.

The coordination of the mind and body through this breathing system contributes a great deal to health, and longevity, as well. The following benefits are quite significant:

First of all, to train the breathing muscles and to expand the capacity of the lungs.

The rhythm of breathing, which alternately increases and decreases the expanded state of the lungs, begins at birth and continues throughout life. The inhalation and exhalation of the lungs can change the capacity of the chest cavity, brought about by the movement of the muscles of respiration. The most important of these muscles is the diaphragm, a broad sheet of muscular tissues which stretches across the bottom of the chest cavity and separates the chest cavity from the abdominal cavity. When the diaphragm moves downwards, air is drawn into the lungs; when it moves upwards the air is expelled. The upward movement is a passive one of relaxation.

With the deep breathing in Tai Chi movements, the capacity of the lungs can be increased through constant training. Its main point is to change the number of respirations consciously and to expand the capacity of the lungs. The breathing, of course, should be deep, long, balanced, and quiet. After a long period of training, the muscles of the diaphragm will be developed and the capacity of the lungs will be expanded. Accordingly, in this way it offers a great deal of improvement to the organs of breathing, as well as a positive effect on the development of health.

Secondly, the aim is to attain the objective of "Inhaling the Ch'i" (energy) for the nourishment of the "Shen". "Shen" may be rendered as "Spirit" or the "Divine Element" or the "Vital Force". It may be referred to as the nervous system, particularly the brain. With emphasis on deep breathing, the oxygen inhaled will surpass the actual need of the body. If this is the case, the various parts of the human organism, particularly the brain, will have plenty of oxygen. On the other hand, during the training period, what is needed is tranquility, re-relaxation, in movement. To be tranquil is to let the various parts of the organism, particularly the brain, have plenty of opportunity to relax. As a result of a long period of practice of these exercises, diseases related to the nervous system such as tension, insomnia, neuralgia, neurasthenia, nervous disorders, nervous type of blood pressure, etc., can be gradually reduced or eliminated. This is the nourishment of the vital energy by rest.

Thirdly, to eliminate the extravasated blood and to strengthen the blood circulation.

In the rhythmic breathing of Tai Chi Ch'uan, the movement in the veins can thus be accelerated. As a result, the blood circulation and the movement in the lymph will also be accelerated. Deep breathing is needed in the movements, and the requirement of lowering the breathing or energy down to the psychic center or "Tan Tien", is actually a type of diaphragm breathing which has a great therapeutic value in its own right. In the contraction and expansion of the diaphragm and the abdomen through continuous deep breathing, the veins, under the pressure, can increase the circulation of the blood to the lungs. On the other hand, the movement of the diaphragm has the effect of massaging the liver, which eliminates the extravasated blood, and this is certainly one of the best methods of improving the function of the liver.

3. The assessment of the value of the "Tan Tien" theory of the Taoists.

The term known as "Tan Tien" or psychic center, which is used by Taoists and found in the medical books in China, is apparently not a term of anatomy, nor a term of physiology. According to the Taoists, the "Tan Tien", the point for the nourishment of life itself, is located about two and a half inches beneath the navel. This is considered as the location for preparing the "Elexir of Life" which makes it fit for immortality and is, therefore, called "Tan Tien", the "Field of Elixir". We have, in the last chapter, already set forth this theory and the practice of this art.

From the anatomical point of view, the part of the digestive apparatus beneath the stomach is known as the intestine. It consists of two sections: the small and the large intestines. The stomach is a bottle-shaped bag with a volume of about sixty-one cubic inches, situated rather transversely in the upper part of the abdomen. There is no such thing as "Tan Tien".

From the point of view of structure and function, man, as a machine, is a combustion engine, like a steam engine. In order to burn up the deposited fuel in the body, an individual breathes the air containing oxygen. The air passes through the respiratory passages into the interior of the lungs. Oxygen passes through the delicate walls of the respiratory passages into the arterial blood vessels. The circulatory passage carries the oxygen to the spot where combustion takes place. Here oxygen (O_2) unites with carbon (C) to form carbon dioxide (CO_2). Heat is produced during this union, and, for this reason, the process is termed combustion. The carbon dioxide flows with the blood to the lungs, passes into the respiratory passages, and leaves the body by way of the nose. Thus, it seems the air does not reach the "Tan Tien", or psychic center.

Judging from modern scientific knowledge, the theory of the "Tan Tien" of the Taoists must be a hypothetical notion and has no scientific value. But we must acknowledge that what we know of this complex subject in science is still rudimentary. We do not know the relationship between consciousness and any nervous process, between the mental and the cerebral. We do not know how thought is born. But no one denies that the mind which controls man is the actual power that exists. The mind has mind-waves just as sound has sound-waves, and light has light-waves. The constant functioning of the cerebrum in man generates these mind-waves. It is not strange to learn then that the energy of these mind-waves creates great power. The idea is derived from a theory and practice of the mind.

From ancient times in China, this "one point" — the so-called psychic center — has been called "Tan Tien", and is regarded as a thing of primary importance. Besides, the Tao Chia and the Buddhists, especially the Zen (Ch'an) School in meditation, are devoted entirely to the training of "Tan Tien" (in Japanese, "Tanden"). India's yoga is more or less a system whose discipline is also based upon this "Tan Tien" training.

In Tai Chi Ch'uan, "Tan Tien" is the base of mental, spiritual, and physical training. In order to attain the greatest benefit for health, as well as the coordination of mind and body, it is absolutely necessary to understand this "one point" — the psychic center —

the so-called "Tan Tien", or the real implication of this art will not be deeply understood.

Despite the metaphysical nature of the Taoists' theory mentioned above, the conception of lowering the Ch'i (breathing) to the "Tan Tien" area still has its own merits by reason of the following explanations:

The man who knows the history of Chinese culture and who has carefully studied the *Tao Tsung* (道藏), books of wisdom which had permeated all Chinese thought for thousands of years, will not wave aside lightly the doubts concerning this theory. He will know, moreover, that in the Chinese sense, the view set forth in the *Tao Tsung* is nothing out of the ordinary; on the contrary, it is quite an inescapable psychological conclusion. Without doubt, the concept is a pure intuitive vision, but one cannot dispense with it if one is trying to understand profoundly the nature of the mind. The Tai Chi Ch'uanists believe the mind is the master. Everybody who studies this art must study the laws of the mind, train his mind, letting the body follow, and thus find the way to coordinate it with the mind. As mind cannot exist without a body, the Tao (law of nature) of "Tan Tien" may thus be described as follows:

A. As a result of the lowering of the Ch'i to the "Tan Tien" area and through the training of the Tai Chi Ch'uan movements, the respiratory capacity of the lungs can be considerably increased. Oarsmen achieve the greatest respiratory capacities. Tai Chi Ch'uanists can achieve the same kind of objective through deep breathing.

B. In the course of walking, resting and moving, if one centers his mind on the psychic center or "Tan Tien", it is apt to lead to the concentration of the mind, At the same time, the central cerebrum may have ample opportunity to take a rest. And through the connection of the nervous system with the internal organs, this again is apt to lead to the harmony of the organs with the functions. This is where the laws of mind and body are joined. Mental, spiritual and physical coordination is possible only when a calm mind is centered on the "Tan Tien".

C. The brain and spinal cord, with nerves and muscles, constitute an indivisible system. But the spinal cord of modern man exercises too little. In order to have a good posture, graceful movements and a healthy spinal column, the exercise of the spine through the method of the Taoist breathing system, in addition to the Tai Chi Ch'uan movements, is the best form of exercise and of absolute importance.

CHAPTER XI

DIAGRAMATIC EXPLANATIONS OF

THE FORMS OF TAI CHI CH'UAN

Form 1.   Commencement of Tai Chi Ch'uan (太極拳起勢)
A.   Terminology

This is a preparatory style for the concentration of the mind in order to set a spiritual mood for the purpose of the exercise.   To use the mind, consciousness, or idea to direct the movements of the whole organism is a basic tenet in Tai Chi Ch'uan.   Hence, the preparatory style is essential.

B.   Diagrams and movements:

General Posture:

Stand upright.   Feet are apart and parallel to each other, at approximately shoulder width.   Place the hands along your thighs, with wrists straight and palms facing the floor. (Fig. 1)

Important Points: Keep the head and neck straight. Lower your shoulders with elbows bent slightly.   Relax the chest muscles — the whole body is relaxed and natural.   The spirit should be concentrated on the exercise.

Movements 1:

Raise the hands gradually to shoulder level, with palms pointing forward, fingers upward and loose, elbows bent. (Fig. 2)

Fig 1   Fig 2

Important Points: During the raising of the hands, the performance should be slow and light. Avoid any tension and do not exert force.

Movements 2:

Set torso erect. Bend your knees and lower torso gradually: Meanwhile lower your arms and palms smoothly to hip level. (Fig. 3)

Important Points: The center of gravity is on the two legs. Bend your knees and relax your waist, with buttocks tucked in. During the downward movement, the lowering of the arms should be harmoniously coordinated with the lowering of your torso. Look straight ahead of you. In the exercise, the method of "relaxing the chest and straightening the back" is important. One may keep the "Chest In" in the reversing form such as the "Repulse of Monkey", and with the relaxing of the chest, one naturally straightens the back. Beware of raising the back in any of the forms and avoid the error of being hunchbacked.

C. Technical Explanations:

In the process of exercising, the body should remain in a state of quiescence, the spirit should be concentrated, with emphasis on "Emptiness". The Chi (breathing) should be lowered down to the "Tan Tien", or psychic center (about two and half inches below the navel). The whole body should be alert and natural. The deeper meanings of the practice can gradually be comprehended from the spiritual, psychological and physical points of view.

Fig 3   Fig 4

D. Benefits:

The commencement form focuses your mind on the movements, which make you relax peacefully and naturally. It restores your internal system and external muscles to their proper placement, which makes you comfortable. The Chi (breathing) is harmonious, the spirit invigorated, and the nervous system is toned up.

Form 2. Grasping the Bird's Tail (Lam Ch'iao Wei) (攬雀尾)
A. Terminology

This is a symbolic term, using the bird's tail to represent the arm of the opponent. The act of grasping it is to follow its movement in rotation upwards or downwards, or to retard its force of advance and take advantage of throwing the opponent away.

B. Diagrams and movements:
(1) The ward-off style (Peng Shih) (掤式)

Movements 1:

Turn right, toes of the right leg slightly outward, with torso turning halfway to the right. Place your right arm in front of the chest and circle your left hand to the right hip level, with left palm facing upwards, right hand downwards. The center of gravity is shifted to the right. Shift the left leg to the inner side of the right, with toes touching the ground. Eyes on the right hand.

Movements 2:

Take a left step forward with bent leg. Meanwhile, the left arm wards off upwards on the left side, shoulder height. Drop the right hand beside the right hip, with palm facing downwards and the right leg straightened. Keep your eyes forward at the left forearm. (Fig. 4)

Movements 3:

After rotating the torso slightly to the left with left arm bent in the front of the chest, circle the right hand before the abdomen, towards the left. When reaching the left rib, both hands oppose each other as if they were embracing a ball, with right palm facing downwards and left palm facing upwards. The center of

Fig 5   Fig 6

gravity is shifted to the left leg.   (Figs. 5-6)

Movements 4:

Lift the right leg and place it at the right, bent. Set the right arm to ward off at the right, with palm facing inwards, at shoulder height. Place the left hand opposite the right elbow, with left leg straightened (but slightly bent). Look at the right forearm. (Fig. 7)

Important Points: In the performance of this style, lower your shoulders and maintain a **bow-shape** with the two arms in front of torso. The separation of hands, the relaxing of the waist and the bowing of the legs should be coordinated harmoniously and naturally. Stretch torso slightly forward.

(2) The pull-back style (Lu Shih) (攦式)

Movements:

Stretch your right hand forward, with palm facing downwards. Raise your left hand forward to the right, with palm facing upwards. Pull the two hands back to the height of the chest, simultaneously turning the waist and legs and shifting weight to the left leg. The eyes are on the left hand. (Fig. 8)

Fig 7   Fig 8

Important Points: Slant the torso slightly, with the buttocks tucked in. The two arms, while pulling backwards, follow the turning waist and take a circular form.

(3) The press-forward style (Chi Shih) (擠式)

Movements:

Place your left forearm against the inside of the right forearm, press both hands levelly outwards, while stretching the torso slightly forward and lowering it so that the weight is shifted from the left leg to the right, and the left leg is straightened (relatively). Eyes should be on the forearm of the right hand. (Fig. 9)

Important Points: Take a slightly forward slant stance and do not bend your back. Relax your waist and hips. All movements, such as the press-forward of the two arms, the relaxing of the waist and the bowing of the legs, should be coordinated with each other.

(4) The push style (An Shih) (按式)

Movements 1:

Fig 9

Fig 10

Separate your two hands, shoulder width, with palms facing downwards. When you have taken the sitting-backward stance, raise the tip of the right leg and shift the weight to the left leg. Meanwhile, draw the hands gradually backwards until they are nearing the chest, with palms facing down. Eyes are straight ahead. (Fig. 10)

Movements 2:

Stretch the torso slightly forward and lower it. Push the two hands out to the front, with fingers pointing upwards. The legs are in the same position as in the preceding style. Eyes are straight ahead. The right leg is changed to a bowing step. (See Fig. 9)

Important Points: The torso is erect, waist relaxed and buttocks tucked in. In the pushing-out of the two hands, lower the shoulders and bend the elbows. In the performance of the "Grasping of the Bird's Tail", focus is on the waist, which is always considered as the axis of the wheel. The palms should turn downwards, each making a horizontal semi-circle, so that they are apart from each other at a distance equal to that between the shoulders. At the beginning stage, the inhalation and exhalation should be natural, keeping the mouth shut but not tightly, with the tip of the tongue touching the upper palate.

C. Technical Explanations:

Although this form is divided into four styles or methods as described above, the movements are continuous. It must also be pointed out that these four styles or methods are very basic in the whole exercise, and they should be carefully distinguished from each other.

D. Benefits:

As this form emphasizes the splitting and enclosing of the limbs and the contracting and expanding of muscles, it strengthens the muscles of the back and abdomen and helps to relieve constipation. The lungs are expanded and become strong, thereby helping to strengthen the heart. The legs and thighs are strengthened and circulation in the organism is improved.

Form 3. Single whip (Tan Pien) (單鞭)

A. Terminology

It signifies the using of a single whip to strike the opponent.

B. Diagrams and movements:

Movements 1:

After sitting backwards with your torso, the weight is gradually shifted to the left leg, while the tip of the right leg turns inward. Meanwhile, with the rotating of the torso to the left, circle both hands horizontally to the left, until the left arm reaches to the left shoulder height, and the right arm is curved before the left side of the chest. (Fig. 11)

Movements 2:

The weight is now gradually shifted to the right leg. Lift the left leg with toes barely touching ground. Meanwhile, pinch fingers of the right hand together, drop hand from wrist forming a "Hooked Hand" and circle horizontally to the right. The center of gravity is shifted to the right. Turn your left hand downwards and circle upwards before the abdomen until it reaches

the right shoulder, with palm facing inward. The eyes
are on the left hand. (Fig. 12)

Fig 11   Fig 12

Movements 3:

With the turning of the torso slightly backwards to the
left, lift left leg to take a big step — bowing. Simultaneously, rotate your left palm and push outward with
the fingers pointing upwards at eye level. The two arms
are slightly bent. The center of gravity is now shifted
to the left leg. The eyes are focused on the left palm.
(Fig. 13)

Important Points: Keep the upper body erect, relaxing the
waist. Avoid leaning forward. While the right elbow is
slightly bent, the left elbow and the left knee form a
vertical line. In the transitional movements, the upper
and lower parts of body are synchronized.

C. **Technical Explanations:**

The whole posture expands and contracts the joints, bones, muscles, hips, and legs.

D. **Benefits:**

Since this form emphasizes "Split Energy", it increases the flow of the blood to the abdominal region and improves digestion. The liver is invigorated, the lungs expanded, and the joints, knees and hips are made more flexible.

Form 4.   Raise hands and step up (Ti Shou Shang Shih (提手上勢)

A. **Terminology**

"Raising" is a technical name for energy, known as "Raising Energy" (Ti Ching).   It signifies the raising of an object upwards.

Fig 13

Fig 14

B. **Diagrams and movements:**

Movements:

Gradually bend the right leg, while the torso sits backwards and turns to the right side. With the tip of the left leg curved inwards, the weight again falls on the left leg. While changing the right "Hooked Hand" to a palm, shift it from the right side to the front. Lift the right leg and put it in front of the left leg, with heel touching the ground — forming a right "insubstantial" (empty) step. Move the left palm to the inner side of the right arm, shoulder height, and the right palm is at eyebrow level (the left one downwards and the right upwards). Eyes are focused on the right wrist. (Fig. 14)

Important Points: In the standing stance, the torso is natural and stabilized and the buttocks tucked in. While the right knee is slightly bent, it should not be straightened. Lower the two shoulders with tips of elbows curved. The two arms are slightly bent and the chest is relaxed.

C. **Technical Explanations:**

There are two methods for the enclosing of the right arm inward toward the left arm:

(1) Enclosing either from an up-to-downward or from a down-to-upward motion.

(2) Lowering the right wrist and raising it upwards while passing the left palm at nose height.

D. **Benefits:**

This form vigorously contracts and strengthens the spinal column, which becomes elastic, thereby helping to maintain an everlasting youthful appearance.

Form 5. White Stork spreads its Wings (Pai Hao Liang Chi) (白鶴亮翅)

A. Terminology

This is a metaphor — the spreading of wings of a white stork. The spreading of the arms and legs, one upwards and one downwards, one extended and one contracted, represents the posture of this form.

B. Diagrams and movements:

With the turning of the torso to the left, the two hands circle to the left as if they were embracing a ball, with the left hand upward and the right hand downward. Meanwhile, with the toes of the right foot turned to the left, the weight is shifted to the right leg. Raise left foot and take half a step to the front, with toes touching the ground, forming a left insubstantial (empty) step. Separate the hands, the right one up above the head and the left down beside the left thigh. Lower your torso and sit on your right leg.

Important Points: The chest should not be thrust forward and the two arms (upward and downward) should maintain the shape of semi-circles. During execution, the energy (Ching) is exerted by the back, pivoting on the arms.

C. Technical Explanations:

In the performing of this form, either one of the two postures may be employed:

(1) Diagonal spreading of the wings.

(2) Upright spreading of the wings.

D. Benefits:

The diagonal or upright opening of the human figure in this form helps to extend and contract the chest and the back, which tones up the spinal nerves, trains the uprightness of the coccyx and strengthens the alertness of the cerebrum.

Form 6. Brush knee and twist step — left (Lou Sih Au Pu) (Tso Shih) (摟膝拗步，左式)

A. Terminology

First, it signifies the use of one hand to brush the knee. Second, the experts of martial art consider the forward movement of the left with the stretching forward of the left hand, or the forward movement of the right leg and the stretching forward of the right hand, as a "Favorable Step". Additionally the forward movement of the left leg and the stretching forward of the right hand, or the forward movement of the right leg and the streching forward of the left hand, is called "Twist Step".

B. Diagrams and movements:

Movements 1:

Move the right hand before the left shoulder, lower it to

Fig 15

Fig 16

the front of the left part of the abdomen and circle it backwards to the side of the right ear. Meanwhile, raise left hand from the back and move it forward passing the side of the left ear, keeping it at the right side of the chest. (Fig. 15)

Movements 2:

Shift the torso slightly to the left and take half a step forward with the left foot, bowing. Brush the left knee with the left palm and place it beside the knee, then push the right hand forward from the side of the right ear, nose-tip height. Stretch the torso slightly forward and lower it, with weight on the left leg. Bend the left leg and straighten (relatively only) the right leg. The eyes are focused on the right palm which is facing outward. (Fig. 16)

Important Points: The torso should not bow forward. During the pushing-out of the palm, it should be co-ordinated with the relaxing of the waist and the bowing of the leg.

C. Technical Explanations:

In the exercise, do not use the limbs to turn the waist and thighs, but use the waist as an axis, pivoting the movements of the limbs. The direction of the two hands take an elliptical (oval) circular form, repeating twice, first from left to right, then from right to left.

D. Benefits:

This form vigorously contracts and strengthens the posterior muscles of the body. It also increases the strength of the legs.

Form 7. Play the Fiddle (Shou Hui P'i P'a) (手揮琵琶)

A. Terminology

In this form, the enclosing of the two hands is similar to the strumming (playing) of a fiddle; hence, its name.

B. Diagrams and movements:

Shift the right leg behind the left one and raise the left leg to take a half step forward, forming an insubstantial (empty) step, with toes raised.   Simultaneously, raise the right hand, with palm up to the height of the tip of the nose, elbow bent. Put the right palm downward so that it faces the left elbow. Lower the body and rest the weight on the right leg.   This form is the same as in "Raise Hands and step up", but the positions of the left and right limbs are on the opposite.   (Fig. 18)

Fig 17   Fig 18

Important Points: The torso should be stabilized and natural.   Lower the shoulders, bend the elbows and relax the chest.   During the raising of the right hand, the movement should take an arc form without jerking.

C. Technical Explanations:

In the moving of the hands outward, the strength of the spinal column should be applied.

D. Benefits:

This form, through the training of the abdomen, waist, shoulders and posterior muscles, increases the extending and contracting strength of the two arms tremendously. The so-called "Crushing Energy" (Chor Ching) is applied.

Form 8. Brush knee and twist step — left-right-left (Lou Shih Au Pu) (摟膝拗步——左，右，左)

A. Terminology

Same as in From 6.

B. Diagrams and movements:

(1) The left style:

Movements 1:

Lower the right hand the front of the abdomen, and circle it backwards to the side of the right ear. Meanwhile, move the left hand backward, passing the side of the left ear, keeping it at the right side of the chest. (fig. 19)

Movements 2:

Shift the torso slightly to the left and take a half step forward with the left foot, bowing. Brush the left knee with the left palm and place it beside the knee and push the right hand forward from the side of right ear, nose-tip height. Stretch the torso slightly forward and lower it, with weight on the right leg. Bend the left leg and straighten the right leg. The eyes should focus on the

Fig 19   Fig 20

right palm, which is facing outward.   (Fig. 20)

(2) The right style

Movements 3:

Turn the torso to the right and take a step forward with your right leg, forming a right bow-step. Simultaneously, raise the left hand from the front and circle backward to the left ear, pushing forward at nose-tip height. Brush the right knee with the right palm and place it beside the knee. Stretch the torso slightly forward and lower it, with weight on the right leg. Bend the right leg and empty the left leg. The eyes are focused on the left palm, which is facing outward.   (Fig. 21)

C. Technical Explanations:

Same as in Form 6.

Form 9. Play the Fiddle

Fig 21   Fig 22

Same as in Form 7

Form 10. Brush Knee and twist step — left

Same as in Form 6

Form 11. Step up, strike, parry and punch (進步搬攔捶)

A. Terminology

Signifies the actions of striking, parrying and punching.

B. Diagrams and movements:

Movements 1:

> Shift the tip of the left leg outward, turn torso to the left, with left palm facing the ground. Simultaneously, change the right palm into a fist, circle it to the left rib with knuckles facing upward and right leg flexed, with heel raised. (Fig. 22)

Movements 2:

While turning the torso to the right, strike down with the fist in a forward motion towards the extreme right at the height of the nose — knuckles facing downward. The right fist completes a vertical circle. Drop the left hand beside the left hip, but step forward with the right foot, the tip turning slightly outward. Eyes are focused on the right fist. This posture is called "striking" (pan). (Fig. 23)

Movements 3:

The weight is shifted to the right leg, circling and raising your left hand forward and parrying. Simultaneously, take one step forward with the left leg. Transfer weight onto left leg, bending left knee and straightening the right leg. This posture is called "parrying" (lan). Punch forward with the right fist, following the stretching forward of the torso and making a downward and up-

Fig 23

Fig 24

ward arc — the knuckles facing upward. Place the left hand against the inside of the elbow and focus the eyes on the right fist. (Fig. 24)

Important Points: The torso is natural. and erect. Clasp the right fist loosely. With the right shoulder following the "fist direction" to stretch forward, keep the shoulders sinking and the elbows flexible.

C. Technical Explanations:

In T'ai Chi Ch'uan, as the masters said, the mystery of neutralizing comes from "parrying", while the mystery of attacking is solved by "punching". There are the so-called "five punches" in the whole series, and this is one of them. In punching, although stretching the torso forward, do not lean too much to the front, and keep body upright. In this way the energy of the spine is strengthened.

D. Benefits:

The benefits of this form are manifested to a greater degree in the actions of striking, parrying and punching. The spinal column is strengthened and the joints of the knees and hips are made more flexible. The important glands of the organs are helped to function more properly.

Form 12. Apparent close up (如封似閉)

A. Terminology

The whole movement is similar to the closing of a door, aiming at the parrying or hindering of the opponent's hands from attacking.

B. Diagrams and movements:

Movements 1:

Changing the right fist into a palm, stretch the left hand outward under the right wrist. Simultaneously, shift weight back to the right leg, bending right knee and flexing left foot. Eyes are gazing straight ahead.

Movements 2:

Draw back the torso, turn your right and left hands (palms facing downward) to the right. Revolve a semicircle, push forward. Separate the two hands as far apart as the shoulders, and push forward, with the palms facing outward. The center of gravity is shifted to the left foot. Eyes are focused first on the two palms, and then on the front. (Fig. 25)

Important Points: Avoid leaning backward while the torso rests on the right leg. While the arms are following the torso to contract backward, the shoulders and elbows should be slightly relaxed in the process of stretching forward. Avoid any mood of stiffness while contracting backward.

C. Technical Explanations:

Immediately after the joining of wrists, the two hands should be separated. Immediately after the separation, the hands should push forward without delay. In the separation of hands, the elbows must be slightly bent downward, beside the ribs, so that the intrinsic energy (Nei Ching) is not dissipated. In pushing, stretch out the fingers and energy is exerted from the ends of the palms.

D. Benefits:

This form tones up the spinal nerves and the abdominal organs. It increases peristalsis of the bowels, invigorates the appetite and clears up gastric troubles.

Form 13. Cross Hands (十字手)

A. Terminology

Fig 25   Fig 26

In this form, the two forearms are joined together to form a cross.

B. Diagrams and movements:

Movements 1:

Turn right toes outward and at the same time shift weight onto right leg, bending right knee and straightening left knee. With these movements, turn torso to the right and move right hand to right side of right leg, keeping palm downward. The left hand remains at the left, the elbow slightly curved. Now in a parallel manner, raise the two arms. The eyes are focused on the right hand. (Fig. 26)

Movements 2:

Shift your center of gravity gradually to the left leg, move the right leg in a half step to the left, forming a "riding-horse" step. At the same time, draw both arms inward (first downward and then upward), crossing the two forearms diagonally in front of your chest (about one foot apart) — the right palm is on the outside of left palm, with palms facing inward, chin high. The eyes are focused straight ahead. (Fig. 25)

Important Points: The torso is natural and erect. The arms maintain the form of two semi-circles, crossing before the upper part of the chest. When standing up, avoid any kind of tension.

C. Technical Explanations:

This form acts as the connecting link between the preceding and the following postures. Although it is ually considered as the signpost for the conclusion of all three sections of the whole series, all the movements, however, are performed continuously without stopping.

D. Benefits:

The complete stretching of the two arms (left and right, upper and lower) helps vigorously the process of inhalation and exhalation. The sympathetic nerves are toned up.

Form 14. Carry Tiger to Mountain (抱虎歸山)

A. Terminology

Assuming that the opponent is a tiger, one should get hold of it and throw it away. This form is also called "Carry Tiger, Push Mountain", in which the act of throwing away is emphasized.

B. Diagrams and movements:

Turn toes of left foot inward, bending the two knees and shifting weight to the left leg. Turn torso on the waist backward to the right, bending right knee and forming a bow-step.

The weight is now on the right leg. When your right leg takes one step forward, brush the right knee with the right palm towards the right, making the right hand circle a half-horizontal round backward to the right and upward to the front, with palm facing downward. At the same time, the left hand circles backward and pushes out horizontally to the right with the left palm, following the turning of the torso. The eyes are first on the right, then on the left. (Figs. 27, 28, 29)

| Fig 27 | Fig 28 |

Important Points: It is important to utilize the waist and torso to move the shoulders backward and forward. The five postures in the operations should continue as one unit.

C. Technical Explanations:

Some masters combine the "cross hands" with this form into

one single unit. The Yang System, classifying these into two distinct forms, combines this form with the following "Diagonal grasping of Bird's Tail" into one posture. Pragmatically speaking, these forms should be so divided as set forth here.

D. Benefits:

This important exercise helps to strengthen the neck area, and assists the various gastro-intestinal functions. It rejuvenates the organs and prolongs longevity.

Form 15. Diagonal grasping the Bird's Tail (斜攬雀尾)

A. Terminology

Same as in "Grasping the Bird's Tail" (Form 2), but the direction is diagonal. As this is the linking movement between this form and the previous one (Carry Tiger to Mountain), the "Ward-off" style may be omitted. Just use the left hand

Fig 29   Fig 30

to join the right one to perform the "Pull Back Style".

B. Diagrams and movements:

Raise the right arm to the front of the chest, shoulder height, with palm diagonally downward. Place the left palm against the right forearm, a few inches apart, to make a "Pull-Back" posture towards the left. While turning torso to the left, keep the balance of the Left and Right performance at the same time. (See Fig. 30)

Weight is shifted to the left leg. Then follow with styles: "Press Forward" and "Push". The movements are the same as those in Form 2; the difference lies in the direction only.

C. Technical Explanations:

Same as in Form 2.

D. Benefits:

Same as in Form 2.

Form 16. Diagonal single Whip (斜單鞭)

A. Terminology, diagrams, movements and benefits:

Same as in Form 3. (With the directions altered) (Fig. 31)

B. Important points:

The direction is diagonal. (See Diagram). Looking at the left palm.

Form 17. Fist under Elbow (肘底捶)

A. Terminology

The real name for this form is "Punch Under Elbow" but in the Chinese terminology, the term "looking at the fist under elbow" is sometimes used.

B. Diagrams and movements:

Movements 1:

After shifting weight to the left leg, move the right foot a half step to the left, paralleling with the left foot. Pivoting on the right foot, turn torso to the left. The

Fig 31   Fig 32

center of gravity is again shifted to the right foot. (Fig. 32)

Important Points: In the turning of the torso to the left, the left leg takes a half step diagonally to the left and forms an insubstantial step, with heel touching the ground.

Movements 2: While the left hand moves to the left and makes a horizontal counter-clockwise semi-circle back to the left side of the waist, turn the right hand to the left in front of the chest and clench it into a fist. At the same time, raise the left hand upward and pass the right wrist, at the height of the mouth, palm facing right, fingers stretched. Eyes are focused on the left thumb. (Fig. 33)

Important Points: When the left foot takes a half step to

the left and backward, the two arms should follow the torso turning to the left. Both movements should be coordinated. The torso is erect and natural, and the buttocks should be tucked in. When the left palm is stretched forward, the weight is on the right leg, with left leg slightly flexed.

C. Technical Explanations:

In the movements, the right hand forms a semi-circle, while the left makes an elliptical (or oval) circle. In punching with the right fist, the torso slants slightly forward. It is necessary to pay attention to the "three external harmonies"; that is, the shoulders and thighs, the elbows and knees, and the hands and legs should be harmonious.

D. Benefits:

In performing this form, you can expect to reduce excess weight and greatly strengthen the legs, thighs, hips and buttocks.

Form 18. Step back and repulse Monkey — right, left, right.
(倒攆猴，右，左，右)

A. Terminology

Assuming a monkey, supposed to be the opponent, is rushing at you, one of your hands is to let it go while the other is to push its head. Hence this name.

B. Diagrams and movements:

Movements 1:

Open the right fist, lower it with palm facing upward, draw it backwards, circle around and pass the right ear. Lower the left hand so that the arm is on the level of the hip and the palm faces upward. Lift your left foot so that the toes are touching the ground. Eyes

Fig 33   Fig 34

are focused on the left palm.   Weight is on the right foot.   (Fig. 34)

Movements 2:

Push the right hand forward (palm facing front), while the left hand draws back, passing the left rib and circling backward, palm facing upward.   At the same time, raise the left leg slightly and retreat half a step backward, toes reaching the ground first.   When the center of gravity is shifted to the left foot, the right leg turns into an insubstantial step.   Eyes are focused on the right palm.   (Fig. 35)

Movements 3:

Reverse the left hand and push it forward, palm facing front, by passing the left ear.   At the same time, draw the right hand backward, passing the right rib, circle it

Fig 35   Fig 36

around and put it beside the right ear. Simultaneously, raise the right leg slightly and retreat half a step backward. When the center of gravity is shifted to the right leg, the left leg turns into an insubstantial step. Eyes are focused on the left palm. (Fig. 36)

Important Points: While the hands stretching forward are not required to extend in straight lines, the hands reversing backward should take a circular movement, avoiding stiffness. The knees of the insubstantial legs are bent. While retreating, avoid jerking high or low, and the torso should be balanced and stabilized. The eyes following the turning of the torso look at the left and right and then turn back to the frontal hands.

C. Technical Explanations:

The movements in this form   should end with an odd num-

ber, that is, in three or five. While the width of the two feet
is equal to that of the shoulders, the retreating feet should
proceed in straight lines.

D.　Benefits:

With the emphasis centering on the spinal cord, the entire
nervous system would be benefited.

Form 19.　Slanting Flying (斜飛式)

A.　Terminology

This form is very similar to the spreading of wings of a flying
bird. Hence its name. It consists of the left and right styles.

B.　Diagrams and movements:

Movements 1:

Shift your left hand horizontally in front of the chest,
palm facing downward, and move the right hand up to
the abdomen, as if you were carrying a ball (the left
hand is on the top, while the right is at the bottom).
Withdraw the right leg to the left, toes touching the
ground. (Fig. 37)

Movements 2:

After turning the torso to the right, take a step forward
with the right leg, forming a bow-step. Separate the two
hands by raising the right one, palm facing upward
slantingly; and by lowering your left hand backward beside your thigh, palm facing downward. The center of
gravity is shifted to the right foot. The right leg is bent
and the left relatively straight. Eyes are focused on the
right palm. (Fig. 38)

Important Points: In turning the torso to the right, do
not over-speed your tempo. It should be stabilized and
natural.

Fig 37   Fig 38

C. **Benefits:**

In this form, as in others, the waist and torso are used to move the hands and legs. This form strengthens the muscles of the back and abdomen and helps to relieve constipation. The legs and thighs are strengthened and circulation in the lower limbs is greatly improved.

Form 20.   Raise Hands and step up.

A. **Terminology:**

Same as in FORM 4.

B. **Diagrams and movements:**

(See Form 4)

Moving the left leg half a step forward, the center of gravity is now shifted to the left leg. Then raise the right leg, knee slightly flexed, heel barely touching the ground.

C. **Technical explanations and benefits:**

Same as in FORM 4.

Form 21. White Stork spreads its Wings.
Same as in FORM 5.

Form 22. Brush Knee and twist step — left.
Same as in FORM 6.

Form 23. Needle at sea bottom (海底針).
A. Terminology
It means that the hand (needle) is used to pressure the vital point, which is known as "Sea Bottom" (Hai Ti) in acupuncture, at the foot of the opponent.

B. Diagrams and movements:
As the right leg takes a half step forward, the left leg moves slightly forward, with toes touching the ground, forming an insubstantial step. At the same time, raise the right hand upward in front of the chest and then bring it down to the height of the left knee. Place the left palm against the inside of the right elbow. Eyes are on the lower front. Part of the center of gravity is shifted to the left foot. (Fig. 39)

Important Points: In order to avoid lowering of the head, do not bend the body slantingly. In the act of bringing the right hand down, do not lean the shoulders forward. The center of gravity is on the right leg, but part of it may shift to the left leg.

C. Technical Explanations:
The spinal cord should be erect, do not bend slantingly forward.

D. Benefits:
This exercise particularly helps the life-force of the spinal cord and the knees.

Form 24. Fan through Back (扇通背).

Fig 39

Fig 40

A. Terminology

Assuming the spinal cord is the axis of the fan and the two arms are spokes in its opening, this form tries to signify that the opening of the arms is very much like the opening of a fan. The so-called "through back" is to say that the strength of the spinal cord can reach the two arms.

B. Diagrams and movements:

Turn torso to the right and take a step forward with the left foot, forming a bow-step. Raise the right hand above the forehead, forming a semi-circle, with palm facing slantingly outward. While the right hand draws back slightly above the temple, stretch the left hand forward and beyond the left knee, palm facing outward. The center of gravity is first on the right foot and then, following the stretching of the left hand, is shifted to the left foot. Lower your torso. The left leg is bent, while the right leg relatively straight. Eyes are focused on the left hand. (Fig. 40)

Important Points:.. The torso is erect, waist and buttocks relaxed. In the stretching of the left hand, the arm must not extend straight out. Stretch your back muscles, lower the shoulders, left hand nose height.

C. Technical Explanations:

In the operation of the energy (Ching), the strength of the left palm should correspond with the left ribs, with a view to moving forward. At the same time, the strength of the right arm should reach (through) the left hand.

D. Benefits:

This form helps to train the strength of the shoulders and the back as well as the legs. The lungs are developed, the neck, shoulders, arms, wrists, back, thighs, knees, calves and ankles are greatly strengthened. The external shape of the body is improved; the internal organs and glands are stimulated.

Form 25. Turn Body — chop with Fist (撇身捶).

A. Terminology

Signifying the turning of the body and striking with fists. This consists in one of the "five punches" in Tai Chi Ch'uan.

B. Diagrams and movements:

Movements 1:

> With the turning of the torso to the right and backward, the center of gravity is shifted to the right foot. While moving, clench your right hand into a fist and make it circle downward — a half vertical circle and stay beside the left ribs knuckles facing downward. The left hand is lifted and stays before the chest with the arm forming a semi-circle and the palm is being pushed slantingly

outward. (Fig. 41)

Movements 2:

While turning body to the right, the right leg takes a half step forward, forming a bow-step. Make the right fist circle vertically upward to the left and chop down forward to the right. Simultaneously, lower the left hand in front of the chest with palm facing downward. The right leg is bent and the left is relatively straight. Eyes are focused on the right fist. (Fig. 42)

Fig 41   Fig 42

Important Points: Reverse the right leg before taking a half step forward. The lowering of the foot and the chopping of the fist should be performed simultaneously.

C. Technical Explanations:

In the turning of the body, the operation of the hands and legs is conducted by pivoting from the waist and spinal column.

D. Benefits:

This form especially helps to activate the strength of the waist and the thighs. It is very beneficial to the waist and leads to the reduction of excess fat.

Form 26. Step up, Strike, Parry and Punch (進步搬攔捶).

A. Terminology. See Form II.

B. Diagrams and movements:

Movements 1:

With the bending of the left leg, weight is now on the left side. Move the right leg and place it next to the inner side of the left leg. Turn the right hand knuckles downward and circle upward by passing the abdomen, and place it beside the left rib. (Fig. 43)

Movements 2:

Fig 43   Fig 44

Take a step forward with the right leg, toes turning outward. At the same time, raise the right fist and strike
down, with knuckles facing upward, while the left hand
is dropped beside the left thigh, palm facing downward.
(Fig. 44)

Movements 3:

Shift the weight to the right leg, while the right hand is
drawn back to the right of the waist, knuckles facing
upward. Push the left hand forward from the left side,
parrying, with palm facing downward. Meanwhile, take
a step forward with the left leg, forming a bow-step, and
then punch forward with the right fist, following the
stretching forward of the torso, making a downward and
upward arc (the knuckles facing the right side). The
left hand makes a half vertical counter-clockwise circle
with the wrist and then draw it backward, placing it
against the inside of your right arm. The eyes are now
focused on the right fist. (Fig. 44)

Important Points: The movement of the waist should follow the action of the step.

Form 27. Step up, grasping the Bird's Tail (進步攬雀尾).
A. **Terminology**. See Form 2.
B. **Diagrams and movements:**

Movements 1:

Shift weight slightly backward and turn torso halfway to
the left. By moving the left toes outward, draw your
left hand downward to the left and leave it there, flexed
horizontally in front of the chest, palm facing down.
Simultaneously, open your right fist, circle downward and
backward, leaving it before the abdomen, palm facing up.

The two hands are facing each other as if they were embracing a ball.

Movements 2:

Step up with the right leg and hereafter continue to perform the "ward off", "pull-back", "press-forward" and "push" styles. The operations and movements are the same as those in FORM 2.

Form 28. Single Whip.

Terminology, Movements and other points are the same as those in FORM 3.

Form 29. Wave hands like Clouds (雲手).

A. Terminology

Indicating the movements of the hands which are similar to the revolving of the clouds. Hence its name.

B. Diagrams and movements:

Movements 1:

Shifting the center of gravity to the left leg, your torso is gradually turned to the left. While the toes of the right leg turn to the right, make the right hand circle vertically down, passing the abdomen to the left side and upward to the left shoulder, the palm facing inward. Before circling, change the right "hooked hand" into a palm. Eyes are now on the right hand. (Fig. 45-46)

Movements 2:

The center of gravity is gradually shifted to the right while the right hand circles vertically a half circle to the left part of the abdomen and stops in front of the chest, the palm turned up. Meanwhile, circle the left hand downward, passing the abdomen to the right up to the right shoulder, with palm facing inward. Simultaneously,

Fig 45

Fig 46

the right leg moves a half step to the left, forming a united paralled step, about five inches apart from the left leg. The eyes are now on the right hand. (Fig. 46)

Movements 3:

While the left hand rotates to the left, the right hand, passing the abdomen, circles vertically upwards to the left shoulder, with palm facing inward. Simultaneously, the left hand is turning outward, with palm facing inward. Now the left leg takes a big step horizontally to the left, and the eyes are focused on the left hand. (Fig. 48)

Movements 4:

The remaining movements are repetitions of the first, second and third movements, which can be performed three times, five times, or even seven times. (Figs. 45-

Fig 47   Fig 48

46-47-48)

Important Points: While pivoting the torso at the waist, avoid jerking up and down. The rotating of the two arms should be active and natural. The movements of the lower limbs, with knees should follow the movements of the left or right hand, whether the direction is up or down.

C.   Technical Explanations:

This is one of the most important forms in Tai Chi Ch'uan and is not easy to perform. Pivoting all the movements at the waist, the two arms, two elbows, two hands, two legs, two knees are considered as wheels. In the operations, they seem to be extending and yet not extending; they seem to be contracting and yet not contracting. All these substantialities and insubstantialities can be comprehended only by gradual study. Generally speaking, the tempo of the two hands should be at the same rate and the turning of the waist must be maintained.

D. Benefits:

In the practice of this form, you can expect to gain tranquility and calmness by directing energy from the psychic center to the whole body. The nerves are calmed, and the mind becomes peaceful and concentrated. Besides the reduction of excess weight in the waistline, it gives a general feeling of joyfulness and well-being.

Form 30. Single Whip ((單鞭).

Same as in FORM 3.

Important Points: After practicing the "Wave Hands Like Clouds" two, three, or five times, while the right hand rotates in the upper direction, change the right palm into a "hooked hand" (pinching the five fingers). Take a step to the left with the left leg. The remaining movements are the same as those in the "Single Whip".

Form 31. High pat on Horse (高探馬).

A. Terminology:

This form symbolizes the riding of a horse, as if you were raising the torso high and patting at the front. Hence its name.

B. Diagrams and movements:

Movements:

Take half a step forward with the right foot and change the right "hooked hand" into a palm. Draw the torso backward and the center of gravity is shifted to the right foot. Draw the left hand back to the front of the left rib, with palm facing upward. Then raise the right hand, pass the right ear and push forward, with the palm turned outward and fingers facing slantingly upward. Simultaneously, raise the left heel with toes touching the ground and forming a left insubstantial step. Eyes are now focused on the right hand. (Fig. 49)

Important Points: The torso is erect and natural. Do not raise the chest nor bow the back. Keep the right hand high at eyebrow level.

C. Technical Explanations:

Stretching the right hand forward, strength is concentrated on the right palm. In the performance of the movements, the rising and dropping of the legs should be coordinated with the raising and lowering of the hands.

D. Benefits:

By doing this form of exercise one can expect to stimulate the energy (Ching) of the two arms; develop chest and im-

Fig 49

Fig 50

prove posture.

Form 32. Separation of right Foot (分右脚).

A. Terminology:

In the separation of the feet, the practitioner has to kick either to the right or to the left. This is the right form.

B. Diagrams and movements:

Movements 1:

Stretch your left hand upward and form a cross by passing over the right wrist in front of the chest, the right hand placed outside of the left hand, both palms facing inward. Immediately after this, separate the two hands on both sides and make them circle vertically downward, and again upward to the front, crossing hands again. Meanwhile, the left foot takes a step slightly backkward and to the left. The center of gravity is shifted to the left. Then draw the right leg to the side of the left foot, with toes touching the ground and heel raised. (Fig. 50)

Movements 2:

Separate the two palms levelly at the left and right, facing outward, and at the same time, kick out levelly with the tip of the right foot at the extreme right side, while the left leg is slightly bent. Eyes are focused on the right leg. (Fig. 51)

Important Points: When stabilizing the torso, do not bend forward or look upward. During the separation of the two hands, the two wrists are at shoulder height. Except for the slight bending of the left leg, the right arm and the right leg should face each other.

C. Technical Explanations:

In the casting step and the separating hands operations, the movements of the hands and the step should be harmonious. During the kicking, the weight of the whole body is on the left foot.

D. Benefits:

This posture strengthens the energy of the legs. The act of balancing the torso and raising the leg will help much in strengthening the muscles. Soon you will be surprised to find how much higher you can lift your legs.

Form 33. Separation of left Foot (分左脚).

A. **Terminology:** See Form 32.

B. **Diagrams and movements:**

Movements 1:

Drop the right leg. The right knee is slightly bent and the weight is on the right foot. Turn the torso halfway to the right. Draw both hands slightly back and to the right, making them circle vertically downward to the right and upward to the front, forming a cross-hands position — the left hand is placed outside of the right hand, both palms facing inward. The center of gravity returns to the right foot. Meanwhile, draw the left foot backward, staying near the right leg, with toes touching in the ground and heel raised.

Movements 2:

Separate the two hands levelly towards the left and right, with palms facing outward. Simultaneously, kick out levelly with the tip of the left foot on the extreme left, with the right leg bending. The eyes are focused on the left leg.

Fig 51   Fig 52

Form 34. Turn and kick with left Sole (轉身蹬脚).

A. Terminology:

This term signifies the posture of turning the body backwards to the left and kicking with the left sole.

B. Diagrams and movements:

Movements 1:

Drop the left foot. Raise your knee with the tip of the foot barely touching the ground. Pivoting on the right leg, turn body backward to the left. Meanwhile, cross the two hands in front of your chest, the left hand is placed outside of the right, palms facing inward.

Movements 2:

Separate the two palms levelly at the left and right, facing outward, and at the same time, kick out levelly, but slowly, with the sole of the left foot. The eyes are now focused on the left leg. (Fig. 52)

Important Points: In the kicking with the sole, the tip of the left foot should reverse inward. In the separation of hands and the kicking with sole, the upper and lower movements should be coordinated.

C. Technical Explanations:

The torso is erect and should not slant forward. During the act of kicking, lower the torso.

D. Benefits:

Same as in FORM 32.

Form 35. Brush Knee and twist step — left and right (摟膝拗步，左，右).

A. Terminology:

Same as in FORM 8.

B. Diagrams and movements:

Movements 1:

Take a step forward with the left leg, forming a bow-step. At the same time, make the left hand brush the left knee. After this, the left hand remains beside the left thigh. Meanwhile, make the right hand pass your right ear and push it forward. The center of gravity is now on the left leg, but the eyes are on the right hand.

Movements 2:

Draw the torso slightly backward. The center of gravity is now shifted to the right foot. Turn the toes of the left foot outward. Take one step forward with the right leg and shift weight to the right. The movements of the two hands are the same as in FORM 8. (See Figs. 15, 16).

Form 36. Step up and punch downward (進步栽捶 **).**

A. Terminology:

Strike right fist to front downward.

The name signifies the movements, that is, to take a step forward, meanwhile punching downward. This is again one of the "five punches" in Tai Chi Ch'uan.

B. Diagrams and movements:

Movements 1:

Move the torso slightly backward and to the right, turning the tip of the right foot outward. Following the turning of the torso, make the right hand circle horizontally backward to the right, clench it into a fist and stop it at the right side of the waist, with knuckles facing downward.

Movements 2:

The left leg takes one step forward, forming a bow-step, with weight shifting to the left foot. After brushing the left knee with the left hand, drop it beside the left thigh. Bend the torso forward and strike downward with right fist to the front below the knee, with knuckles facing outward. The center of gravity is shifted to the left foot, bending, while the right leg is relatively straightened. The eyes are now focused on the right fist. (Fig. 53)

Important Points: The torso is erect, waist and thigh are relaxed.

C. Technical Explanations:

Do not slant the head beyond the toes. In striking with the fist, use the strength of the spinal column.

D. Benefits:

This form helps one to gain strength and flexibility throughout the spine, back and neck. It also develops the energy of the right hand.

Form 37. Turn Body — chop with Fist (轉身撇身捶).

A. Terminology:

See Form 25.

B. Diagrams and movements:

Movements 1:

Stand up, open the right fist, raise the two hands above the head and finally make them circle vertically to the right. The center of gravity is shifted to the right foot. After turning the toes of your left foot to the right, put the left hand in front of your forehead and clench the right hand into a fist in front of the chest, with knuckles facing upward. (See Fig. 42)

Movements 2:

The center of gravity is first shifted to the right foot and then to the left, and again, finally, to the right. In the shifting of weight to the right, raise your right foot and move it half a step to the right. Raise your right fist and chop down to the front forward toward the extreme right, while lowering the left hand to put it against the right forearm. The right leg is bent, and the left leg relatively straight. The eyes are now focused on the right fist.

Important Points: The direction of the blow should take the form of a circle.

Form 38. Step up, strike, parry and punch (進步搬攔捶).

A. Terminology:

Same as in Form 26.

B. Diagrams and movements:

Movements 1:

With the turning of the torso to the left, move your right fist and left palm back and rest in front of the waist on the left side with knuckles and palm facing downward.

The rest of the movements are the same as those in Form 26.

Form 39. Kick with right Sole diagonally (右蹬脚).

A. Terminology:

Same as in Form 34, except for the direction which is diagonal.

B. Diagrams and movements:

Movements 1:

Separate and circle the two hands vertically and downward, toward the right and left, and cross hands at the front of your chest, with the right hand outward, palms facing inward. At the same time, turn the tip of the left leg slightly outward and place the right foot beside the left leg, with toes touching the ground. The eyes are on the front.

Fig 53

Fig 54

Movements 2:

> Raise the right leg and kick with sole, the toes facing backward. Simultaneously, separate the two arms levelly at the right and left. Eyes are now focused on the right leg. (Fig. 54)

Form 40. Hit Tiger at left (左打虎).

A. Terminology:

Practitioners consider this form as the fiercest one in the beating of an opponent. Hence its name.

B. Diagrams and movements:

Movements 1:

> Draw the right leg backward and drop it beside the left leg. Meanwhile, shift the left hand to the inner part of the forearm of the right hand. Eyes are focused on the right hand. (Fig. 55)

Movements 2:

> Taking a step backward to the left with the left leg, turn your torso to the left, forming a left bow-step. At the same time, draw the two hands to the chest, with right hand clenched into a fist, the knuckles facing upward. Make the left hand (which is being changed into a fist) circle downward to the left and upward before the forehead, knuckles facing inward. The two fists oppose each other, and the eyes, following the turning of the torso to the left, are focused at the front. (Fig. 55)

> *Important Points:* The arms maintain the form of two semi-circles; the muscles of the chest are relaxed.

C. Technical Explanations:

The direction of the movements of the two fists should take the form of circles at the right and the left, the crossing line of which is at the front of the abdomen.

D. Benefits:

This important exercise helps to promote the health of the back area, promotes freedom from nervousness, discourages old age, and strengthens the elasticity of the knees and ankles.

Form 41. Hit Tiger at Right (右打虎).

A. Terminology:

Same as in the preceding form.

B. Diagrams and movements:

Movements:

First shift the weight backward, then, turning the toes of the left foot inward, shift weight again to the left leg. At the same time, after turning the torso backward to the right, take a step forward with the right leg, forming a bow-step. Changing the two fists into palms, make them

Fig 55

Fig 56

circle to the right by passing the abdomen, while the left palm, changing into a fist, remains in front of the chest, the knuckles facing upward; draw the right palm, changing into a fist in front of your forehead, with the knuckles pointing inward. While the fists oppose each other, the eyes are focused on the front. (Fig. 56)

Form 42. Right Foot kicks upward (右蹬脚).

A. Terminology:

The term signifies the direction of the movements of the kicking foot.

B. Diagrams and movements:

Movements 1:

While bending the left leg, the center of gravity is shifted to the left leg. Turn toes of the right leg inward and move the torso towards the left. Meanwhile, raise the left fist upward, separate the two arms before the forehead, and cross the hands in front of the chest, with the right palm outward and the left palm inward. At the same time, place the right foot beside the left leg, the toes barely touching the ground and the heel raised. The eyes are focused on the front. (Fig. 57)

Movements 2:

While lifting the body, turn palms outward levelly and kick upward with the tip of the right foot, while the left leg is slightly bent. (Fig. 57)

Important Points: The same as those in the "separation of right foot", but the point of using strength is concentrated at the tip of the right foot.

C. Technical Explanations:

Pivoting at the waist, open the body and exercise the two

Fig 57

Fig 58

Fig 59

Fig 60

arms. In kicking with the right foot, the left leg should bend slightly so that the weight is on the left leg.

D. Benefits:

Same as in Form 34.

Form 43. Strike Ears with Fists (雙風貫耳).

A. Terminology:

Using the two fists to strike the two ears of the opponent, hence its name.

B. Diagrams and movements:

Movements:

Drop the right leg in the front, forming a right bow-step. Simultaneously, after brushing the right knee downward with the two palms, change them into fists, and extend upward and strike the two ears of the opponent on both sides with the knuckles facing inward, forehead height. At the same time, the torso is extended slightly forward. The weight is now on the right foot. The right leg is bent and the left leg is straightened. The eyes are focused on the right fist. (Figs. 58, 59, 60).

Important Points: The head and neck are erect. Avoid hunchbacking. The fists are loosely closed. Maintain the circular forms with your two arms.

C. Technical Explanations:

The advance and retreat of the two arms should be coordinated with the legs, activated and without stopping.

D. Benefits:

This posture makes the spine supple and elastic. The muscles of the arms are strengthened.

Form 44. Kick with left Sole (左踢脚).

A. Terminology:

Signifying the kicking with the sole.

B. Diagrams and movements:

Movements 1:

After shifting your center of gravity backward, turn toes of the right leg outward. Cross your hands before your chest, while changing your fists into palms, with left palm outward. At the same time, after the shifting the center of gravity to the right foot, draw the left leg beside the right one, with toes touching the ground and heel raised. The eyes are focused on the left side. (Fig. 61)

Movements 2:

Separate the two arms levelly to the left and the right, with palms facing outward. At the same time, raise the left leg and kick upward with the sole towards the left side, toes reversed. The eyes are focused on the left leg. (Fig. 61)

Important Points: The same as those in "Turn and Kick with Left Sole", but there is difference in the direction.

C. Technical Explanations:

In the posture of kicking, focus the energy (Ching) on the sole of the left foot, and the right leg should bend slightly, so that the weight of the body is concentrated on the right leg.

D. Benefits:

With the relaxing of the waist and buttocks, this form helps to improve the digestion.

Form 45. Turn around and kick with right Sole (轉身蹬右脚).

A. Terminology:

Same as in the preceding form.

B. Diagrams and movements:

Fig 61   Fig 62

Movements 1:

Raise the knee of the left leg by taking a standing stance, with the tip of the foot suspended in the air. Meanwhile, cross the hands again in front of the chest, with the right hand staying outward. Pivoting on the right sole, turn torso 180° to the right, with left leg bowing and weight shifting to the left side. While the toes of the right foot are touching the ground, the eyes are now focused on the right side. (Fig. 62)

Movements 2:

With the lowering of the torso, separate your two hands levelly to the left and the right, palms facing outward. Meanwhile, lower the torso, kick with the right sole, with the tip of the foot reversed. The eyes are focused on the right leg. (Fig. 62)

Form 46. Step up, strike, parry and punch (進步搬攔捶 **).**

A. Terminology:

Same as in Form 11.

B. Diagrams and movements:

(See Form 11)

Movements:

>Drop the right leg and take a step forward to the front, with toes turning outward. Meanwhile, clench the right palm into a fist, turn it downward to the left, pass the left side of the waist, raise it, and then strike down and forward (the arm being level with the shoulder), making a vertical circle, with knuckles facing downward. The left palm is flexed beside the left thigh, with palm facing the ground. The eyes are focused on the right fist. The other succeeding movements are the same as those in Form 11.

Form 47. Apparent close up (如封似閉 **).**

Following the preceding posture, all the movements are the same as those in Form 12.

Form 48. Cross-hands (十字手 **).**

Following the preceding posture, all the movements are the same as those in Form 13.

Form 49. Carry Tiger to Mountain (抱虎歸山 **).**

Following the preceding posture, all the movements are the same as those in Form 14.

Form 50. Diagonal grasping of Bird's Tail (斜攬雀尾 **).**

Following the preceeding posture, all the movements are the same as those in Form 15.

Form 51.   Diagonal single whip (斜單鞭).

Following the preceding posture, all the movements are the same as those in Form 16.

Form 52.   Partition of Wild Horse's Mane—right, left and right (野馬分鬃，右，左，右).

A.   Terminology:

The posture of this exercise is similar to the running of a wild horse and the parting of its mane to the right and left. Hence its name.

B.   Diagrams and movements:

(1)   Right Style

Movements 1:

After turning torso to the left, curve the left arm levelly before the chest. Change the right "hooked hand" into a palm. Move the waist slightly to the left, with right palm facing upward, (on the lower part) and left palm facing downward (on the upper part), as if they were embracing a ball. At the same time, draw the right foot backward beside the left leg, toes touching the ground. The eyes are focused on the left hand.   (Fig. 63)

Movements 2:

Take a step forward to the right with the right leg, forming a bow-step. Meanwhile, stretch the torso slightly forward and raise the right forearm slantingly to the right, eyebrow high, with palm facing slantingly upward over the right leg. Lower the left hand and place it beside

Fig 63   Fig 64

the left thigh, palm facing downward. The eyes are
focused on the right hand. (Fig. 64)

(2) Left Style

Movements 3:

Draw the torso backward, with weight shifting to the
left leg. Lift the right toes slightly outward, forming a
bow-step. At the same time, draw the right hand to the
front of the chest, flexing levelly. Circle the left hand
to the right, stopping under the right hand. The two
palms thus face each other, as if they were embracing
a ball. Draw the left foot back beside the right leg, with
toes touching the ground. The eyes are focused on the
right hand.

Movements 4:

The left leg takes one step to the left, forming a bow-step.   Meanwhile, stretch the torso slightly forward and raise the left forearm slantingly to the left, eyebrow high, with palm facing slantingly upward over the left leg.   Put the right hand downward and place it beside the right thigh, palm facing downward.   The eyes are focused on the left hand.

(3)   Right Style

Movements 5:

Draw the torso backward, with weight shifting to the right leg.   Lift the left toes slightly outward, forming a bow-step.   At the same time, draw the left hand to the front of the chest, flexing levelly.   Circle the right hand to the left, stopping under the left hand.   The two palms thus face each other, as if they were embracing a ball.   Draw the right foot backward beside the left leg, toes touching the ground.   The eyes are focused on the left hand.   (Fig. 63)

Movements 6:

The right leg takes one step to the right, forming a bow-step.   Meanwhile, stretch the torso slightly forward and raise the right forearm slantingly to the right, up to the height of the eyes, with palm facing slantingly upward over the right leg.   Lower the left hand and place it beside the left thigh, palm facing downward.   The eyes are now focused on the right hand.   (Fig. 64)

C.   Important points:

Do not lean forward too much; relax the chest.   In the separation of the two arms, maintain a circular form.   While turning, use the waist as an axis.

D.   Technical explanations:

In operation, this form should take an odd number. For instance, if the right styles are performed two times, the left style is done once. But in the first operation, a half step is to be taken while the rest should take one step.

E. Benefits:

It helps to invigorate the whole nervous system. One can expect to strengthen the muscles throughout the face and the neck, and help the improvement of the circulation and the complexion.

Form 53. Step up, Grasping the Bird's Tail (進步攬雀尾).

A. Terminology:

Same as in FORM 2.

B. Diagrams and movements:

(See Form 2)

Movements:

After sitting backward, the center of gravity is shifted to the left foot. Draw the right hand back to make a horizontal half circle and stay in front of the chest. At the same time, cause the left hand, following the movement of the upper part of the body, to make a small horizontal circle beside the waist, and put it below the right elbow, with palm facing upward. Take one step forward to the left with the left leg. The center of gravity is shifted to the left. The eyesight is focused on the left hand. The rest of the movements are the same as those in the Grasping the Bird's Tail. (See Form 2)

Form 54. Single Whip.

The movements are the same as those in Form 3.

Form 55. Fair Lady works at the Shuttles (玉女穿梭).

A. Terminology:

This form takes the following four steps: First, advancing. Second, revolving backward. Third, turning. Fourth, revolving backward, — directing to the four corners continually — just like a shuttle going through a piece of embroidery. Hence its name.

B. Diagrams and movements:

Movements 1:

> A. *The first Diagonal Corner Style.*
>
> After turning the toes of the left foot inward, the center of gravity is again shifted to the left leg. The toes of the right foot then turn outward, following the turning of the torso to the right and backward. Open the "hooked hand" and curve the palm of the right hand in front of the chest, facing downward. The left hand circles downward and upward, staying before the abdomen, with palm facing upward. Then raise the left leg and take a step toward the left corner, forming a bow-step. Raise the left hand in front of the forehead with the palm facing outward, and slantingly upward. Simultaneously, push the right hand outward near the elbow of the left hand, palm facing outward. The eyesight is now focused on the right hand. (Fig. 65)

Movements 2:

> B. *The Second Diagonal Corner Style.*
>
> After shifting the centre of gravity to the right leg, the toes of the left foot turn inward, and the torso shifts to the right, backward. Raise the right leg and drop it at the

diagonal right corner, forming a bow-step. The center of
gravity is shifted to the right foot. Simultaneously, draw
the left hand and put it before the elbow of the right hand,
as if they were embracing a ball, with the palm of the right
hand facing upward. At the same time, raise the right
hand slantingly upward. Push your left hand outward
near the elbow of the right hand, palm facing outward.
The eyesight is now focused on the left hand. (Fig. 66)

Fig 65   Fig 66

Movements 3:

C. The Third Diagonal Corner Style.

After turning the left hand downward in front of the
abdomen, with palm facing upward, drop the right hand
down before the chest with arms flexing levelly, palm
facing downward, as if they were embracing a ball.
Meanwhile, after turning the torso slightly to the left,

raise the left leg and drop it before the diagonal left corner, forming a bow-step. At the same time, raise the left hand upward in front of the forehead with the palm facing outward, and slangtingly upward. Simultaneously, push the right hand outward near the elbow of the left hand, palm facing outward. The eyes are now focused on the right hand. (Fig. 67)

Movements 4:

    D. *The Fourth Diagonal Corner Style.*

After shifting the center of gravity to the right leg, the toes of the left foot turn inward, and the torso turns to the right and backward. Raise the right leg and drop it at the diagonal right corner, forming a bow-step, while the center of gravity is shifted to the right foot. Draw the left hand and put it near the elbow of the right hand, as if they

    Fig 67   Fig 68

were embracing a ball, the palm of the right hand facing upward. At the same time, raise the right hand upward in front of the forehead, with palm facing outward and slantingly upward. Simultaneously, push the left hand outward near the elbow of the right hand, palm facing outward. The eyes are now focused on the left hand. (Fig. 68)

Important Points: The torso should maintain its erectness without too much slanting forward. In the raising of the hands, avoid the raising of the shoulders. In the pushing of the hands, following the bowing of the knees, the upper and the lower limbs should be coordinated. In the turning or revolving of the torso, one should have his leg placed backward, the toes touching the ground, and then take a step forward.

C. Technical Explanations:

The movements of these postures take the four corner directions. The series is divided into four parts, each having two operations. There are differences between "turning torso" and "revolving torso". The movements (1) and (3) are "revolving torso" while the (2) and (4) are "turning torso". The movements follow a definite order. If the exercise starts from South to North, the first corner is NW, the second SW, the third SE and the fourth NE. The movements in the third style are the same as in the first, and those in the fourth are the same as in the second.

D. Benefits:

This form relieves cramps and stiffness of the neck. The entire chest and spinal cord area are strengthened. The hands and legs are expanded and benefited.

Form 56. Step up, Grasping the Bird's Tail (進步攬雀尾).

A. Terminology:

Same as in FORM 2.

B. Diagrams and movements:

(See Form 2)

Movements 1:

Turn the left palm downward, and the right palm upward, as if they were holding a ball. Then take a step to the left with the left leg, forming a bow-step. Meanwhile, separate the two hands upward and downward toward the left and the right, the left hand chest high, and the right hand down to the thigh.

Movements 2:

After shifting weight slightly backward, then turn the toes of the left foot slightly outward, following the turning of the torso to the left. At the same time, curve the left arm levelly in front of the chest, and circle the right hand downward to the left of the waist, facing the left palm with the right palm, (the left palm faces downward, the right one upward). The eyes are focused on the left hand. The following movements are the same as those in FORM 2 — "The Grasping of the Bird's Tail".

Form 57. Single Whip (單鞭).

Same as in FORM 3.

Form 58. Wave Hands like Clouds.

Same as in FORM 29.

Form 59. Single Whip.

Same as in FORM 3.

Form 60.   Snake Creeps Down (蛇身下勢).

A.   Terminology:

This form is also known as the style of "Creeping Down of the Single Whip."   Here the snake is used as a metaphor.

B.   Diagrams and movements:

Movements 1:

Draw the upper part of the torso backward and slightly to the right, and lower it gradually.   The center of gravity is shifted to the right foot.   The left leg is straightened, while its toes turn slightly to the right. The right leg is bent, with buttocks as low as possible. (Fig. 69)

Movements 2:

Following the lowering of the torso, circle your left hand, beginning from the right shoulder downward and forward inside the left leg (fingers pointing upward and the palm facing right) to the height of the nose, and draw back in front of the chest.   The eyesight is focused on the left hand. (Fig. 69)

Important Points: Sit down wholly on the right leg, with knee turning outward, as low as possible, and the left leg is straightened slightly with toes curved inward.   The toes of the left foot should touch the ground.   Put the left hand below the left knee and stretch it forward beyond the toes of the left foot.   Coordination should be paid to the flexing and stretching of the knees and arms and the raising and lowering of the torso.   The torso should not be bent forward and the spinal cord should be straight.

C. Technical Explanations:

The direction of the right hand at back of the torso takes a semi-circle. The stretching of the left hand downward and forward takes the next semi-circle, together forming a whole circle.

D. Benefits:

This form strengthens and invigorates the whole organism. The neck, shoulders, arms, thighs, knees, calves, ankles, back and abdomen are greatly benefited. It also helps in increasing the elasticity of thighs and buttocks.

Form 61. Golden Cock stands on One Leg (R) and (L) (金鷄獨立，右，左).

A. Terminology:

In this form, while one leg is standing, the other is being raised.

Fig 69   Fig 70

Besides, the raising of the arms is similar to the spreading of the wings of a golden cock. Hence its name.

B. Diagrams and movements:

A. Right Style

Movements 1:

> After raising the torso gradually and standing on the left leg, let the right knee form an "independent style" (i.e. raising upward). The center of gravity is now shifted to the left leg. Meanwhile, change the right "hooked hand" into a palm and turn it down to the right side of the right knee, where it makes one horizontal circle clockwise. Raise the right hand so that the elbow is above the right knee, which is bent upward, with fingers of the right hand pointing upward and the palm facing left. Lower the left hand and put it beside the left thigh, with palm facing downward. The eyes are focused on the right hand. (Fig. 70)

B. Left Style

Movements 2:

> Drop the right leg behind the left leg, weight shifting to the right foot. After standing up on the right leg, lift the left knee, as shown in the "independent style". Meanwhile, turn your left hand to the left side of the left knee, where it makes one horizontal circle clockwise. Raise the left hand so that the elbow is above the left knee, which is bent levelly upward, with the fingers of the left hand pointing upward, and the palm facing right. Lower the right hand and put it beside the right thigh, with palm facing down. The eyesight is focused on the left hand. (Fig. 71)

> *Important Points:* The "independent leg" should bend

slightly; the torso is erect, emphasizing balance and stability.

C. Technical Explanations:

In the right style, when the right palm is raised upward in front of the right forehead, its elbow should more or less be in contact with the right knee, forming a semi-circle. The same should be done in the left style.

D. Benefits:

This form tones up the spinal nerves and the abdominal organs, with the center of gravity of the whole body concentrating on one leg without wavering. It also vigorously contracts and strengthens the abdominal muscles.

Form 62. Step Back and Repulse Monkey (R), (L) and (R). (倒攆猴，右，左，右).

A. Terminology:

Same as in FORM 7.

B. Diagrams and movements:

(See Form 7)

Movements:

Following the preceding style, turn the left palm upward and draw it back to the left side of the waist. The center of gravity is shifted to the left. Push the right hand forward bypassing the right ear, with palm facing forward, making a vertical circle counter-clockwise. Turn the heel of the right foot to the right. Lower the torso and rest on the right leg. The left leg is bent and the right one straightened relatively. This movement is followed by the Left Style and Right Style.

Form 63. Slanting Flying.

Same as in FORM 19.

Form 64. Raise Hands and Step Up.

Same as in FORM 4.

Form 65. White Stork Spreads its Wings.

Same as in FORM 5.

Form 66. Brush Knee and Twist Step (L).

Same as in FORM 6.

Form 67. Needle at Sea Bottom.

Same as in FORM 23.

Form 68. Fan through Back.

Same as in FORM 24.

Form 69. Turn Body and White Snake Puts Out its Tongue
（ 轉身白蛇吐信 ）.

A. Terminology:

The pushing-out right palm is supposed to be associated with
the tongue of a snake.

B. Diagrams and movements:

Movements 1:

While turning the torso backward to the right about 45°,
the weight is again shifted to the right foot, forming a
bow-step. Meanwhile, clench the right hand into a fist
and strike down in the right, with knuckles facing downward. The left hand stays before the abdomen, with the

Fig 71   Fig 72

eyesight fixed at the right palm.   (Fig. 72)

Movements 2:

Push the left hand forward, with the fingers pointing upward above the right fist.   Meanwhile, change the right fist into a palm and place it beside the right side of the waist, with the palm facing upward.   The eyesight is focused at the left hand.   Push palm forward beneath the left hand, knuckles facing downward. The left palm is not attached to the inner side of the right forearm.   The eyesight is now focused at the right palm. (Fig. 72)

Important Points: The torso is erect, shoulder relaxing and elbows flexing.

C.   Technical Explanations:

This posture is very much similar to that of the "Turn Body and Chop with Fist" (see FORM 24), but in the pushing out of the palm, emphasis is laid on the "Sinking Energy" (Chin Ching) of the palm.

Form 70. Step up, Strike, Parry and Punch.
Same as in FORM 11.

Form 71. Step up, Grasping the Bird's Tail.
Same as in FORM 27.

Form 72. Single Whip.
Same as in FORM 3.

Form 73. Wave Hands like Clouds.
Same as in FORM 29.

Form 74. Single Whip.
Same as in FORM 3.

Form 75. High Pat on Horse.
Same as in FORM 31.

Form 76. Cross Palms (穿掌).
A. Terminology:
This form is also known as "Penetrating Hands" on account of its posture.
B. Diagrams and movements:
Movements:

While the right hand is drawn downward, chin high, stretch the left hand forward under the right forearm. Meanwhile, take a step forward with the left leg, forming

a left bow-step.   Eyesight is focused on the two hands.
(Fig. 73)

Important Points: The stretching of the palm, the bowing
of the leg and the loosening of the waist should be coordinated.   Raise the height of the palms to the level of
the eyes.

Form 77.   Turn, and Cross Legs (轉身十字腿).

A.   Terminology:

In Chinese martial art, the stretching of "favorable fist" and
the kicking of "twisted leg" are called "Cross Legs" (Kicking
with the right sole) while the "Horizontal Kicking" is called
"Pai Lien Tuei" (Lotus Swing Leg).

B.   Diagrams and movements:

Movements:

Fig 73   Fig 74

Now the weight is on the left leg, bending. Pivoting on it, turn the body to the right and backward, the two hands crossing in front of the chest, with the palms facing inward, (right one on the external) forming a "Cross Hands" style. Then separate the two arms toward the left and right, and kick with the right sole at the height of the waist. The eyesight is focused at the front. (Fig. 74)

Important Points: Stabilize the torso. Raise the right leg first, and then kick out at the central front.

C. Technical Explanations:

During the turning of the torso, the center of gravity of the whole body should be laid on the left leg.

Form 78. Brush Knee and Punch the Pubic Region (摟膝指襠捶).

A. Terminology:

After performing the posture of the "Brushing Knee', punch the opponent at his pubic region. This is one of the five "Punches" in Tai Chi Ch'uan. Hence its name.

B. Diagrams and movements:

Movements:

Drop the right leg at the front, the toes turning outward. While the torso is turning to the right, clench the right hand into a fist and place it beside the right side of the waist. Take a step forward with your left leg, and brush the left knee with the left palm. Immediately following this, punch the opponent's pubic region with the right fist in a downward and upward arc, knuckle facing the right. (Fig. 75)

Important Points: Do not slant your body to the front, and the right arm should not stretch out too far.

C. Technical Explanations:

In the act of punching (with the fist), the strength starts from the spinal cord, right shoulder expanding and the right leg stretching.

Form 79. Step up, Grasping the Bird's Tail (上步攬雀尾).

A. Terminology:

Same as in Form 2.

B. Diagrams and movements:

Movements:

While shifting weight slightly backward, turn your toes of the left foot outward. Open the right fist and place it in front of the abdomen with palm facing down. Cause the left hand to circle backward and turn to the right. Put it in opposition to the right palm as if they were embracing a ball, the left palm facing downward, the right up. Meanwhile, draw the right leg backward to the side of the left foot, toes touching the ground. The eyesight is focused on the left hand. The rest of the movemnts are the same as those in Form 2.

Form 80. Single Whip.

Same as in Form 3.

Form 81. Snake creeps down.

Same as in Form 60.

Form 82. Step up to form Seven Stars (上步七星).

Fig 75   Fig 76

A. **Terminology:**

The practitioners of martial arts consider the crossing of the
hands with the two fists as the "Seven Stars" style.

B. **Diagrams and movements:**

While the toes of the left leg turn slightly outward, lift
up the torso forward gradually.   The center of gravity
is shifted to the left foot.   Clench the left and right
hands into fists forming the "cross fists" in front of the
chest.   The right fist is placed at the outer part of the
left fist, knuckles facing the front.   Simultaneously, kick
with the tip of the right foot, about one foot above the
ground.   The left knee is bent.   (Fig. 76)

Important Points: While the two wrists are crossing, the
two arms form naturally a circle.

C. **Technical Explanations:**

In the forming of the "Seven Stars", the weight of the body is placed on the left leg, with right leg stretching.

D. Benefits:

One can expect this form as an aid to improve blood circulation in the upper areas of the body.

Form 83. Retreat to Ride Tiger (退步跨虎).

A. Terminology:

The practitioners of martial arts consider the following movements as the style of "Riding Tiger": (1) spreading out the two arms with left palm hooking backward; (2) the two legs are bending, the right one curving, the left toes touching the ground. Hence its name.

B. Diagrams and movements:

Movements:

Draw the right foot one step backward. The weight is shifted to the right foot. Turn the left foot slightly to the right, with toes touching the ground, heel raised Change the two fists into palms. The right one is lifted up, staying in front of the right side of the forehead, palm facing outward. Lower the left hand and place it beside the left hip, palm facing down. With the toes of the left leg touching the ground, forming an insubstantial step, the eyesight is now focused at the front. (Fig. 77)

Important Points: The two shoulders should be on a level; the chest should be relaxed and expanded; the right leg should slightly bend.

C. Technical Explanations:

The five fingers of the left hand change into a "hooked form" (the so-called "Monkey Fist") and brush diagonally toward

Fig 77

the left with finger tips pointing backward (optional).

D. Benefits:

One can expect to strengthen the spine, develop the chest, improve posture, and streamline the legs, thighs, hips and buttocks.

Form 84. Turn Round, Kick Horizontally (轉身擺蓮).

A. Terminology:

As pointed out previously, the "side kicking" is called "Pai Lien T'uei" (Lotus Swing Leg), which is here rendered into "kicking horizontally".

B. Diagrams and movements:

Movements 1-2:

With the sole of the right foot on the ground, turn the body 360 degrees circling. Then take a step to the left

with your left leg, bowing. At the same time, circle the
two hands vertically downward and upward, forming
parallel-hands in front of the chest. The eyes are
focused at the front. While the torso turns continually
to the right, the toes of the left leg is shifted inward.
Raise the right leg and kick horizontally and upward to
the right (Lotus Swing Leg). At the same time, circle
the two palms from the left and pass the front of the
forehead, down to the right, striking at the edge of the
right foot with the two palms, first by the left palm, and
then by the right palm. Finally, drop the right leg to the
ground at the further right side. (Fig. 78)

Important Points: During the swinging of the right leg, it
actually circles from the left to the right. Avoid any
tension.

Fig 78

C. Technical Explanations:

During the kicking of the right leg, the toes of the left leg should be directed slightly inward so that they would facilitate the swinging movement.

D. Benefits:

The practice of this form increases the flexibility of the waist and the vitality of the body. It gives a general feeling of activation and well being.

Form 85. Shoot Tiger with Bow (彎弓射虎).

A. Terminology:

This form symbolizes a man, riding on horse back, shooting with an arrow. Hence its name.

B. Diagrams and movements:

Movements:

After putting the right leg at the extreme right diagonally, as stated in the preceding form, the center of gravity is shifted to the right foot, forming a bow-step. Meanwhile, clench the two palms into fists, circle them downward-backward to the right. Raise the right fist so that it passes the right ear, and the left fist is in front of the chest. Strike with knuckles of both pointing upward. Lean torso slantingly forward to the right. The eyesight is focused at the left fist. (Fig. 79)

Important Points: During the turning of the two hands backward, your head should follow the motion, looking first at the right fist, and then at the left one. The two arms maintain a circle form, with each fist opposing the other, the right one slightly up, the left one down.

C. Technical Explanations:

Fig 79

In striking forward with the two fists, it implies the idea of "screwing energy".

D. Benefits:

This form vigorously contracts and strengthens the muscles of the back and increases tremendously the energy of the shoulders.

Form 86. Step up, Strike, Parry, and Punch (進步搬攔捶).

Terminology and other points same as in Form 11.

Movements:

While the center of gravity is shifted to the left foot, the torso turns slightly to the left. Draw the right leg to the side of the left one, at the same time, cause the right fist to stay at the right side, knuckles facing downward. Change the left fist into a palm, moving from the upper side downward to the thigh. The rest of the movements are the same as those in Form 11.

Form 87. Apparent Close Up.

Same as in Form 12.

Form 88. Cross Hands.

Same as in Form 13.

Form 89. Conclusion of the Tai Chi (合太極).

A. Terminology:

This form signifies the end of the exercise in Tai Chi Ch'uan. Hence its name.

B. Diagrams and movements:

(See also Form 13)

Movements:

Raise the two hands, to the height of the head and lower them gradually to the right and left as far as the stomach. The center of gravity is first shifted to the right foot, and then shifted to the left one. Draw your right foot half a step to the left, forming a parallel step. Stand up, and cross the two hands in front of the chest, the right palm placed outside of the left, with the palms facing inward. Attention must be given to the central equilibrium. Lower both hands downward beside the thighs as in the "Preparatory Style". Finally return to the same place where one stood during the "Commencement". In conclusion, use your mind to direct the breathing (Chi, or energy) down to the "Tan Tien" or Psychic Center. (Figs. 80, 81, 82, 83)

Fig 80

Fig 81

Fig 82

Fig 83

NOTE: The exercise can also be performed on the left side (or "reversed style"). When one is so familiar with the whole series of the forms that continual movements can be made, and that the breathing system has been comprehended thoroughly, one may try the "reversed style" as well. The starting point of this style should commence at the opposite direction of the right style. For instance, if the right style starts from North to South, the left style should start from South to North. The initiative movements of the right hand and right leg are now taken by the left hand and left leg. Left turns change to right turns, and vice versa. When the right style and left style are performed perfectly well, one would be able to avoid all the short-comings that arise from "unbalance". In order to derive the full benefits from this exercise, it is highly recommended to perform both styles daily. It is interesting to mention here that Jason Ying-ang Lee of Hong Kong has developed the "Lee modified Tai Chi Ch'uan for Health" (written in Chinese and English).

PART III: TECHNICAL AND APPLICATIONAL

CHAPTER XII

EXPLANATION OF CHART SHOWING THE SEQUENCES OF FORMS AND THE DIRECTIONS OF THE MOVEMENTS IN TAI CHI CH'UAN

1. Commencing the movements from the North end, first perform the Preparatory Style by facing the West.

2. Having taken a step to the Left, turn torso to the Right and perform the Second Form — the Grasping of the Bird's Tail.

3. Including the postures: Ward Off Slantingly Upward, Pull Back, Press Forward and Push. The face is towards the North. Take a left step, turn torso to the South, and then perform the Single Whip.

4. Move the right step to the front, perform the Raise Hands and Step Up.

5. Opening the Left Step by facing the South, perform The While Stork Spreads Its Wings.

6. Then perform the Brush Knee Twist Step (Left Style) at the same place.

7. Unite the right leg with the left, and perform the Play the Fiddle.

8. Opening the left step facing South, perform the Brush Knee Twist Step (Left). Take a right step forward and perform the

Brush Knee Twist Step (Right). Again take a left step and perform the Brush Knee Twist Step (Left).

9. Unite the right leg with the left, and perform the Play the Fiddle.

10. Take the left step and perform the Brush Knee Twist Step (Left).

11. Advance the right step, and perform the Step Up, Strike, Parry and Punch.

12. In the same place, perform the Apparent Close Up.

13. Turning to the right and facing West, unite the step (the space btween being equal to the distance of the shoulders) and perform the Cross Hands. (End of the First Section.)

14. **Open the right step by turning backwards to the right diagonally, and perform the Carry Tiger to Mountain by facing** Northeast.

15. Standing at the same place, perform the Diagonal Grasping of the Bird's Tail.

16. Turning the torso to the left by facing Southwest, open the left step and perform the Diagonal Single Whip.

17. Advance the right foot parallel to the left, and turn torso facing the South with left heel raised, then perform the Fist Under Elbow.

18. While the Left Leg is withdrawn backward, the right hand is being stretched forward, perform the Step Back and Repulse Monkey.

19. Withdraw the Right Leg backward and stretch the left hand forward, then perform the Step Back and Repulse Monkey (Left). Again, withdraw the left leg backward and stretch the right hand forward, in this way perform the Step Back and Repulse Monkey (Left). Again, withdraw the Left Leg backward and stretch the right hand forward, in this way

perform the Step Back and Repulse Monkey. Advance the right step in the direction of Northwest and perform the Slanting Flying.

20. Move the right leg to the front, and perform the Raise Hands and Step Up.

21. At the same place, perform the White Stork Spreads its Wings.

22. Open the left step facing South and perform the Brush Knee and Twist Step (Left).

23. Withdraw the left leg by half a step with bending knee and perform the Needle at Sea Bottom.

24. Taking a step to the left, perform the Fan Through Back.

25. Turn backwards and perform the Turn and Chop with Fist.

26. Step up left leg, then perform Step Up, Strike, Parry and Punch.

27. Again, take a right step forward and perform the Grasping of the Bird's Tail.

28. Open the left leg and turn body back facing South, then perform the Single Whip.

29. Unite the right leg with the left leg at a distance of half a step and perform the Wave Hands like Clouds. (1) Take a step to the left and perform the Wave Hands like Clouds. (2) Again unite the right leg with the left and perform the same form. (3) One may again repeat the (1) posture by stepping once more to the left.

30. Take a left step and perform the Single Whip.

31. Withdraw the left leg about half a step and perform the High Pat on Horse.

32. Kick with right foot and perform the Separation with the Right Foot.

33. Kick with left foot and perform the Separation of Left Foot.

34. Turn backwards and perform the Turn and Kick with Sole.

35. Drop the left leg downward and perform the Brush Knee Twist Step (Left). Advance the right leg and perform the Brush Knee Twist Step (Right).

36. Again take a left step forward, and perform the Step Up and Punch Downward.

37. Turn right and backwards and perform the Turn and Chop with Fist.

38. Take a left step forward and perform the Step Up, Strike, Parry and Punch.

39. Take one step forward and perform Kick With Sole Diagonally.

40. Drop the right foot, open the Left Leg, direct the torso to the left and perform the Hit Tiger at Left.

41. Turn feet and torso to the right (and backward), and perform Hit the Tiger at the Right.

42. Standing at the same place, perform the Right Foot Kicks Upward.

43. Drop the right foot at the front and perform the Strike Ears with Fists.

44. Immediately afterward, raise the left leg and perform the Left Foot Kicks Upward.

45. Turn backward to the right facing East, drop the left foot and kick with the right foot, then perform the Turn Round and Kick With Sole.

46. Take a left step forward and perform the Step Up, Strike, Parry and Punch.

47. Standing at the same place, perform the Apparent Close Up.

48. Unite the step on the right side and perform the Cross Hands.

(End of the Second Section.)

49. While turning backwards to the right, take a right step and direct torso towards Northeast and perform the Carry Tiger to Mountain.

50. At the same place, perform the Grasping the Bird's Tail.

51. Turn the torso back, open the left foot and perform the Diagonal Single Whip.

52. Take a right step forward and perform the Partition of Wild Horse's Mane (R); take a left step forward and perform the Partition of Wild Horse's Mane (L); again, take a right step forward and perform the same Form on the right.

53. Take a left step, perform the Step Up and Grasping the Bird's Tail.

54. Take a left step, turn torso to the South and perform the Single Whip.

55. Take a left step in the direction toward Northwest, perform the Fair Lady Works at Shuttles (Style 1). Turn right in the direction toward Southwest and perform the Fair Lady Works at Shuttles (Style 2). Again take a left step, directing the torso to Southeast and perform the Fair Lady Works at Shuttles (Style 3). Lastly, turn the torso around to the right, facing Northeast, and perform the Fair Lady Works at the Shuttles (Style 4).

56. At the same place, open the Left Leg and perform the Grasping the Bird's Tail.

57. Open the left foot, turn torso to the South, then perform the Single Whip.

58. Move the right leg and take a half step to the left, then perform the Wave Hands like Clouds movements. Take a left step to the left, perform the Wave Hands Like Clouds movements. Again, move the right leg half a step to the left and

perform the Wave Hands like Clouds movements:

59. After completing this posture, do the Single Whip.

60. Standing at the same place, bend the right leg and perform the Snake Creeps Down.

61. Standing up, raise the right leg and perform the Golden Cock Stands on One Leg (R). Drop down the right leg, raise the left one and perform the Golden Cock Stands on One Leg (L).

62. Withdraw the left leg and perform the Step Back and Repulse the Monkey (R); withdraw the right leg and perform the Step Back and Repulse Monkey (L); withdraw the left leg and perform the Step Up and Repulse Monkey (R).

63. Reverse the right leg and direct it to northwest; then, perform the Slanting Flying.

64. Move the right leg to the front and perform the Raise Hands and Step Up.

65. Standing at the same place, perform the White Stork Spreads Its Wings.

66. Take a step forward with the left leg, facing South, perform the Brush Knee and Twist Step (L).

67. Withdraw the left leg half a step, bending, and perform the Needle at Sea Bottom.

68. Take a left step and perform the Fan Through Back.

69. Turning backward to the right, perform the White Snake Puts Out its Tongue.

70. Advance the left leg, and perform the Step Up, Strike, Parry and Punch.

71. At the same place, perform the Step Up and Grasp the Bird's Tail.

72. Take a left step and perform the Single Whip.

73. Unite the right leg with the left one at a distance of half a step, then perform the Wave Hands Like Clouds (1). Take a left step, perform the Wave Hands Like Clouds (2), and unite the right leg with the left at half a step's distance, then perform the same form (3).

74. Take a left step and perform the Single Whip.

75. Withdraw the left leg half a step and perform the High Pat on Horse.

76. Take a left step and perform the Cross Palm.

77. Turn backwards and perform the Turn and Cross Legs (Kicking With Right Sole).

78. Drop the right leg to the ground and perform the Brush Knee and Punch Pubic Region.

79. Take a right step forward and perform the Step Up, Grasping the Bird's Tail.

80. Take a left step and perform the Single Whip.

81. Standing at the same place, bend the right knee and perform the Snake Creeps Down.

82. Stand up, take a step to the front with the right leg and perform the Step Up to Form Seven Stars.

83. Reverse the right leg and raise the left leg, and thus perform the Retreat to Ride Tiger.

84. Turn to right backward and round and perform the Turn Round and Kick Horizontally.

85. Drop the right leg to the right side and perform the Shoot Tiger With Bow.

86. Take a step forward with right leg and perform the Step Up, Strike, Parry and Punch.

87. Standing at the same place, perform the Apparent Close Up.

88. Turning to the right and facing West, unite the step (the

space between the feet being equal to the distance of the shoulders) and perform the Cross Hands.

89.　Lower the two hands slowly, return to the Preparatory Style, closing the complete performance by the "Conclusion of the Tai Chi". (Third Section.)

Appendix I:　Notes on the Use of the Chart.

1. In the movements of Tai Chi Ch'uan, the starting point is also the concluding point. For the purpose of showing the directions of the various forms in the movements, the commencement and conclusion cannot be shown at the same point.

2. Those forms which have to be performed at the same place are represented in the chart, thus:

3. Forms that have to be performed in the same place, with positions slightly changed, are to be shown thus:

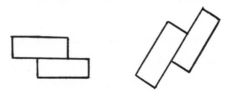

4. In the moving of steps, the two positions are to be connected by a straight line showing the advance of movements, thus:

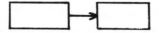

5. Forms that have to be performed diagonally are connected by diagonal lines, but the length of the lines have nothing to do with the degree of advancing.

6. The diagonal or uprightness of the forms to be performed are to be shown by the directions of the positions represented in the Chart.

7. The directions of the forms in the movements are to be connected by arrows.

8. The indicating lines concerning the separations of the left and right legs are intended to signify the directions of the toes.

9. There is a coordinate indicating the directions of the whole Diagram which should be followed carefully in the movements.

Appendix II: Attention in practicing

Attention should be paid to the following points in the first stage of learning:

a) Equal Speed: In the performance of the movements, whether they are done slowly or speedily, it is necessary to maintain the same speed, — that is equal speed.

b) Selection of Postures: There are three types of postures: high, middle, and low. At the moment of practicing, the selection of posture which one has to follow is of vital importance. The sudden change of posture while moving is to be discouraged. Aside from the posture known as the "Creeping of the Snake". in which the torso has to be lowered, the whole series should be performed on about the same level. During the first stage, especially for older people or people weakened by illness or injury, it is advisable to adopt a higher posture. Thereafter, in the progressing stage, the medium or low postures may be adopted according to the wish of the practitioner.

c) Repetition: The question of how many times a man or woman should practice the whole set of Tai Chi Ch'uan a day may be determined by the practical needs and the condition of the body. One may practice one to three times in a certain period of time, say for half an hour, or one may take up one section or one posture such as "Grasp the Bird's Tail" or "Wave Hands like Clouds", and the "Joint Hands Operation" as well as the art with equipment, and practice them repeatedly.[1]

d) Gradualness: In the studying of the postures, one should proceed with one at a time, and from "simple to complex". After mastering the first section, one may proceed to the second section and then to the third. There is no speedy method of learning the forms or postures; they must be done gradually. The techniques for self-defense and the "Joint Hands Operation" as well as the art with equipment, should only be taken up in the last stages if desired. Over-eagerness will naturally lead to absolute failure.

e) Perseverance and Constancy: Perseverance and constancy are some of the fundamental conditions for the success of acquiring the art of Tai Chi Ch'uan. A learner should devote at least twenty minutes a day to practicing.

f) Training Place and Practice Clothes: Any floor which will not obstruct the feet and does not create too much sliding or friction will do. For the beginner, a space of about five or seven square feet is sufficient. As a wide space is not necessary, the practice can take place even in a hotel room during traveling. The space should be well ventilated and spacious enough to allow freedom of movement. As to practice clothing, any suit of light material that permits freedom

[1] A simplified system which omits the duplicate postures such as advocated by Cheng Man-Ching, Yang Chien Chung and others, may be taken with benefits, but most of the Masters in China still persist in performing the whole set without revision.

of bodily movement will suffice. Bare feet are not required and low heels are appropriate.

g) Before and After Practice: Heavy meals and drinks should be avoided immediately before or after practice. It is advisable to wipe off the perspiration, if any, and wet clothes should be changed. After the practice, one should walk for a few minutes before sitting down.

The Terminology and Sequence of the Forms of Tai Chi Ch'uan

CHAPTER XIII

PRACTICAL APPLICATION OF THE TECHNIQUES

IN TAI CHI CH'UAN FOR SELF-DEFENSE

A person who has mastered the forms and techniques of Tai Chi Ch'uan can successfully defend himself against any opponent from attacking. Altogether there are thirty-seven patterns, or methods, which are basic for defense purposes. As to the sub-techniques, they are always changeable, unlimited in number, and cannot be comprehended fully or intuitively without oral teaching from experienced masters.

The aim of the art of Tai Chi Ch'uan is for the promotion of health and well-being. It is utterly not intented for aggression; our labour is love not hate. However, in order to increase the interest of those who have already mastered the forms, it is probably advisable to explain very briefly the whole set of techniques in practical application. Those who are not interested in the techniques of self-defense need not pay attention to all the aspects described in this chapter.1

Pattern 1: Grasping The Bird's Tail.

A. The Ward Off Style (Peng).

In the Preparatory style, or Commencement, one has to concentrate his mind and stabilize the body in order to observe correctly the coming direction of the opponent. Always remember the maxims in the strategy of Tai Chi Ch'uan: "To deflect the momentum of a thousand catties (Chinese pounds), with a trigger strength of four toels (Chinese ounces), shows anything cannot be achieved by sheer force." "Do not move if he (opponent) does not move, but move ahead of him if he does move slightly".

After the Preparatory style, if B (the opponent, with dark pants) strikes A (the defender, with white suit) from the right side at his rib with his left fist, A should turn his body immediately to the right and lift up his right hand to ward it off. (Using the Ward-off style.) Following this, if B uses his right hand to strike A's chest, A must lift his left hand again to ward it off. Meantime, A should take one step to the left, with leg bending at the front. (Figure 1)

After avoiding B's aggressive act, A should circle his right hand inward-outward-downward and strike directly at the opponent's chest. Take one step forward with the right leg bent. Use the "integral energy" to ward-off the opponent. (Figure 2)

1 In the preparation of this Chapter, the author has consulted Tung Fu-ling's, *The Application Method of Tai Chi Ch'uan,* 2nd edition, 1957, Hong Kong with permission.

The writer is indebted to Mr. Kwang Yung-cheng (with white suit) who supplied us with the pictures taken with his friend (with dark pants) in Taipei, Taiwan, China. Kwang, an engineer graduated from N.Y.U. with Master's degree, has practised Tai Chi Ch'uan for over 30 years. He is unique in one respect. After a medical test on his lung capacity in the Veterans' General Hospital in Taipei, December, 1964, Dr. Kao Feng-tien found to his surprise that Kwang could hold his breath for as long as five minutes, longer than the world record established by a specially trained skin diver.

Through a physical check-up, what the doctor found indicated that in terms of biological function he was as young as a man of 20. (Actually he was 48). Asked to give an explanation for all this, Kwang attributed the unusual physical phenomenon to Tai Chi Ch'uan. He has a large number of disciples, both Chinese and American, men and women. Among the dignitaries who have taken lessons from him is Vice Admiral Doyle, former commander of the U.S. Taiwan Defense Command. Being an expert in this exercise, he has recently (since 1968) been appointed as the personal tutor of Mr Houphouet Boigny, the President of Ivory Coast, Africa.

Fig 1

Fig 2

B. Pull Back Style (Lu).

Following the Ward off style, B, taking the advantage, strikes A's chest with his left hand. At this critical moment, A should use the left hand to hold B's wrist, and attach B's upper arm with his right wrist. (Fig. 3)

Fig 3

Meanwhile, A, sitting on the hind leg, slightly turns his torso to the left. Pulling B's left hand with both hands backward (Lu style), A must try to uproot B's hind heel from the ground so that the latter's center of gravity is out of balance. (Fig. 4)

C. Press Forward Style (Chi).

Following the Pull Back style described above, B, because of his disadvantage, desires to withdraw his hand. A should turn his right palm upward and attach B's upper arm in order not to let B flee. A also puts his left palm against his own right wrist on B's upper arm. (Fig. 5)

Fig 4

Fig 5

At this critical moment, if B attempts to pull away, A should bend his front leg (right) and strengthen his hind one, finally releasing his intrinsic energy (Ching), thereby pressing B forward instantly. (Fig. 6)

Fig 6

D. Push Style.

Following the previous style, if B uses his right hand to pull A's right hand, A should immediately turn his right hand upside down and sit backward on the left leg. Taking advantage of B's changing tendency, A should stick to B's elbow (right) with the left hand and to B's right wrist with the right hand so as to close him up. (Fig. 7)

Simultaneously, A bends the right leg in the front, while strengthening the left leg in the back. Finally, he should push (An) B away by releasing his own intrinsic energy. (Fig. 8)

Pattern 2: Single Whip.

Following the preceding pattern, if B comes from the right side

Fig 7

Fig 8

and strikes A's right ribs, A should turn his torso immediately to the right and circle his right hand upward and downward and ward off B's attacking hand. (Fig. 9)

Fig 9

Meanwhile, if B changes his position and comes from the left, raising his right fist and striking downward toward A's head or chest, A should turn immediately to the left side, and, when B's fist has not yet reached A's head or chest, A should take the initiative of attacking B first. A, raising the left leg, takes a step forward, bending in the front. While circling his left hand upward with palm facing outward and then forward, he pushes B on his chest, using intrinsic energy. (Fig. 10)

Pattern 3: Raise Hands and Step Up.

Following the Single Whip pattern, B (the opponent) strikes directly from the front with his left hand. At this moment, A should close his two hands, right one in front, holding B's elbow; left hand in the rear, holding his wrist. Meanwhile, he should raise his right

Fig 10

leg, putting it before B's left leg. By strengthening the "enclosed energy", A thus raises and uproots B's legs from the ground. This is the technique of raising and striking (Fig. 11 & Fig. 12)

Fig 11

Another technique is: Employing the "enclosed energy", A uses his two palms, applying on B's coming hand and twist it, thus pulling the opponent downward to the ground. (Fig. 12)

Fig 12

Pattern 4:   White Stork Cools Its Wings.

Following the preceding pattern, if B uses his right fist to strike at A directly from the left, A should sit backward, hollowing his chest and avoiding the direct attack. Meanwhile, circling a small cycle with the left hand upward and downward, he should stick to B's coming right hand. He must use the left hand to neutralize B's striking hand or foot kicking at A's middle or lower part of the body. (Fig. 13)

Taking one step forward, A raises his right hand and uses his forearm to uphold the armpit of B and expand upward. He then takes half a step forward with left leg. While neutralizing the coming attack with the left hand, he lowers it for the sake of balancing the right hand. If B strikes with his left hand, A uses the right hand to ward off the approaching fist and hits at the other's temple. Meanwhile, he may kick the opponent in his pubic region with the left foot. (Fig. 14)

Fig 13

Fig 14

Pattern 5: Brush Knee and Twist Step, Left.

Following the preceding Pattern, if B attacks the middle or lower part of A's body with his hand or foot, A should circle his left hand upward-inward-downward and ward it off, and hit the opponent's chest or face with the right palm. (Figures 15 & 16)

Fig 15

Sitting down substantially on the left leg, A, meanwhile, should strengthen his right leg.

In the right pattern, the application of the technique is just reversed.

Pattern 6: Play the Fiddle.

Following the preceding Pattern, if B strikes with his right hand on A's chest, A, sitting backward on his hind leg, raises his left hand and holds his opponent's elbow, while using his right palm to press forward on B's wrist, applying the "enclosed energy" with both hands on the opponent's forearm. At the same time, A should draw his left leg backward to form a half step, and uproot the opponent's

Fig 16

heel and throw him backward with "total intrinsic energy". (Figures
17 & 18)

Fig 17

Fig 18

Pattern 7: Step Up, Strike, Parry and Punch.

Following the preceding pattern, if B attacks A with his right fist directly on the upper part of the body, A immediately turns his two hands upward to form two circles, and holds B's fist with his right fist and press downward. If, at this juncture, B continues to attack A at his head or neck, A should use his left hand to parry it and then hit or punch his opponent with the right fist at his solar plexus or navel. (Figures 19 & 20)

When A stretches his left hand outward, he should take a step forward with the left leg, bending.

Pattern 8: Apparent Close Up.

Following the preceding Pattern, if B grasps A's right fist, A should immediately draw back his left hand and put it under the right arm and neutralize the opponent's grasping hand by pushing it off. In this favourable position, he continues to use the two palms to close the opponent's elbow or arm so that he is immovable and

Fig 19

Fig 20

changeless. With the left leg in the front, bending, the right leg in the rear, he forms a straight line without lifting the heel from the ground. (Figures 21 & 22)

Fig 21

Fig 22

Pattern 9: Cross Hands.

Following the preceding Pattern, if B comes to attack from the right and pushes with the two hands, A should turn to the right, separate the two hands, and circle from downward to upward and close the two arms to criss-cross the opponent's striking hands and ward them off. (Fig. 23)

Fig 23

A's left leg should be substantial and the right one insubstantial. (Figure 24)

Pattern 10: Carry Tiger to Mountain.

Following the preceding pattern, if B comes from the right or the back of A by striking at A's ribs directly with right fist, A should immediately turn the left foot inward, revolving the body to the right. Simultaneously, he should turn right hand downward and ward-off the coming fist. Meanwhile, he must circle the left hand upward and outward from the ear. (Figures 25 & 26)

Fig 24

Fig 25

A, taking one step to the right, bends. After circling the left hand outward, A may use it to push the opponent on his shoulder or on his upper arm. Another technique is to hold B with the right hand around his waist and push him away. (Fig. 26)

Fig 26

Pattern 11: Fist Under Elbow.

Following the preceding pattern, if the opponent B comes from the back and attacks A's left ribs, A, seeing this, should instantly turn to the left and take one step facing the opponent. Meanwhile, he circles the left hand upward and holds fast or pushes the opponent's elbow upward with it. (Figures 27 & 28)

At the same time, while taking one step forward with the left leg, A clenches his right fist under the left elbow and strikes at the waist of B, using the total intrinsic energy. (Fig. 28)

Pattern 12: Step Back and Repulse Monkey.

Following the previous pattern, if B attacks A with his right hand, A, while retreating one step with the left leg, uses the left hand

Fig 27

Fig 28

to ward it off downward or to stick to B's wrist. Meanwhile, he
circles the right hand upward to the level of the ear and strikes at the

opponent's face with the right palm.　This is the technique of advancing by retreating. (Fig. 29 & 30)

Fig 29

Fig 30

Sitting substantially on the left thigh, A's right thigh becomes insubstantial. By using the "sinking intrinsic energy", A would thus eliminate the coming force of B's right hand. He may also stretch the right hand as an insubstantial (empty) one without touching the opponent.

This is right style. The movements of the left style are the same as those on the right, except that the left and the right hands change positions.

Pattern 13:   Slanting Flying.

Following the previous pattern, if B strikes A's right ribs with his right fist from the right side, A should turn instantly to the right and hold the opponent's wrist with the left hand while pulling his armpit with the right hand.   (Fig. 31)

Fig 31

While stepping up with the right foot, A also strikes slantingly upward and ejects the opponent away, using both hands, by applying the "long intrinsic energy". (Fig. 32)

Fig 32

This technique can be applied on both sides.

Pattern 14:   Needle at Sea Bottom.

Following the preceding Pattern, if B grasps A's right wrist, A must first sit backward on the hind leg and then pull the opponent's hand downward by lowering his body at the waist and legs. (Fig. 33)

Meanwhile, A, because of his retreating half step from the front leg, prolongs the opponent's hand by pulling it downward. And because of A's sudden sinking of the right hand, the opponent may lose his central gravity. If possible, A can circle his left hand from outward to inward and ward off the striking hand. (Fig. 34)

Pattern 15:   Fan Through Back.

Following the preceding pattern, and after warding off the opponent, if B again attacks A with the right fist over his head, A should quickly circle his right hand upward, holding his wrist and lifting it overhead. Meanwhile, raising the left hand upward and stretching

Fig 33

Fig 34

it forward to the left or to the front, A should push on the armpit of the opponent. (Figs. 35 & 36)

Fig 35

Fig 36

While the left foot in the front or left side is bending, the hind leg is strengthening. By using the "total intrinsic energy" of the whole body, A may also push on the chest or ribs of B, and "long intrinsic energy" may be applied. (Fig. 36)

Pattern 16: Turn, Chop with Fist.

Following the preceding pattern, if A discovers that B is prepared to attack him from the back, he should turn immediately to the right and turn the left leg. Also turn right hand downward placing it before the chest with clenched fist. Simultaneously, he should turn left hand upward to the temple for the purpose of pushing the opponent backward or slapping his face. (Figs. 37 & 38)

The legs of A should turn to the right in coordination with the body.

Fig 37

Pattern 17: Wave Hands Like Clouds.

Following the previous pattern, if the opponent B is attacking A on the upper part of the body, A should circle his right hand

Fig 38

upward, sticking to the coming forearm near the elbow and thus ward off the other. The same technique must be applied on the left, if necessary. In fact, this is a technique to ward off the opponent at the right, left and front. But what A should use is the "neutralizing energy" instead of "resisting-intrinsic energy". When B's strength goes to the "void", his "one thousand catties of force", so to speak, would come to "nothingness". (Figs. 39 & 40)

Pattern 18: High Pat on Horse.

After the previous pattern, if B attacks directly toward A's chest, the latter should grasp B's wrist with the left hand, drawing it towards his left side, with left leg retreating a half step. (Fig. 41)

After controlling the opponent by this simple technique, A, in the meantime, hollows his chest and pushes his right hand forward, attacking the opponent's nose or elsewhere with palm in the pattern of "High Pat on Horse", so as to cause the opponent to lose his central gravity. (Fig. 42)

Fig 39

Fig 40

Fig 41

Fig 42

Pattern 19: Separating of Foot.

Following the previous pattern, and after controlling the opponent, A, with the left foot on substantiality, raises his right foot and kicks towards the opponent's waist (Figs. 43 & 44). Applying the Left Pattern, he raises the left foot and kicks at B's abdomen. Simultaneously, he separates the two hands by using the right one to ward off the opponent's left arm, with the left hand for balancing. The foot and hand should use the energy at the same moment, this being called "total intrinsic energy".

Fig 43

Pattern 20: Turn Left and Kick with Sole.

Following the previous pattern, if B attacks A's left side at the back with his right hand, A should turn body to the left and kick the opponent's abdomen with left sole. (Fig. 45) He may use the separated left hand to bolt the attacking fist, while the right hand is for balancing. After stabiliizing the right leg, he applies the "total intrinsic energy" and kicks with sole. (Fig. 46)

Fig 44

Fig 45

Fig 46
Pattern 21:　Step Up and Punch Downward.

Following the Right Brush Knee and Twist Step style, if B attacks A with fist directly, A should ward it off with left hand. (Fig. 47) If B kicks with his right foot slantingly at A's thigh, A should

Fig 47

take one step with left foot and strike slantingly at the-opponent's leg with downward punch by using the right fist. While the left leg is bending at the front, the right one is strengthened at the rear. (Fig. 48)

Fig 48

Pattern 22:   Kick with Right Sole Diagonally.

If the opponent B attacks A's face with his left fist, A should use the left hand to bolt his wrist, with body slanting toward the left in order to avoid the coming force. (Fig. 49)

After stabilizing the left leg, A should raise his right foot and kick at the opponent's waist or abdomen. For the purpose of balancing, both hands should be separated and the "total intrinsic energy" applied in attacking. (Fig. 50)

Pattern 23:   Hit Tiger at Left or Right.

If B attacks with his right hand directly on A, A should turn to the right and grasp the opponent's wrist and pull it downward. Meanwhile, he uses the right fist to strike at B's neck. This is "Hit

Fig 49

Fig 50

Tiger at Right". At this time, right leg is bending and left strengthening. (Figs. 51 & 52)

The technique of "Hit Tiger at the Left" is just the reverse of the "Right".

Fig 51

Fig 52

Pattern 24:   Right Foot Kicks Upward.

Following the preceding pattern, if B attacks A from the left or front with right hand, A should sit on the left leg, withdrawing half a step from the right leg.   Meanwhile, he must circle the right hand upward, holding B's arm and controlling him.   (Fig. 53)

Fig 53

In the process of balancing the two hands, the right foot is raised and kicks at the opponent's abdomen or waist or leg in order to push him away.   (Fig. 54)

Pattern 25:   Strike Opponent's Ears with Both Fists.

Following the preceding pattern, if the opponent B attacks A with both fists at the middle part, A should separate his two hands and circle downward along both sides of the right leg so as to neutralize the attacking fists to the left and right with the backs of the hands. (Fig. 55)   Immediately after this movement, he circles both hands upward and strikes at the opponent's ears with both fists. (Fig. 56)

Fig 54

Fig 55

Fig 56

With right leg in front, bending, the left leg is strengthening in the rear. For the neutralizing of the opponent's hands, "Sinking intrinsic energy" is applied.

Pattern 26: Partition of Wild Horse's Mane.

Following the "Slanting Single Whip" style, if B attacks A with the left fist, A, taking one step to the right corner, with right leg bent, uses the right hand to grasp the opponent's left wrist and stretches the right arm upward to strike his face or ward him off by the armpit. (Fig. 57 & 58)

The same technique can be applied on the left side when A and B stand opposite to each other.

Pattern 27: Fair Lady Works at the Shuttles.

Following the Single Whip style, if B comes from A's back and grasps his right hand, A should turn body backward to the right and circle the left hand upward to ward off the attacking hand. Meanwhile he should push his opponent's chest with the right palm, which

Fig 57

Fig 58

circles downward by passing the inside of the left elbow.

First, sitting on the left thigh, A withdraws his right foot half a step backward, but, when the right hand comes down by passing the left elbow, he must take one step forward to the first corner with the left leg and with the right hand pushing at the same time. (Figs. 59 & 60)

Fig 59

Fig 60

If B comes from A's back, striking with his right hand, A should turn backward and ward off the attacking hand with the right arm in coordination with the revolving body. He must use the left hand, which is circling downward, passing the right elgow, to push at his opponent's chest.

This pattern can be applied on all the four corners with the turning of the body.

Pattern 28: Snake Creeps Down.

Following the Single Whip style, if B, the opponent, raises the right foot kicking fiercely, A should lower his body backward in order to avoid his blow and use his left hand to hit at the solar plexus of B, or hold his sole and raise it forward with both hands in order to throw him out of balance. (Fig. 61 & 62)

Fig 61

Fig 62

Pattern 29:   Golden Cock Stands on One Leg.

If the opponent B Strikes A with his fist at the chest, A must raise his left hand upward as the body is rising.   (Fig. 63)

Fig 63

Meanwhile, as A's left leg is substantial, and as the right hand is holding B's elbow, A, in coordination with the movement of the right hand, again kicks at the thigh or pubic region of the opponent with the right foot. The left foot is standing, slightly curved, similar to the "Standing of a Golden Cock". (Fig. 64)

Fig 64

A may raise left or right hand to hold either of the opponent's elbows. The use of foot or knee for kicking is optional.

Pattern 30: White Snake Puts out its Tongue.

Following the Fan Through Back style, if A discovers B preparing to attack him from the back, he should turn to the right immediately and circle the right hand downward in front of the chest, while the left hand is turned upward before the forehead, palm facing outward. (Fig. 65)

At this juncture, if B attacks A with his right hand, A should use his left palm to hold the opponent's wrist. Taking advantage of the opponent's withdrawal, A, furthermore, should turn the right palm upward and strike at the chest of the opponent, with right foot bowing. (Fig. 66)

Fig 65

Fig 66

Pattern 31: High Pat on Horse and Cross Palms.

Following the High Pat on Horse style, and after pushing the opponent backward, if the opponent B again pushes forward with both hands, A should hold B's forearm with the right hand and attack B's upper chest or the neck or the face with the left palm by stretching upward above the right wrist. Simultaneously, he must take half a step forward with the left foot. (Fig. 67 & 68)

Fig 67

Pattern 32: Turn and Cross Legs.

Following the preceding style or pattern, if B tries to make a sneak attack at the back, A should turn body immediately to the right with left foot bending, right foot withdrawing. (Fig. 69)

While watching for the next movement of the opponent, if B attacks A at the head with left hand, A should stretch his right hand to hold it, with left hand opening for the purpose of balancing. He

Fig 68

Fig 69

then raises his right foot to kick at the pubic region of the opponent with the sole. (Fig. 70)

Fig 70

Pattern 33: Brush Knee and Punch Opponent's Pubic Region.

Following the preceding pattern or style, and after   kicking of the opponent. A taking this advantage for the purpose of advancing, puts down his right foot horizontally. If B again attacks back with the right hand, A should brush it off with his left hand and take a step forward with the left foot bent. Finally, he should strike at B's abdomen or the pubic region with the right fist. (Figs. 71 & 72)

Pattern 34: Step up to Form Seven Stars.

Following the Snake Creeps Down Style, if B attacks with his right fist, A, after clenching both fists, should grasp the coming hand horizontally with his left hand. (Fig. 73)

With the right foot taking a step forward, he raises the right fist in coordination with the left one to strike the opponent at his upper torso, or to stop his attacking fist. In this case, A's body and hand

—358—

Fig 71

Fig 72

Fig 73

movements should be very well coordinated. This is the applying of
the total "intrinsic energy". While the left leg is substantial, the right
one, which is advancing, is insubstantial. (Fig. 74)

Fig 74

Pattern 35: Retreat to Ride Tiger.

Following the preceding pattern, if the opponent is aggressively advancing, or tries to grasp A's right wrist, A should retreat in order to avoid his blow or prolong the right hand of the opponent in order to eliminate his force. Meanwhile, after opening the left fist and warding off the opponent's right hand with it, A also raises the right palm, attacking the temple of the opponent. The left one reach the thigh, forming a semi-circle. With body slightly slanting to the right, it resembles the style of Riding the Tiger, defending with the posture of attacking. This is the technique of advancing by retreating and the energy applied is known as "Open Intrinsic Energy". (Figs. 75 & 76)

Pattern 36: Turn Around and Kick Horizontally.

Following the precding style, if B attacks A at the head with his right fist, A should turn left hand to the right and right hand to

Fig 75

the left, resting them in front of the chest with a guarded gesture.
(Fig. 77)

Fig 76

Fig 77

Supposing the opponent sweeps horizontally with his right foot, A, for the purpose of retreating and avoiding the coming attack, should turn 360 degrees to the right. Meanwhile, after this circular movement, and sitting on the left thigh, A should raise his right leg and sweep horizontally from left to the right aiming at the sacrum of the opponent. However, if B still attacks with his right fist, A should pull the opponent's hand to the left with both hands. This is the pattern which employs hands and feet simultaneously. (Fig. 78)

(Briefly speaking: If B strikes A with right fist at the first instance, A might pull the opponent down with both hands by using pulling backward technique, emphasizing the "Pull Down" energy. Meanwhile, he uses the 'flying right foot' to kick at B's chest. If B strikes at the back, A should use the 'turn and kick' technique.)

Fig 78

Pattern 37: Shoot Tiger with Bow.

Following the preceding pattern or style, if B attacks A from the front, A should turn waist to right and use both hands to hold the opponent's wrist and elbow so as to eliminate his coming force. At the same time, he takes one step to the right, the right leg being substantial. (Fig. 79)

Fig 79

At this juncture, if the opponent resists fiercely, A should take the posture of 'curving the bow' and then release his 'total intrinsic energy' so as to eject B away to a far distance. (Fig. 80)

Other method: If B's striking palm's energy is tremendous, A should stick to his wrist with the right hand; meanwhile, he applies the left palm to strike at B's right elbow. It may be advisable to use the "Raising Energy" to disperse B's 'heel-root' and then apply the "Push Energy" to strike him diagonally.

Fig 80

Notes: (1) Although the above 37 patterns are the fundamental techniques or methods for self-defense in Tai Chi Ch'uan, it has been pointed out that "the ultimate test of one's abilities in practicing Tai Chi Ch'uan for self-defense comes with the practical utilization of all the movements learned in both solo and hand pushing exercises through free-style bouts." The latter is called "Style of Free Hands (Shan Shiu 散手) consisting of 92 patterns which are not included in this book because of the lack of space. Those who are interested in this aspect of Tai Chi Ch'uan are requested to consult Hsiung Yang-ho's famous book, "Tai Chi Ch'uan Shih I," Revised edition, Taipei, 1970. (熊養和，太極拳釋義，1970 年訂正版，台北).

It may be added that in studying the techniques for self-defense, one must also learn four difficult techniques: "effectively using applied contact (敷) which prevents one's opponent from making an effective counter-move; maintaining the advantage over an opponent by application of covering pressure (盖) which prevents the opponent from freely manoeuving; effectively applying opposing force (對) at the right moment and point to knock the opponent off balance; and enticing an opponent towards oneself while at the same time, dissipating his strength and efforts (吞)." (quoted from Stanley E. Henning, "An Introduction to Tai Chi Ch'uan, a Branch of the Inner School of Chinese Boxing." See "Special Research Collections on Tai Chi Ch'uan," No. 52, 1971, Taipei.)

CHAPTER 14

JOINT HANDS OPERATIONS —

THEIR MEANINGS AND METHODS

I. The Meaning of Joint Hands Operation (推手).

It is a known thesis in the Chinese healing art that those who pattern themselves after the Yin and Yang (the two principles or forces in nature) and live in harmony with Tao (the Reality, the 'Logos' or the way of the universe), no doubt can escape old age and keep their bodies in perfect condition for a long life.[1] The practice of Tai Chi Ch'uan, in accordance with the above thesis, serves to help people in fulfilling their alloted span of life, extending it to a hundred years or more. However, with regard to the applicational aspect of this exercise, it must be complemented by the practice of Joint Hands Operation, without which it is uninteresting to practice Tai Chi Ch'uan on the one hand, and relatively impossible to understand the "intrinsic energy" and the "self-defense techniques" on the other.

Methodologically speaking, the fundamental 'kung-fu' of the Joint Hands Operation is to help the practitioners to practice and

---

[1] For the theory of Tao and Yin Yang applied to medicine, see *The Yellow Emperor's Classic of Internal Medicine*, trans. by Ilza Veith, University of California Press, 1966, (New edition). The Section on Acupuncture (針灸術) is very important, particularly for those who are interested in health-seeking.

understand the 'intrinsic energy' (Ching): (1) "To adhere and lift", (Chan), (2) "To Join", (Lien), (3) "To adhere horizontally" (T'ieh), and (4) "Neither let go nor resist" (Pui Tiu Ting) by applying the four methods or movements or energies: (a) "Ward-Off Slantingly Upward", (Peng), (b) "Pull Back" (Lu), (c) "Press Forward" (Chi), and (d) "Push" (An), in the Four Sides or Four Directions of Joint Hands Operation. Besides these four methods, there are the Four Corners or the Four Angles Joint Hands Operation, known as Ta Lu (Great Pullings). The additional four methods, or movements, or energies, are: "Pull Down" (Ts'ai), "Bend Back-ward", (Leh), "Elbow-Stroke" (Chou), and "Shoulder-Stroke" (Kou). The meaning of these technical terms has been explained thoroughly in Chapter Ten. With regard to this aspect, it is expected that it will be studied more attentively here. However, all the details, particularly in action, should be personally taught by a well-qualified instructor.[2]

In brief, the Joint Hands Operation is the way leading to the understanding of the opponent's "intrinsic energy" (Ching). During the operation, should any part of the opponent's hand or body come into contact with yours, you will instantly sense the source or direction of his energy — substantiality (Yang) or insubstantiality (Yin), overweight or underweight. Thus, one can "grasp" or "attach" the opponent's hand or any part of his body, preventing him

---

[2] Besides the four most important methods of Ta Lu, another two methods may be mentioned here: (1) "Slap" (Shen): After the applying of "Pull Back", if one tries to prevent the opponent from attacking by "Shoulder-stroke", he should "Slap" the opponent's face with his palm. (2) Arm Twist: This technique is sometimes used in connection with "Pull Back", after which one holds the opponent's wrist with one hand, twists his arm, and places the forearm of the other hand on his elbow, while stooping towards the front and bringing him down.

from fleeing. Taking the initiative, if any, one can skillfully borrow his "energy" and "attack" him as well. This is one of the most important implications of Joint Hands Operation, without which one is hardly able to apply or understand what is "intrinsic energy", or the techniques for self-defense. To quote Wang Tsung Yueh, the well-known theoretician of Tai Chi Ch'uan: "Having understood what is meant by "intrinsic energy", the more you practice it, the more you are on the way to refinement." The dexterity in application is, of course, finally dependent upon how much time you devote to the practice of the various types of Joint Hands Operation described in the following sections.

II. The Eight Essentials in the Practice of Joint Hands Operation.

A. Quiescence of the Mind.

During the practice of Joint Hands Operations, the mind must be in a state of quietitude and the attention concentrated on the practice. In opposing the aggressor, whether he be a man of great power or not, one's mind or consciousness should go ahead of his. Attention must always be given to his movements, which are to be closely watched and followed. Do not cast him away or oppose him with force. By concentrating upon this essential principle, one will be able to learn how to apply the techniques properly in one or two years. The main point is that one has to use the mind or consciousness without using any awkward strength. The opponent will thus be controlled by you in time through the application of the fundamental strategy of Tai Chi Ch'uan.

B. Alertness of the Body.

If one's body remains in a state of alertness, the opponent will not be able to advance or retreat at ease. However, it is of utmost importance that the body should always be kept alert. If the opponent attacks you on the left, you must keep the left in a state of insubstantiality so that he may not attain his purpose. If he attacks you on the right, contract your right shoulder so that his coming fist will unable to reach it. To repeat, in the process of using the techniques, one must always keep the body in alertness.

C. The Concentration of the "Chi". (Breathing)

In order to prevent the movements from disintegration, the concentration of the Chi is needed. "To inhale is to accumulate; to exhale is to attack." In inhaling, one is capable of sinking deep prior to attacking the opponent. Here, one has to concentrate the mind or consciousness in order to circulate the Chi over all the body. Little strength has to be used in attaining one's aim.3

D. The Integration of "Energy".

The "energy" (or 'intrinsic energy') in the internal organs should be trained to move like a chain. To attack with "energy", one should understand its source, which, as a matter of tact, "stems from the soles of the feet, commanded by the waist." Furthermore, the "energy can be escalated from the sacrum along the spine, expressing in the fingers" (by means of the concentration of the mind, of course). One's spirit should always be on the alert. When the opponent's energy does not appear, you should prepare to utilize your energy to control his. This is what we call the technique of borrowing the opponent's strength to attack him. The characteristic of Tai Chi Ch'uan, as it is often said in the classics, is to deflect a thousand catties (Chinese pounds) with the trigger of four taels (Chinese

3 It should be noted that it is important to "exhale at the proper movement of exhaling and inhale at the proper movement of inhaling. The air inhaled should be sunk to the "Tan Tien", and that exhaled should be sent out of the finger tips. "

ounces) of strength.   This is its efficiency."4

E. Concentration of the Spirit.

With all the foregoing conditions mentioned, the most important one, however, is to concentrate on the Spirit (or Shen).   Upon its concentration, one will be able to "split" or "enclose" so as to differentiate the insubstantiality (Yin) from the substantiality (Yang).   "To enclose is to collect; to split is to open."   If one knows what is meant by "split" and what is "enclose", he knows what is meant by Yin and Yang.   If his right side is substantial, the left should be insubstantial, the reverse also being true.   The strength has to be borrowed from the opponent; the Chi (energy, breathing) has to stem from the Tan Tien, emanating to the spine, expanding to the shoulders, and expressing itself in the fingers.   Usually this Chi, or "intrinsic energy" has to be escalated from the lower part of the body or the vital points of 'Bubbling Well' at the soles upward. If one comprehends all these principles, one's technique will be very advanced.

F. Central Equilibrium.

In Joint Hands Operations, one has to take a favorable position,

---

4 The *Song of the Joint Hands Operation,* which is very popular, written by an unknown author, has been translated by Professor T. T. Liang of New York, at the request of the writer.   It runs as follows:
"In Peng, Lu, Chi and An,
You must find the real technique
If he goes up, you follow...
Then he cannot attack.
Let him attack you with great force,
and use four ounces to deflect one thousand pounds.
Neutralizing him until he becomes powerless,
and then use 'withdraw-attack'.
Also adhere and lift, support from below,
Stick horizontally, and attach from rear;
Without letting go and with no resistance."

and next, a good opportunity. When a favourable position is secured, one must keep his "central equilibrium" (Central gravity) in order to avoid being placed in a disadvantageous position. This is particularly true when a movement is about to start and the energy is out of balance. Hence in applying the technique of "press forward", the knees should not pass the toes, and the elbows should not go further than the knee. The body should neither lean forward to the left nor to the right.

G. The Direction of the Eyes.

In Joint Hands Operations, besides the quiescence of the mind, the alertness of the body, the sinking and circulation of the Chi or breathing, the integration of the energy and the concentration of the spirit (or Shen), the direction where the eyes look is also of great importance. For instance, one must look upward in "Ward-Off Slantingly Upward", look backward in "Pull Back", look forward in "Press Forward" and "Push".

H. Observation of Order.

In the first stage of the practice of "Fixed Steps Joint Hands Operations" one should devote one's whole attention to the practice of "Ward Off Slantingly Upward", "Pull Back", "Press Forward" and "Push". The waist, legs and other parts of the body must be so trained as to be capable of becoming proficient in "Adhere and Lift", "Join", "Adhere Horizontally", "Attach from the Rear".

In the second stage, after mastering the above techniques to an excellent degree, all the other techniques such as "Pull-Down", "Bend-Backward", "Elbow-Stroke", (also "Split", "Enclose", "Slap", "Twist", "Feint", "Neutralize", "Fast-Hold" and "Attack") may be freely employed at one's own will.

In the third stage, one must see that every movement is to be made circular, without angles, before pugilism can have any practical result. This is a movement which is similar to that of a rotating wheel. If something angular in form is thrown at the wheel, it will naturally be expelled by the roundness of the wheel. It is this important principle that shows why, in Tai Chi Ch'uan, every movement takes the form of a circle.

III. The Three Important Styles of Joint Hands Operations

In the final analysis, there are really no definite formulae or styles in Joint Hands Operations. Their changes are almost infinite and mystic. Beginners should try to master the following three basic styles before they can attain an incredible rate of success. They are as follows:

A. Style I: Joint Hands Operations with Fixed Steps may be divided into two types:

    a. Joint Hands Operations with United Steps in which the two practitioners' right feet are in the front, left in the back.

    b. Joint Hands Operations with Favourable Steps in which one practitioner's left foot is in the front, while the other's right foot follows the same direction.

B. Style II. Joint Hands Operations with Active Steps. Both practitioners may start with right or left feet at will — advancing or retreating. The change of the step, however, has to follow the change of the hands in action.[5]

~~~~~~~~~~~~~~~~~~~~~~~~~~~~~~~~~~~~~~

[5] In both styles, the four methods or movements — "Ward Off Slanting Upward", "Pull Back", "Press Forward", and "Push" must be clearly distinguished and practiced. The meanings and methods of both styles, together with Ta Lu, will be explained in the following section with illustrated pictures. Naturally, the beginners should start with circling, hence our explanation and illustration will begin with the Single Joint Hands Operation.

C. Style III. Ta Lu (or Great Pulling) can be divided into two types:

    a. The Fixed Type, in which the movements and directions are fixed.

    b. The Unfixed (Free) Type, in which the movements and directions are not fixed.

The meanings and practicing methods of each style are to be given in the following sections:

IV. The Basic Methods of the Joint Hands Operations with Fixed Steps.

1. Single Joint Hands Operations.

A (wears white cloth) and B (wears dark pants) stands opposite each other, both with right legs at the front, keeping the Central Equilibrium steps. The wrists of A and B touch each other on the back, shoulder height. The thumbs of both practitioners are opposite their noses. A attention centers on the direction of the movements. (Fig 1)

Fig 1

2. The Method of pulling on a plane-circle.

1. A, taking a substantial step with the front leg, applies his right palm in order to "Push" B. B, sitting on the hind leg, applies her right palm attaching the wrist of A, who turns his waist to the right by the use of "Pull Down" towards the right on a plane-level. (Fig. 2)

Fig 2

2. B, taking a substantial step at the front, applies her right palm (turning to Yin) to attach the wrist of A, who is sitting on the hind leg. He turns his waist, and applies his Yang palm to "Pull Down" towards the right on a plane level. (Fig. 3)

Note: Applying the methods of "Push" and "Pull Down", A and B are operating cyclicly and repeatedly on a plane-circle movement. All the operations should be in proper correlation with one another. The movements are designed to train the mo-

Fig 3

mentum of the waist and legs, enabling the practitioners to
master the methods of the "Push" and "Pull Down" as well as
the "Neutralizing". The postures should be exact, measuring
to the requirements of "Adhere and Lift" (Chan), "Join"
(Lien), "Adhere Horizontally" (Tieh), "Attach from the
Rear" (Sui) and "Neither let go nor Resist" (Pui Tiu Ting).
When the right-form posture is learned with proficiency, one
may proceed to practice the left form.

3. The Pulling Method of Cubic-Circle Movements.

(1) Continuing from the Right Single Joint Hands Operations,
A, raising the right elbow, applies the right palm to go forward toward
the chest of B — the Yin palm is used. B, applying her right palm
(Yang) to attach A's palm on the back, sinks her right elbow, and
turns body (waist) to the right. Now, she is sitting on the left leg
and "Pulls Down" in the same direction — applying the method of
'neutralizing'. (Figs. 4 and 5)

Fig 4

Fig 5

(2) Raising the right elbow, B now turns to Yin palm and attacks toward the chest of A, who, lowering the right elbow, applies

the right palm — attaching to the back of B's right palm — to "Pull Down" towards the right — 'neutralizing'. He is now sitting on the hind leg and turning body (waist) in the same direction. (Figs. 6 & 7)

Fig 6

Fig 7

Note: After mastering the right form with proficiency the left form
        should also be practiced.

V. Joint Hands Operations with Fixed Steps — Their Essential Meanings.

Preparatory Posture: The same as in the fundamental movements mentioned above.

Method 1:   "Ward Off" (Peng).   Explanation: This technique is used to ward-off the "Push" technique of the opponent with
a view to preventing his pushing hands from reaching your own chest.

A (wears white pants) and B (wears dark pants) each take
a step forward with the right leg.   A puts both hands on the right
forearm of B, who, in order to slow down the kinetic action of A, sits
solidly on the left thigh with lowered waist and relaxed sacrum, using
the intrinsic energy and the momentum of the waist and legs to "Ward
off" diagonaly the hands of A upward to the right. (Figure 8)

Fig 8

Method 2: "Pull Back" (Lu). Explanation: This technique is used to attach the opponent's elbow and wrist in order to "Pull Back" his or her hand and body. In the application of this technique, do not oppose or go into direct conflict with the opponent. The technique of "Neutralizing" (Hua) is often used in this case.

B circles both hands downward and adheres to the right wrist of A with right hand, and his elbow with the left hand. Actions are caused by the intrinsic energy. A applies the momentum of the waist and legs to "Pull Back" (Lu) his hand towards the right. This is the kinetic action known as Lu. (Figure 9)

Fig 9

Method 3: "Press Forward" (Chi). Explanation: This technique is the exact opposite to that of the "Pull Back". When one is pulled back by the opponent, he should change the position from "Retreat" to "Advance" and use the front hands to "Press Forward" against the opponent's chest.

A, after being "pulled back" to his disadvantageous position by

B, turns partly to the right and changes the right arm into a form of semi-circle. The left hand attaches to the opponent's right arm. Now, A uses both hands to "Press Forward" against B's chest; the action of A comes from his intrinsic energy, and the momentum of the waist and legs. This is known as the kinetic action of Chi. (Figure 10)

Fig 10

Method 4: "Push" (An).

Following the previous methods, B, while being pressed forward, has to relax the chest (Chest-in), raise the back, loose the waist, and sit firmly on the left thigh. Finally, B "neutralizes" the coming hand of A towards the left. This is the kinetic action known as "Neutralizing" (Hua).

Simultaneously, A should grasp the right wrist of B with the right hand, holds her right elbow with the left hand, and finally "push" his hands towards the chest of B. This is the kinetic action known as "Push", (An). This action, as usual, starts from the intrinsic energy, and the momentum of the waist and legs. (Figure 11)

Method 5: In short, the whole method, which comprises all the above methods, may be stated as follows:

A (or B) after being "Pushed" (An) by B (or A), turns from the method of "Ward-Off" (Peng) to the method of "pull" pulling the right arm of B (or A) by the method of "Pulling Back" (Lu).

B, after being "Pulled Back" by A to a disadvantageous position, changes immediately his (or her) right arm to the form of semi-circle, and "Presses Forward" against A's chest, using the intrinsic energy of the waist and the legs, shoulders sinking and elbows hanging. This is "Press-Forward". (Chi)

Notes:

(1) The above methods actually consist in Peng, Lu, Chi, An (and Hua), the last of which, an additional important method, must not be omitted in the Joint Hands Operation.

Fig 11

(2) The five "Steps" are known as "Advance", "Retreat", "Look to the Left", "Look to the Right", and "Central Equilibrium". Attention must be paid to the last "Step", which is the center of gravity in the cyclic and repeated movements.

(3) The whole sequence of Joint Hands Operation runs thus: (A) Starting from Peng (Ward-Off); (B) Changing to Lu (Pull Back). (C) From Lu, changing to Chi (Press-Forward). (D) From Chi, Changing to Hua (Neutralizing). (E) After Hua, it goes to An (Push).

To solve 'An', one must use 'Peng'; to solve 'Peng', one uses 'Chi', and to solve 'Chi', one uses 'Hua' and 'An'.

(4) In fact, the cyclic runs thus:

When you apply "Pull Back" (Lu) on me, I must apply the method of "Pushing" (An) on you. When I change to apply the method of "Press Forward" (Chi), you should apply "Push" (An). When you turn to "Push" (An), I prepare to "Ward-off" (Peng). When I turn to "Ward-off", you again apply "Push" (An). Meanwhile I may also apply the "Diagonal Pull Back", which is often called "Neutralizing" (Hua). The four movements or methods should be performed upward and downward, forward and backward, in cyclic actions. The "To adhere and lift — palm down" (Chan) (Stick-to-Upward) and "To Join" — palm up (Lien) ("Joins" are up and down movements.) "To adhere horizontally" (Tieh) (Attack), and "To attack from the rear" (Sui) (Follow up), are backward, forward and lateral movements.

(5) The sequence of the movements (methods) in the Four Sides may also be performed by A and B according to the following formula with considerable effectiveness:

A—"Press Forward" "Ward Off Slantingly Upward" "Pull Back" "Push"

B—"Pull Back" "Push" "Press Forward" "Ward Off Slantingly Upward"

VI. The Methods of Ta Lu (Great Pullings) (大擺).

1. Explanations:

When a practitioner has attained a high degree of proficiency in
the art of Joint Hands Operations with Fixed steps and Active Steps,
he must proceed to learn and practice Ta Lu or the Great Pulling
System, by using the eight methods, viz: "Ward-off Slantingly Upward", "'Pull Back", "Press Forward", "Push", "Pull Down",
"Bend Backward", "Elbow-Stroke" and "Shoulder Stroke" to move
within the Four Corners and Eight Directions. However, in this
system, the latter four methods — "Pull Down", "Bend Backward",
"Elbow-Stroke", "Shoulder-Stroke" — are generally considered as
the four fundamental movements, the value of which can be compared to that of the vowels AEIOU in the English alphabet. If there
were no such vowels, pronounciation would be impossible. [7] In addition, the movements of the hands should be coordinated with the
steps: "Advance", "Retreat", "Look to the Left", "Look to the
Right", and "Central Equilibrium". The body also changes in accordance with the changing of the steps. After all, holism, or the
integration of the whole body, is what matters in this ststem ——
the ultimate in Tai Chi Ch'uan.

---

[7] See Yearning K. Chen, *Tai Chi Ch'uan, Its Effects and Practical
Applications*, Shanghai, 1947, pp. 155-182. Mr. Chen said: "In Tai Chi
Ch'uan, the circles are not only round, but are also square. It is said the
Tai Chi is a circle, and that the interior and the exterior, the left and the
right, are all included in the circle. It is said that Tai Chi is a square, and
that the interior and the exterior, the left and the right, are all included in
the square. The going out and the going in of the center, and the advance
and the retreat of the square, follow the square and correspond to the circle.
The square is for development and the circle for intensity. When one understands the circle and the square, the outer forms and the inner significance
of the Four Sides, one's technique is perfect and there is no need for the
Four Corners Operations." This is admitted, still we consider the Four
Corner Operations indispensible.

GENERAL RULES GOVERNING THE PRACTICE OF TA LU

Stepping

1. The first of beginning corner (direction) is the only slight modification of the practice. Since it is the beginning, the starting positions of A and B are not in an actual corner. Thus the beginning corner requires one less step than what the other corners take to complete. Naturally, when the first corner is repeated, it would utilize the full number of stepping motions.
2. A and B move the same foot simoultaneously whether stepping, pivoting or turning.
3. A and B work harmoniously to arrive at each corner.
4. Generally speaking, regardless of direction of corner, the first two steps of either A or B will be in one direction while the third and final step will be at 90 degrees to the former steps and direction.
5. If A steps forward, B pivots and steps back. The reverse is also true.
6. A and B turn around each other in a clockwise direction while the steps are anticlockwise toward the four corners.
7. For visual clarity in this book, A and B will start facing West and East respectively. However, should they start facing North and South, each corner could be arrived at in the exact same sequence and direction that is found in the "Fair Ladies Working the Shuttles" in T'ai Chi Ch'uan. This presumes the practice of T'ai Chi begins by facing South.

Pulling

1. In corners 1 and 3, A initiates the action by pulling B.

2. In corners 2 and 4, A follows B and counters with elbow and shoulder stroking.
3. In corners 2 and 4, B initiates the action by pulling A.
4. In corners 1 and 3, B follows A and counters with elbow and shoulder stroking.
5. The right wrists of A and B remain in contact at all times.
6. The left arms circle in clockwise direction to attach or face toward the opponent's right hand.
7. Left and right arms of both A and B move simoultaneously.

General Concepts

1. Each arm and leg action is divided into three parts.
2. Speed is not necessary. Sensitivity and balance are vital throughout.
3. When pulling do not grasp the opponent's wrist tightly nor press with the other arm fiercely. Maintain steady, moderate control.
4. Ta Lu (Great Pulling) implies the step size should be as large as possible without becoming awkward. In the beginning one may not be able to take great strides. With practice one can advance however.
5. All actions cease simoultaneously and momentarily at the completion of a corner.
2. Methods:

There are two methods in Ta Lu —— the Fixed Type and the Unfixed (Free) Type. Beginners have to start with the first one.

A. The Fixed Type:
GENERAL DIRECTIONS —— CORNER # 1

B attempts to slap A's face with her right palm. As he is about to be slapped A wards off B's right hand with his right hand diagonally upward and retreats two steps toward the southwest applying methods of Pull Down and Bend Backward. Simoultaneously B proceeds to advance two steps and strikes A with her Elbow stroke and Shoulder Stroke. (figs. 12, 13, 14.)

(Fig. 12)

A (white, facing west) and B (black, facing east) touch together right wrists. Knees are bent and left palms face the floor. (Fig 12)

(Fig. 13)

A inititates the action by turning inward his left foot. A guides B's right arm in a downward arc. As A turns his left, B steps forward with her left foot. Her body also turns to face the direction of her left foot. Both begin to revolve their left hands in a clockwise pattern. (Fig. 13)

(Fig. 14)

A steps back with his right foot to the first corner (southwest) B follows A with her right foot by stepping forward. A has pulled B's right arm by grasping her wrist and also by guiding her arm with his left hand. B's left hand is facing A's right hand, but not touchng it. (Fig. 14)

GENERAL DIRECTIONS —— CORNER # 2

A attempts to slap B's face with his right palm. As she is about to be slapped, B wards off A's right hand with her right hand diagonally upward and retreats three steps toward the second corner (southeast) applying methods of Pull Down and Bend Backward. Simoultaneously, A proceeds to advance three steps and strikes B with his Elbow Stroke and Shoulder Stroke. (Figs. 15, 16, 17.)

[*Fig. 15*]

B initaiates the action by taking a half step back with her right foot. A follows with a half step forward with his right foot. As B sits back on her left leg she lifts A's right arm to the neutral position overhead. Both drop left hands and begin a clockwise circular pattern as in the first corner. (Fig. 15)

(Fig. 16)

B now pivots a quarter turn in place. She pivots on her left foot. (Note: this is similar to A's beginning action in fig. 13) A follows her by stepping forward with his left foot. The engaged right wrists continue in the clockwise direction. The left hands continue their arcs without stopping or hesitation. (Fig. 16)

(Fig. 17)

B steps back with her right foot into the second corner. A follows with his right foot stepping forwad. B has pulled A's right arm and guided it with her left hand in the same manner A did to her in the first corner. Likewise A has turned his left palm in to face B's left hand, though not touching it. The final position is exactly the opposite to fig. 14. (Fig. 17)

GENERAL DIRECTIONS —— CORNER # 3

This is a repeat of corner one.

B attempts to slap A's face with her right palm. As he is about to be slapped, A wards off B's right hand with his right hand diagonally upward and retreats three steps toward the third corner (northeast) applying methods of Pull Down and Bend Backward.

Simoultaneously, B proceeds to advance three steps and strikes A with her Elbow Stroke and shoulder stroke. (fig. 18, 19, 20.)

(Fig. 18)

A initiates the action by taking a half step back with his right foot. B follows with a half step forward with her right foot. As A sits back on his left leg he lifts B's right arm to the neutral position overhead. Both drop left hands and begin a clockwise circular pattern as in the other corners. (Fig. 18)

(Fig. 19)

A now pivots a quarter turn in place. He pivots on his left foot. B follows him by stepping forward with her left foot. The engaged right wrists continue in the clockwise direction. The left hands continue their arcs without stopping. (Fig. 19)

(Fig. 20)

A steps back with his right foot into the third corner. B follows with her right foot stepping forward. A has pulled B's right arm and guided it with his left hand in the same manner as he did in the first corner. Likewise B has turned her left palm in to face A's left hand though not touching it. The final position is the exact oppposite to fig. 23. (Fig. 20)

GENERAL DIRECTIONS —— CORNER # 4

This is a repeat of corner two.

A attempts to slap B's face with his right palm. As she is about to be slapped B wards off A's right hand with her right hand diagonally upward and retreats three steps toward the fourth corner (Northwest) applying the methods of Pull Down and Bend Backward. Simoultaneously, A proceeds to advance three steps and strikes B with his Elbow Stroke and Shoulder Stroke. (figs. 21, 22, 23.)

(Fig. 21)

B initiates the action by taking a half step back with her right foot. A follows with a half step forward with his right foot. As B sits back on her left leg she lifts A's right arm to the neutral position overhead. Both drop left hands and begin a clockwise circular pattern as in the other corners. (Fig 21)

(Fig. 22)

B now pivots a quarter turn in place. She pivots on her left foot. A follows her by stepping forward with his left foot. The engaged right wrists continue in the clockwise direction. The left hands continue their arcs without stopping..(Fig. 22)

(Fig 23)

B steps back with her right foot into the fourth corner. A follows with his right foot stepping forward. B has pulled A's right arm and guided it with her left hand in the same manner as in the other corners. Likewise A has turned his left palm in to face B's left hand though not touching it. The final position is exactly the opposite to fig. 20. (Fig. 23)

Note: The above instructions complete the basic Ta Lu. When they are mastered one can further develop his skill by practicing the Four Corners in the opposite direction. Thus A and B will do the same actions, only the opposite hand and feet will be utilized in the same way. Thus the first corner could be initiated by A who would pull B's left hand with his left. He would turn in his left. He would turn in his right foot and step back with his left foot to the Southeast. B would follow by stepping forward with her right foot. Both would still apply the same offense-defense techniques. All four corners can be practiced in clockwise and anticlockwise directions.

The cyclic practices are of utmost importance. In general, the two hands or at least one hand must stick to the opponent's otherwise the energy is disconnected. In retreating, two steps and one pivot have to be taken, and in advancing three steps. Retreating is always done toward the four corners.

3. The Unfixed (Free) Style.

According to this type, the operational methods of Left-Right "Pull Down", "Bend Backward", "Elbow Stroke" and "Shoulder Stroke" are the same as those in the Fixed style described above, but the "Slapping" and "Pushing" are unfixed. One can apply any methods at his own will, and because the directions are also unfixed, one may take the East, West, North or South. In general, he, who is slapped, should retreat diagonally two steps and turn his body to apply the methods of "Pull Down" and "Bend Backward" in changing direction. Again, he, who is pushed, should retreat horizontally two steps and turn his body to apply "Pull Down" and "Bend Backward" in changing direction. As to direction, there is no fixed procedure, one may change voluntarily. If one has attained a high degree of proficiency, and the steps are staged in an orderly manner, any of the eight methods can be applied. At this stage, one is confined neither to a particular method nor to a special direction. Every method and every direction can be applied as the opportunity is presented. After all the various changes are infinite and mystic: to describe them is utterly impossible. It is up to the grasp and intuitive illumination of the practitioner himself.

VII. The application Methods of the Four Sides and Four Corners.

NOTE:

The following applications are presented in classical form for clarity of principles and application. Naturally a real self-defense altercation would dictate how the technique must be used and what limitations are required.

Explanations:

The Ward Off (Peng), Pull Back (Lu), Press Forward (Chi) and Push (An), are the methods applicable to the Four Sides, while the Pull Down (Picking, Chai), Bend Backward (Twisting, Lieh), Elbow-Stroke (Elbowing, Chou) and Shoulder-Stroke (Leaning, K'ao) are methods applicable to the Four Corners. For the theoretical explanations of these methods, see Chaper 8.

Ward Off.   fig 24, 25, 26.

(fig. 24)

A face B. B steps forward with her right foot and punches with her right. (fig. 24)

(fig. 25)

A sits back absorbing B's punch while deflecting slightly upward the force of B. (fig. 25)

(fig. 26)

A shifts his weight forward immediately and thrusts B backward.
(fig. 26)

2. Pull Back   fig. 27, 28, 29, 30.

(fig. 27)

A faces B. B steps forward with her right and punches with left.
(fig. 27)

(fig. 28)

As B is punching A, A grasps her left wrist and guides her arm with his right hand. (fig. 28)

(fig. 29)

B counters A by reaching over A's right arm and grasps his right with her right hand. (fig. 29)

(fig. 30)

A steps back twisting B's right arm and grasps it with his left hand causing her to fall down. (Fig. 30)

3. Press Forward fig. 31, 32, 33.

(fig. 31)

A faces B. B steps forward with her left foot and punches with her right. (fig. 31)

(fig. 32)

Neutralizing B's force, A causes B's arm to bend against her. B is now off balance. (fig. 32)

(fig. 33)

A pins B's arm against her torso by stepping forward with his right causing B to fall. (fig. 33)

4. Push   fig. 34, 35, 36.

(fig. 34)

B faces A. A steps forward with his left foot and punches with his right. B begins to deflect (as in ward off). (fig. 34)

(fig. 35)

Sensing this, A relaxes his right arm and turns B's arm and torso horizontally by utilizing B's force (as in press forward). A also turns his palm on B's arm. (fig. 35)

(fig. 36)

Stepping forward with his right. A attaches his left hand against B's arm pushing against her causing B to fall. (fig. 36)

5. Pull Down A   fig. 37, 38

(fig. 37)

A faces B. B steps forward with her right foot and punches with her right. A deflects her punch by grasping her right wrist with both of his hands. (fig. 37)

(fig. 38)

A takes the advantage by sitting back, turning his waist to his right and pulls B's force forward so she is off balance. (fig. 38)

Pull Down B   fig. 39, 40.

(fig. 39)

A faces B. B steps forward with her right foot and punches with her right. A deflects (as in ward off) to neutralize B's force. (fig. 39)

(fig. 40)

Now A turns his right palm and grasps B's right wrist. Next he steps back pulling B off balance. (similar to pull back) (fig. 40)

Note: Pull back is a horizontal pull while Pull Down is a downward pull.

6. Bend Backward A   fig. 41, 42, 43.

(fig. 41)

A faces B. B steps forward with her right and punches with her left. A sits back to avoid being struck and neutralizes B's force by hooking his right hand over B's left forearm or wrist. (fig. 41)

(fig. 42)

Shifting forward, A sharply swings B's left arm around horizontally causing her to be spun about. (fig. 42)

(fig. 43)

A can further counter by stepping forward and push against B. A may also take what other action he feels necessary to defeat B. (fig. 43)

Bend Backward B   fig. 44, 45, 46.

(fig. 44)

A faces B. B steps forward with her left foot and punches with her right. A sits back to avoid being struck and deflects slightly upward with his left arm. (fig. 44)

(fig. 45)

A continues by rotating his left over B's right forearm and thereby grasping it. Observe how B's right fist is cought under A's arm and that this causes her arm to be locked at the elbow. (fig. 45)

(fig. 46)

While B is trapped and securely held A can further counter with a punch at B's chest or take what other action he feels necessary to defeat B. (fig. 46)

7. Elbow Stroke A   fig. 47, 48, 49.

(fig. 47)

A faces B. B steps forward with her right foot and punches with her left. A deflects (as in ward off). (fig. 47)

(fig. 48)

Continuing, A grasps B's wrist with his left hand and steps forward his right foot attaching his right hand against B's left elbow. This action will straighten or lock her elbow so she is trapped and held securely. (fig. 48)

(fig. 49)

By turning his torso A sharply strikes B's shoulder causing B to fall away. (fig. 49)

Elbow Stroke B   fig. 50, 51, 52.

(fig. 50)

D faces A. A steps forward with his left and punches with his right. B deflects A's force slightly upward by grasping A's right wrist. (fig. 50)

(fig. 51)

Sensing this, A relaxes his right arm and bends it so his right elbow is pointing at B. A also attaches his right hand inside his elbow for support and for maintining control. (fig. 51)

(fig. 52)

A now steps forward with his right foot and strikes B's chest with his elbow. B falls backward from the force of A's thrust. (fig. 52)

8. Shoulder Stroke A   fig. 53, 54, 55.

(fig. 53)

A faces B. B steps forward with her right foot and punches with her right. A sits back to avoid being struck and deflects horizontally by grasping B's right arm at her elbow. (fig. 53)

(fig. 54)

Shifting his weight forward, A pushes against B causing her to turn about. (fig. 54)

(fig. 55)

A follows through by sinking under B's right shoulder and while still holding B's arm, A thrusts his Shoulder sharply against B causing her to fall away. (fig. 55)

Shoulder Stroke B fig. 56, 57, 58.

(fig. 56)

B faces A. A steps forward with his right foot and punches with his right. B counters by grasping A's arm with her right hand (as in Pull Down). (fig. 56)

(fig. 57)

Sensing this A relaxes his right arm, bending his elbow (as in Elbow Stroke B). He also supports his right arm with his left hand for control. (fig. 57)

(fig. 58)

Shifting his weight forward, A thrusts his Shoulder against B's left arm and torso, thus trapping her and knocking her backward. (fig. 58)

The operations and functioning of the forgoing methods would involve a great deal of energy, time, practice, and understanding.

Note: In learning how to practice the above techniques, it is necessary to follow the instructions of an expert in the beginning stage.

CHAPTER 15

THEORY OF SELF-DEFENSE IN

TAI CHI CH'UAN

1. The Three Characteristics of Tai Chi Ch'uan in the matter of Pugilism.

The phrase 'Tai Chi Ch'uan' in Chinese is a combination of two terms: 'Tai Chi' — the basic principle of Chinese philosophy, and 'chuan' — fist or pugilism. The main objective of martial art (Wu Shou), in China as elsewhere, is, of course, its emphasis on pugilism. However, there is a great difference between the system of Shao Lin and that of Tai Chi (Wu T'ang): the first and lowest use of martial art recognizes mainly the pugilistic aspect; the second and highest includes also the spiritual one. While speaking of the pugilistic use as the lowest, it is not our intention to imply that it is of no value to humanity. We simply wish to assign to it its comparative value in relation to the higher use. On the higher plane of cultural development, the primary objective of Tai Chi Ch'uan is to teach human beings how to attain the goal of spiritual and physical fitness as well as eternal youth, but pugilism, a by-product of the same art, is purely a secondary matter. However, viewing it from the standpoint of pugilism, this system has at least three general characteristics which are:

(A)   The pugilistic aim of Tai Chi Ch'uan is mainly for self defense. "If the opponent does not attack me, I have no desire to attack him". Hence, its first characteristic is manifested in its law of non-aggression.

(B)   The application of Tai Chi Ch'uan in pugilism is based on strategy rather than on brute strength or force. Its second characteristic is, therefore, manifested in its law of emphasis on intelligence or strategy.

(C)   Tai Chi Ch'uan, as a system of exercise, is based usually on the principle of 'yielding'. This comes from the instruction of Laotzu, who said: "The softest (yielding) of all things overrides the hardest of all things". Admitting that unyielding (yang) and yielding (yin) are complimentary, in nature, its general characteristic in performance is by all means "yielding".

2. Laws concerning the application of strategy in Tai Chi Ch'uan.

It has been repeatedly pointed out that, once developed through regular and proper practice, in not too long a period, a new form of energy — the "Intrinsic Energy" (nei ching) cultivated in the body will certainly show its beneficial effects on the practitioner. "It will help improve the circulation of blood, tone the muscles and relax the nerves. It slims down the obesity and builds up the skinny. It is even reputed to heal incurable diseases and such chronic ailments as neurastenia, hypertension, and paralysis".[1] But the pugilistic achievement of this art cannot be learned except through a prolonged period

[1] Quoted from Tung Fu Ling, "The Manly Art of Self-Expression", The Asian Magazine. December 31, 1961.

of training. The main reason is that, as far as the application of all the strategy and techniques in Tai Chi Ch'uan is concerned, one has first of all to comprehend deeply and to apply skillfully those laws, principles and techniques such as the Law of Non-Opposition, the Law of Non-Separation, the Law of Central Equilibrium, and the Law of Circular Movements, all of which will be described as follows:

(A) The Law of Non-Opposition. (no resistance)

In the application of Tai Chi Ch'uan, what we particularly emphasize is the use of the "method of neutralizing". Prior to the discharge of one's own "energy" (attack), one should first gain a more favourable position than the opponent occupies and only then begin to strike. Again, Wang Tsung-yueh has stated: "To deflect the momentum of a thousand catties (Chinese pounds) with a trigger force of four taels (Chinese ounces) of strength". That is the chief merit of Tai Chi Chuan. In essence, the emphasis here lies on technique rather than physical force. Hence, what we attempt to unhold is obviously not the instinctive use of strength, rather, it is the recondition of the strength in order to use it in a strategic way with better results. NON-OPPOSITION is therefore an important law responsive to this need.

In the application of this law, however, two points should be noted. First, one should take an initiative by adjusting himself to any movement started from the side of the opponent. To stay on the side of softness (yielding) is to be tough, and not passive. Next, one should use his sense to "listen" (understand) to the actions of the opponent before taking counter actions. If the opponent advances one inch, you may retreat one inch. But do not yield too much or too little. If less, you commit yourself to the pitfall of 'opposition', if more, the pitfall of 'disattaching'. Hence, the technique of non-opposition is not solely in using less strength, but in using lesser strength to 'feint' (induce) the opponent to an unfavorable position before changing techniques and "charging".

(B) The Law of Non-Separation. (not letting go)

The Law of Non-Opposition emphasizes the importance of 're-treating' and 'yielding', while the Law of Non-Separation emphasizes 'Following' — a transitory period prior to 'charging' or attacking. Speaking in terms of directions and effects, these two techniques seem to be contradictory. However, viewing them as part of a circular movement, the two are actually supplementary to each other. For the former stresses the use of the energy of 'running' and the latter, 'attaching'. In the "Theory of Tai Chi Ch'uan", it is said, "Attaching is running; running is attaching". The Yang (positive force) cannot be divorced from Yin (negative force), the Yin also cannot be divorced from the Yang. The mutual coordination of Yin and Yang is a way to comprehend the "energy" (Ching). From this dialectic process, we understand how important these two techniques and energies are.

In application, when one engages the opponent in a struggle, it is most important to attach to his movements in order not to let him get away. One should use one hand to 'follow' the hand of the opponent, and the other to attack. Should the opponent oppose you obstinately, you might return to the techniques of 'grasping and releasing', or 'sticking' to the opponent and raising him up for the sake of dislocating his center of gravity.

Although the techniques of Tai Chi Ch'uan are variable and changeable, the important ones cannot be divorced from the following two laws.

(C) The Law of Circular Movement.

In the practice of Tai Chi Ch'uan, no brute strength is needed. All movements are deliberately slow and always travel in arcs or circles. Indeed, all the postures of Tai Chi Ch'uan are composed of numerous circles — plane or vertical, big or small. It is required that the movements of the limbs be preceded by circular forms. Within the big circles, there are small circles, and within the small circles there are still tiny circles. In all the circles, there are nuclei and segments, the latter, like the universe, are basically divided into two separate but mutually independent and complementary parts (Yin and Yang), substantiality and insubstantiality, negative and positive.

Thus, for instance, in the basic postures of the "Grasping of the Bird's Tail" one may have to do five basic circles which may also be considered as five methods, viz: (1) the plane circle; (2) the vertical circle; (3) the oblique circle; (4) the front and backward circle, and (5) the auto-turning circle. When all these methods are mastered, one may employ all these circles at will in self-defense. And, during the first stage of practicing, the circles drawn may be big and inactive, but in the second stage, they must be small and active. Furthermore, according to the comprehension of the Tai Chi Ch'uan masters, the drawing of circles is not only in the externality, but also in the internality, that is to say, one should have the idea of a circle, even without the form of a circle. And in a twinkling, the marvel — in application, of course — of the circles appears.

The circular movements of Tai Chi Ch'uan, which are very similar to the movements of the wheel of a machine, enable the various parts of the body to acquire balanced activities on the one hand, and are suitable to the physiological needs of the body on the other. The marvels of the circular movements in pugilism may be said to consist of the following principles: (1) forming the state of adjustment in order to avoid the state of damage; and (2) forming the state of lightness in order to avoid the state of heaviness. Not only the principles of "Stick-to Upward", "Attach", "Join", "Follow-Up", and the "Listening", "Neutralizing", "Hold Fast" and "Attack" are to be operated skilfully within the numerous big and small circles, but also all the movements of the hands and legs from the 'Commencement' to the 'Conclusion' should be performed in conformity with the circles. In each circle, there are insubstantiality and substantiality, which are changeable and infinite. Consequently, in the event of a struggle with an opponent, the resistance or "Ward-off" means attacking, and attacking means resisting or "Ward-off". Because of the fact that in every circle there must be insubstantiality and substantiality, one half of the circle is used for sticking, and the other half is for attacking; one half is running in order to neutralize the strength of the opponent, and the other half is sticking in order to subdue the enemy. The more advanced the technique is, the smaller circles will be performed. Here lies the mystery of the Law of 'Circular Movement'.

(D) The Law of Central Equilibrium.

The psychological factor instrumental in the training of the body to attain a state of Central Equilibrium (center of gravity) is considered a part of the Tai Chi Ch'uan exercise. According to science, we know that mental and moral disciplines bring about a better central equilibrium of the sympathetic system and a more complete intergration of all organic and mental activities. These agencies can be divided into two categories: those acting from without, and those acting from within. To the first category belong all reflexes and states of consciousness caused on the subject by other individuals, or by social environment. The second category comprises the factors which modify the subject from within, such as meditatlon, concentration, will power, etc. In Tai Chi Ch'uan, whether in the matter of exercise, or a struggle with an opponent, one must concentrate one's mind and maintain one's utmost quiescence so that the Equilibrium could always be observed. The agency comes, therefore, from the second category of the above mentioned factors.

The center of gravity in the human body, as the Tai Chi Ch'uan practitioners see it, is in the 'Psychic Center' or 'Tan Tien'. In order to stabilize the central equilibrium of the body, we must lower the Chi (breathing) to the psychic center upon which our meditation is also focused. From the pugilistic point of view, the way leading to victory in combat is first of all to overthrow the Central Equilibrium of the opponent, and attack him next. A well-known principle, therefore, is: "to subdue the motion with quiescence" hence in Tai Chi Ch'uan, the mastering of the Law of Central Equilibrium is, of course, of utmost importance.

3. Problems concerning Pugilism from the Standpoint of Tai Chi Ch'uan.

(A) The Problem of Speed.

As time is an important factor in pugilism, there is no doubt that practically all the schools of martial art focus their attention on the 'speed' of the movements. Wang's *Theory of Tai Chi Ch'uan,* expounds specially the principle "to subdue the speed with slowness". Why? This is because one does not expect to conquer the opponent with strength but with intelligence, or strategy. Besides, there is no absolute standard governing the rate of motion. In the advanced stage of the applied techniques, one is always expected to observe the rule: "If the opponent moves very quickly, you should respond in kind; if the opponent moves slowly, you should follow him slowly".

(B) The Techniques of 'Intrinsic Energy' (Nei Ching)

What is 'intrinsic energy'? Can we make a distinction between 'energy' (Ching) and strength or force (Li)? In order to answer these questions, let us take note of the following examples.

Example I: When one is required to use both hands to lift up an iron bar from the level of the chest to a spot above his head, what is needed in this case is pure strength or force, which has nothing to do with the circumstances or the posture of the performer. Example II: An athlete, prior to the act of throwing a disc, first of all, inhales deeply and makes some circular movements in preparation. The strength or force involved in the circular movements of the body here is called 'energy', or 'intrinsic energy' by the practitioners of Tai Chi Ch'uan. In the above examples, the distinction between what is "force" and what is "energy" is manifestly self-explanatory. Furthermore, the direction of strength or force, according to their interpretation, is straight, while that of energy is circular; the nature of the former is 'superficial', while the latter is 'sinking'; the rate of speed of the former is equivalent to stagnation, while the latter is 'expressive'. The object of Tai Chi Ch'uan, after all, is to help people to release this type of 'intrinsic energy'.

(C) The Types of Intrinsic Energy.

The types of 'intrinsic energy' (or Ching) are as follows:

'Stick-Upward', 'Attach', 'Listening', 'Interpretative', 'Running', 'Neutralizing', 'Borrowing', 'Releasing', 'Feint', 'Raising', 'Sinking', 'Hold Fast', 'Split', 'Enclosing', 'Parrying', 'Ward Off', 'Pull Back', 'Press Forward', 'Push', 'Pull Down', 'Bend Backward', 'Elbow-Stroke', 'Rolling', 'Drilling', 'Chopping', 'Cooling', 'Discontinuing', 'Inching', etc. Among these, the most important are the 'Stick-Upward', 'Attach', 'Listening', 'Interpretative', and the 'Neutralizing' Energies. How to apply is the chief method of Tai Chi Ch'uan. If it is properly comprehended and applied, one will have understood deeply the mysteries of this art.[1]

(F) The Three Stages of Applying Energies.

In fact, all the principles regarding the releasing and applying of the different types of 'energy' have been thoroughly examined in the "Theory", "Treatises" and "Classics of Tai Chi Ch'uan". (See Appendices). Due to the limitation of space, what we can do here is to show briefly how we can apply them in action. To counter an attack, the application of 'energies' in different stages may be conveniently illustrated as follows:

[1] The above is by no means an exhausative list of all the types of energy. According to Tung Ying-chieh's classification, there are still some other Ching or Energies, the names of which are: Stick-dynamic, Follow-Close, Light, Alert, Sinking, Raising, Crushing, Twisting, Attaching, Prop-up, Rubbing, Pressing, Penetrating-the-bone, Dashing-Down, Hanging-Up, Wavering, Discharging, Shaking, Prompting, Departing, Suddenness, Tenth-of-an-Inch, Accumulating and Releasing of the Arrow Energy. (See Tung Ying-chieh, *A Treatise on Tai Chi Ch'uan,* 5th edition, p. 70, 1966, Hong Kong.)

A. When the blow from the opponent is imminent.

B. When the blow from the opponent is being felt.

C. When the blow from the opponent has been received.

A. First Stage: The use of 'Feint Energy'.

When the blow is imminent, rely on the 'listening energy' and the 'interpretative energy' to detect the direction of the opponent's strength, and use the 'Feint Energy' as if you were attacking him. Having done this, if the opponent attacks you directly, you should "borrow" or "neutralize" his strength in order to throw him out of balance. If all these techniques are employed skillfully, there should be no difficulty in throwing the opponent swiftly to the ground. In the application of 'Feint Energy', one, of course, has to employ not only hand technique, but also body, step, and waist techniques.

B. Second Stage: The use of 'Neutralizing Energy'.

When the blow is being felt on the body, first one should withdraw from a direct perpendicular blow. Next, the circular movement of the technique of Tai Chi Ch'uan has to be applied in order to 'neutralize' the strength of force of the opponent. The application of the 'Neutralizing Energy', which, as has been pointed out repeatedly, is one of most important techniques of its kind. It depends upon the successsful use of the 'Attaching Energy', and 'Running Energy'. In the meantime, it is also important to apply the 'Ward Off Energy' without which the purpose of 'neutralizing' may not be achieved. Under favorable circumstances, when the 'Neutralizing Energy' is well applied, the opponent will hardly be able to maintain his central equilibrium and would fall if the center of gravity is upset — depending, of course, on the magnitude of the strength on both sides. The main strength in neutralizing the force of the opponent comes from the motivation, the intrinsic energy, and the momentum of the waist and legs.

C. Third Stage: The use of 'Borrowing Energy'.

When the body has received the blow, stand courageously firm and utilize 'Feint Energy' to lead the opponent's strength or force to give way diagonally on the one hand, and to apply the 'Neutralizing Energy', to eliminate or shift his central equilibrium on the other. Under favorable circumstances, one can also use 'Borrowing Energy' — to borrow the opponent's strength or force so as to overcome him. The result would lead to his disintegration. The 'Borrowing Energy', in the light of experience, is, in fact, the most mystic energy (method) that can be applied for self-defense in this art.

The foregoing description deals only with the nature, types and application of 'Intrinsic Energy'. Experienced masters can usually predict with great accuracy when a blow is struck, where it will from and what tactics would be used by the opponent. Finally, under all the conditions mentioned above, one will have no difficulty in solving all the problems that he might encounter.

APPENDICES

I

TAI CHI CH'UAN CHING*
（太極拳經）

* All the classics here have been rendered into English by the present
writer.

In any action, the entire body should be light, alert and coordinated like a string of pearls. The Chi (vital energy, prana in Sanskrit) should be actively excited, but the Shen (spirit) must remain
calm internally. Do not leave any place with defect, uneveness, or
discontinuity and severance. It (energy) is rooted in the feet, stems
in the legs, is commanded or directed by the waist, and functions
through the fingers. Starting from the feet, leading to the legs and
up to the waist, all movements must be acted as an integral whole.
In this way, the favourable chance (time) and the suitable position
(space) can be grasped. In case one fails in mastering these advantages, his body will be in disorder and confusion. The only way
to avoid the pitfall of disintegration is by adjusting one's legs and
waist. This principle applies irrespective of all the directions, above
or below, front or back, left and right.

All these movements are motivated by the mind (or consciousness), not from the externality. When attacking above, one must
not forget below. When striking left, you must pay attention to the
right. When advancing, one must have regard for retreating. If one's

mind is to go upward, one must have the idea of exerting his effort downward. It is similar to the act of lifting something; one has to push down first and the 'root' or attachment will be easily broken, immediately rendering the object free to manoeuver. In principle, it is of utmost importance to distinguish the difference between insubstantiality (emptiness) and substantiality (solid) — (or Yin and Yang); there is distinction at every place, and each place should be taken care of. To repeat, all parts of the body must always be thought of as threaded together, not allowing the slightest severance.

The original note on this classic by Yang Lu-Ch'an (1799-1872) adds: "This is the theory transmitted by Master Chang San-feng of Wu Tang Mountain, with a desire toward helping all the able people of the world to attain longevity and rejuvenation. The technique and art are the least things to be concerned with."

*Note: This classic has been attributed to Chang San-feng, the founder of Tai Chi Ch'uan. It might have been written by Wang Tsung Yueh.

II

THEORY OF TAI CHI CH'UAN
(太極拳論)

by

WANG TSUNG YUEH

Tai Chi — the Supreme Ultimate, evolving from Wu Chi (The Ultimateless), is the origin of movement and quietude, and the Mother of Yin and Yang.

In movement, the two act independently, and, in quietude, they fuse into unity. There should be no excess and no insufficiency.

One should yield at the opponent's slightest pressure and adhere to him at his slightest retreat. To conquer the strong by yielding is termed "withdrawal" (tsou) (走). To improve your position to the detriment of the opponent is called "adherance" (chan) (黏). One should respond quickly to fast action (of the opponent), slowly to slow action. In spite of the myriad changing techniques, the principle remains the same. Through diligent practice, one can gradually "comprehend intrinsic energy" (or tenacious strength), and from this he can advance to the stage of spiritual enlightenment (the knowledge of supernatural). This, however, can never be attained by intuition without arduous and persistent effort for a long time.

The head-top should be emptied, alert, and straight. The chi (breath-energy) should be sunk to the "tan t'ien". The body is held balanced without leaning to any direction. Your opponent should not be able to detect your change from solid to empty or vice versa because of your speed in effecting this change. When your opponent brings pressure on your left side, the left side should be empty. The same holds for the right side. When he pushes upward or downward against you, let him feel as if there were no end to the emptiness he encounters. Advancing, he feels the distance incredibly long; retreating, he feels it exasperatingly short.

The entire body is so sensitive that not a feather will be able to be added and so pliable that a fly cannot alight on it without setting it in motion. Your opponent cannot detect your move, but you can anticipate his. If one can master all these techniques, he will become a peerless hero.

In pugilism there are many unorthodox schools. Although

they differ in form and scale, they can never go beyond reliance on the strong defeating the weak or the swift conquering the slow. Yet these are the results derived from the application of physical endowments (ā priori) and have nothing to do with practical learning and experience.

The saying: "To deflect the momentum of a thousand catties (Chinese pounds) with a trigger force of four taels (Chinese ounces)", shows this cannot be achieved by sheer force.

In view of the fact that an old man can successfully defeat a great number of people, how can this be achieved through reliance on speed?

Stand like a balanced scale; in movement be as a whirling wheel.

Keep your weight sunk on one side. If it is spread onto two feet, the result is stagnant.

There are many who have scored brilliantly in practicing for a number of years, yet are still incapable of performing unpredictable operations and changes. This is due to the lack of comprehension of the fallacy of "Double Weightiness".

In order to avoid this type of fallacy, one must understand Yin and Yang. In the matter of applied techniques, — to "adhere" (stick to) (黏) is also to "withdraw" (走). "To withdraw" is also "to adhere", hence Yin cannot be separated from Yang, nor can Yang be separated from Yin. It is by their complementary nature that one can comprehend what is "intrinsic energy" (tenacious strength).

After having comprehended "intrinsic energy", the more the practice, the greater will be one's own ingenious refinements.

Then, by calm awareness and deliberate consideration, one will gradually find himself to be able to do just as he desires to do.

Basically, one should forget oneself and yield to others, but the prevailing mistake is to overlook the "near", and to attempt what is far "away".

The saying has it: "The slightest divergence leads one far astray". The student should, therefore, distinguish this logically and in detail, — hence the theory.

III

TREATISE ON THE PRACTICE OF THE
THIRTEEN POSTURES (METHODS) —

A Psychological Interpretation

（十三勢行功心解）

by

WU YU-HSIANG

Using the mind to move the Chi (breath, energy, prana) with quiet effort, the Chi may, therefore, be "occluded", (i.e., gathered or stored) into the bones.

Using the Chi (breath) to mobilize the body without hindrance, the body may, therefore, be serviceable and at the desire of the will.

If then Shen (Spirit) can be roused, then there is no reason for anxiety about the clumsiness and heaviness. To achieve this, one would feel as if the top of the head were suspended from above.

Both the Yi (consciousness or idea) and the Chi (breath) must be able to interchange with alertness; then one comes to feel the happiness of activation. And yet these are to be achieved by the changes of insubstantiality (emptiness) and substantiality (firmness).

In the releasing of the Ching (intrinsic energy or tenacious strength), one must be calm and relaxed — concentrating in one direction at a time.

The trunk must be kept standing in perfect erect, centrally-balanced, comfortable and relaxed, so that it can deal with the impacts from any direction.

For the guidance of the Chi (breath), it should be done as if it were circling the "nine-curved string of beads", reaching the tiny cells.

To operate the Ching (intrinsic energy), the flexibility should be like the most refined steel, capable of destroying all the hardness in the world.

In configuration or appearance, one should be alert as a falcon, ready to pounce on a rabbit, — the spirit, as a cat seizing a mouse.

In quietude , one resembles the mountain; in motion, a river.

In storing the Ching (intrinsic energy), the act should be similar to that of drawing a bow. To release it — as if discharging an arrow.

In the midst of the curve, seek the straight. Store first, then release. Strength initiates from the spine. Steps follow changes in the body. To receive (i.e., to "join" or "neutralize") is to release (to attack); to release is to receive. To break is, again, to continue.

To go to and fro, one must have "folds" and "alternations." Advancing and retreating must have "turnings" and "changes."

Through what is extremely "pliable" and "yielding," one achieves what is extremely "rigid" and "unyielding". To be able to regulate inhaling and exhaling, the body can be light and active.

The Chi (breath) must be nourished naturally without hindrance — then no harm will manifest. The Intrinsic Energy (Ching) must be stored in a curve — then there is surplus.

The mind is the command. The Chi (breath) is its banner and the waist is its flagpole.

In postures, first attempt to develop and expand; later, attempt to contract and collect. Then one is capable of attaining perfection and integration (to connect the movement closely together).

It is again said:

First pay attention to the mind — next to the body. Keep the stomach relaxed and calm; the Chi (breath) is gathered into the bones. The spirit is peaceful and the body in a state of tranquility. At every moment, attention has to be paid to the mind.

It must be remembered: One action must involve all actions, and partial quietude leads to total quietude.

In the movements of going forward and backward, the Chi (breath) attaches to the back, gathers into the spine. Inwardly, the spirit is consolidated; outwardly, the expression is leisurely calm.

In steps, one must be as alert as a cat's pawing, whereas in the operation of the Ching (intrinsic energy), it should be similar to that of "reeling of silk", (i.e., circling).

In the entire body, the idea (Yi) centers upon the Spirit (Shen), not upon the Chi (breath). To center upon the Chi leads to stagnancy. To be with the Chi (breath), there will be no strength — not to be with the Chi, there will be pure firmness. (In the Chinese text, it literally reads: "If there is Chi (breath), there will be no strength." This is not easy to understand. But actually, this seems to say that, in the highest stage, the Chi escalates into and unites with the function of Shen (Spirit). Through the Shen, it mobilizes the Chi in an instant — this becomes "Spiritual Strength" or "Spiritual Speed", which resembles thunder or electricity. This is the highest stage — which is known as "Spiritual Enlightenment" and can be attained in Tai Chi Ch'uan.

The Chi (breath) resembles the wheel; the waist is like the wheel's hub.

It is again said:

(In Self-Defense) If the other is not moving, the self does not move. At the other's slightest move (stir), the self moves sooner than he. (The self has already anticipated the movement.)

The Ching (intrinsic energy) seems relaxed but not relaxed (i.e., in the releasing of the "intrinsic energy" — attacking — the act seems loose, yet not loose); about to expand, but not to expand. (In the stretching of the hands, they are not to be absolutely straight.)

The Ching (intrinsic energy) breaks off, but the Yi (consciousness or idea) still continues.

IV

TAI CHI CH'UAN CLASSICS — A REVIEW
by
WEN-SHAN HUANG

Included in the voluminous literature on Tai Chi Ch'uan, particularly those works written in the last few hundred years in China, there are about six or seven Treatises, known as P'u (譜), some important chapters of which should be studied conscientiously and com prehended deeply by students who study this art in its theoretical and practical aspects.

With a view to this goal, a list of the P'us, with explanation, is given as follows:

I. The Sung Family Ch'uan P'u, entitled: *The Tai Chi Kung — Its Origin and School,* is generally attributed to Sung Yuan-Chiao of the Ming Dynasty (A.D. 1368-1644), who traced the origin of the art of Li Tao-tze and Hsu Hsun-ping to the T'ang Dynasty (A.D. 618-907). In this Treatise, Sung mentioned the fact that he had had the benefit of being taught by Chang San-feng in the Hung Wu Period (c. A.D. 1368) of the Ming Dynasty when he visited Wu Tang Mountain, where Chang originated his art.

As far as can be ascertained, this is the earliest and most important ancient historical document in existence regarding Tai Chi Ch'uan or Tai Chi Kung. However, it only became available to the present century when it was publicized by one of their descendants — Sung Shu-ming in Peking in 1919. When Hsu Yu-Sang (1879-1945) wrote his famous book, *The Explanations of the Patterned Movements (Postures) and Diagrams of Tai Chi Ch'uan* in 1919, he based his historical research mostly on this P'u.

The following classics have been attributed to Hsu Hsun-ping by Sung Yuan Chiao himself:

(A) *Song of Eight Characters;*

(B) *The Important Secret of Mind-Realization;*

(C) *Song of the Great Function of the Entire Body;*

(D) *The Secret of Sixteen Key Points,* and

(E) *Song of Functional Application.*

II. Wang Tsung-Yueh's *Tai Chi Ch'uan Treatise* (P'u), another important exposition, was handed down to us by Chen Ch'ang-hsing (1771-1853) of the famous Chen Family in Chen Chia Kuo, Honan Province. According to Wang Yu-yang of the early Ch'ing Dynasty, "In the art of Pugilism, Shao-lin is known as the Exoteric School, while the art of San-feng of Wu Tang is known as the Esoteric School." After Chang (San-feng), Wang Tsung-Yueh, a man of Shi-an, who had obtained the authentic secrets handed down from his Master (Chang), was famous in the whole world. He wrote many ·treatises, exploring the hidden meaning of Tai Chi Ch'uan. Indeed, he is a genius of both civil and military ability. His art was handed down to Chen Chou-tung (陳州同) of Wen Chou (i.e., the Southern School) and Chiang Fa (蔣發) of Honan (i.e., the Northern School).

It was believed that Wang lived in the period of the Emperor of Shih Tsou (Koblai) of the Yuan Dynasty, c. A.D. 1280. Modern research, however, comes to the unproved conclusion that he lived in the Chien Lung Period (1736-1795) of the Ch'ing Dynasty (1644-1912), and prior to his time, Tai Chi Ch'uan consisted only of thirteen postures (methods). Credit is given to him for joining them together into the present continuous structure. Furthermore, due to his brilliant expositions, we have now a systematic and theoretical base of the fundamental principles of Tai Chi Ch'uan, which finally becomes a most successful and independent school of martial art, synthesizing and revolutionizing all the martial arts in China.

His two masterpieces of Treatise, which we have rendered into English here, are:

(A)   *The Theory of Tai Chi Ch'uan*

(B)   *Treatise on the Thirteen Postures* (*methods*) — *a Psychological Interpretation.*   (This has also been attributed to Wu Yu-hsiang 1812-1880).

III.   Chen Hsin's *"The Diagrammatic Explanation of Tai Chi Ch'uan"* is believed to have been handed down by Chen Chang-hsin (陳長興 1771-1853) of Chen Chia Kou (陳家溝). In recent years, Chen Hsin (1849-1929) published his masterpiece by using the above title, the structures and songs of which are so different from the Yang (楊) or Wu (吳) Systems that people begin to suspect that Tai Chi Ch'uan might not have been originated by Chang San-feng, but thought it might be the incorporation of the popular arts among the Northern people and the adoption of some of the postures originated by General Chi Chih-Kuang (戚繼光) (1528-1587) of the Ming Dynasty.   But, in spite of modern criticism, we find that, in the genealogy of the

Chen Family, it has been recorded that their distant ancestor (ninth generation of the Chen family of Chen Chia Kou), Chen Wang-ting (陳王庭), lived in the latter part of the Ming Dynasty and had learned Tai Chi Ch'uan from his servant Chiang Fu, who again had learned it from others.

In the middle of the Ch'ing Dynasty (A.D. 1644-1911), the technique of Tai Chi Ch'uan of the Chen Family was most popular. This is the reason why Yang Fu-Kwei (or Yang Lu Ch'an 1799-1872), the forerunner of the Yang School, went to learn it from the Chen Family, and finally had it transmitted to Peking; hence, the famous Yang School in the contemporary world, Yang Chan-fu (楊澄甫) being the grandson of Yang Lu Ch'an.

IV. Huang Pei-Chia's (黃百家) *Ch'uan P'u.* Huang was the son of Huang Tsung-hsi (黃宗羲) (1610-1695), a foremost social thinker, philosopher, and historian of the Ming-Ching Periods. In his Treatise, he did not use the name Tai Chi Ch'uan, (neither did his father), but he says: "With the Shao-lin (Chinese Karate), the pugilism of the Extoric School (Wai Chia) has attained the climax of its achievements. Chang San-feng, who was a master in Shao-lin himself, again revolutionized it into a new system which is now called Esoteric School (nei Chia). Those who have learned one tenth or two tenths of his art can overcome the Shao-linists very easily." However, in spite of the fact that the principles mentioned in this treatise are the same as those of Wang Tsung Yueh's, the names of the forms and the songs are quite different from what we now have in the Yang System. It is generally believed that the art of this Southern School has been lost altogether.

V. *Yang Chia Chuan P'u.* Altogether in nine chapters, it

consists mainly of the oral teachings of the Yang masters, edited by their pupils.

The famous Treatise known as *"Tai Chi Ch'uan Ching"* (a classic, which we have rendered into English in the above), has been generally attributed to Chang San-feng, but, as a matter of fact, the appendix was written by Yang Fu-Kwei (Lu Ch'an) who added that this was originally handed down by Chang San-feng.

V. Li Yik-She's (李亦畬) (1833-1892) *Chuan P'u.* Li learned Tai Chi Ch'uan from his mother's brother, Wu Yu-hsiang (1812-1880), an eminent master, who acquired his knowledge of this art from Chen Ching-ping (陳淸萍) (1795-1868), also of the Chen Family of the Chen Chia-Kuo. The ten chapters of his treatise were written by Li himself.

Although the above list may not have exhausted the sources of Tai Chi Ch'uan, it, we believe, includes all the important documents exploring the secrets of this art — an art for the prolongation of life, or rejuvenation on the one hand, and for self-defense on the other.

For some of the recent publications and writings on the subject, see the bibliography in Chinese and English at the end of this book.

THE SONG OF THE THIRTEEN POSTURES

The thirteen postures should never be overlooked. The source of Ming (命) (Ming is the beginning of Chi or breath, yet itself is not Chi, but is where Chi is produced; Ming connotes material form, while I (意) is idea and connotes spiritual form.) is in the waist. Attention must be paid to the changes from substantiality to insubstantiality, and vice versa. The Chi should be rendered to flow through the the entire body without stagnation.

When one meets a forceful action while in quietude, one's reaction should not be separated from quietude (calmness). In this way, the changes of the technique in accordance with the attacking of the opponent express the mystery of the art. Moreover, one should pay attention constantly to every posture, and try to understand what its function is. It really takes lots of work to be successful.

Attention should also be paid to the waist at all times. When the abdomen is completely relaxed, the Chi can be moved upward instantaneously.

When the spine is held erect, the spirit moves to the top of the head. Holding the head as if it were suspended from above, the whole body feels light and nimble. If one carefully considers his posture, the movements of 'curve-expansion' and 'open-close' can be made automatically.

Oral guidance for the studying and its attainment are indeed necessary. Practice should be continued without stoppage, while its method must depend upon one's own diligent study.

With regard to the standard of reality and function, the mind and the Chi command all the movements, while the bones and muscles become obedient.

If one asks what is the chief purpose of this exercise, the answer is: the prolongation of life and rejuvenation without feeling senility.

The above song consists of one hundred and forty characters (in Chinese), of which every word implies truth, nothing but truth. If one does not study and consider it carefully, he may end in absolute failure with deep repentance.

THE ART OF GLOWING HEALTH:

A MODERN SYSTEM OF BALANCED EXERCISE,

SELF MASSAGE, AND BREATHING RHYTHMS

DRAWN FROM THE WISDOM OF TAOISM, ZENNISM AND ACUPUNCTURE OF ANCIENT CHINA

TABLE OF CONTENTS

INTRODUCTION

by

James C. Ingebretsen, President

Academy of Creative Education, San Jacinto, Calif.

In seeking ways to help modern man live in more creative relationships with himself and other persons, and the physical and psychic gains and strains of a technologically oriented society, the
Academy explores and uses many techniques of self-enhancement and
renewal — spiritual, psychological, physical, artistic, mental. Among
the most valuable and stimulating of these we must include the Cultural Exercises developed, and simplified for western use by Professor
Wen-Shan Huang out of his wide knowledge and experience of the
ancient psycho-physiological methods used by the Chinese elite to
promote spiritual and bodily vitality and well-being.

It is impossible in a few words to praise this little book highly
enough. Only a few moments a day devoted with thoughtful attention to Professor Huang's suggestions could add years to one's life,
and undreamed of dimensions to one's conscious vitality and effective
relationships.

What makes these exercises uniquely valuable to contemporary
men and women, especially those of the West, is the fact that they are
primarily based on the ideas of drawing in, conserving and channeling
energies normally untapped. Much of western calisthenics seeks to
promote physical well-being mainly by strengthening muscles through

the outpouring of energies which might better be used for other purposes. Whatever might have been said, in earlier days, in favor of
those strenuous exercises which give us bigger and tenser biceps and
thighs, it is clear today that what man needs is not more bigness or
more tension, but more suppleness, more lightness. We need the
ability to move freely, especially at the mental, emotional and psychological levels, in continuous response to new and unexpected challenges and developments at every hand. Our world is in constant
flow and we need great resources of pliant energy to maintain creative
harmony with our changing surroundings. Thus these ancient exercises, which aim at linking body, mind and spirit in supple flowing
relationships, are virtually made to order for the demands of modern
life.

The emphasis in these exercises is always on the discovery and
containment of new energy, and its transformation to higher levels,
not on energy expenditure. The strength and skill sought is not
direct physical strength and skill to overcome adversaries, or to tame
the outer world of nature (though such skill and strength may follow).
The emphasis is rather on the development of one's own deeper inner
resources and on the tapping and drawing in of energy from cosmic
levels. Energy is not poured out, but is drawn in. Though this must,
and can, be experienced more fully than it can be described, one need
only watch a master like Professor Huang at work to feel in the most
direct way the tremendous energy expressed and held in by the quiet,
sweeping, circular, cyclic movements of the exercises. In the more
advanced form of the ritual Tai Chi Ch'uan described by Professor
Huang in this volume, one sees vividly how sharply different the
movements are from the harsh, angular movements which characterize
much of western physical culture.

Perhaps most significant is the fact that these are not mere physical exercises. They are exercises in psycho-physiological control and relationship. It is through focused attention and intense concentration on both the letter and spirit of what one is doing that results come. These are not violent actions to engage the arms and legs while our mind flits here and there. These are basically intellectual and spiritual disciplines which use the body to complete the expression of a growth at much deeper levels.

Even at the level of physical expression, there is a difference. It is not arms and legs or muscles so much as it is the wrists, ankles, fingers, knees and spine with which we're working. The key is not at all brute strength in muscles but suppleness in joints.

Finally there is the always present emphasis on rhythmic interchange between firmness and softness, the feminine as well as the masculine, what the Taoists know as the Yin and the Yang — almost altogether missing in western life and exercise. Yet, as the Chinese believe, and as our Academy experiments confirm, here is a key concept on which a balanced and harmonious life in the midst of today's distractions may wisely be based for integration and growth.

It is a great pleasure to recommend this book and all it teaches in the conviction that any who seriously try to implement its teaching will find a new and satisfying way of life always and increasingly opening towards new horizons of awareness and vitality.

PREFACE

by Wen-Shan Huang

Glowing health is the objective of every man and woman.
Glowing health means to be active, dynamic, happy and peaceful,

in body and mind, on the one hand, and to build an effective prevention against tension, pain, sickness and infection, on the other.

To enjoy glowing health, exercise is absolutely necessary. Physical exercise is important, but it is not enough. Oriental philosophy has long testified that spirit and body are inter-related — not only inter-related, but are unified into an integral organism. Thus, according to the Chinese idea, the physical and the spiritual aspects of man's health are not dualistic, as many people are apt to believe, but are monistic.

The Chinese cultural system of exercise, as synthesized in this guidebook, is intended, if practised regularly as a whole, for fitness, both physical and spiritual, of the individual organism.

Most of the elements of this system have a tradition of more than a thousand years of history in the Far East. First originating in China, they were gradually transmitted to Japan, Korea and other countries.

The system consists of three aspects which are:

A. CULTURAL PHYSICAL EXERCISES

B. CULTURAL SELF MASSAGE

C. CULTURAL BREATHING RHYTHMS

The three aspects can be learned in a short time as a whole, and are suitable to every individual, man or woman, young or old. One may take one aspect and practice it regularly and omit the others, but for older people, the practice of the three aspects is more preferable. All the aspects can be taken in the morning and evening for about 15 to 20 minutes each time, but older people who have more leisure at their disposal may spend about 25 to 30 minutes for their own benefits.

To summarize, it may be said that this system may have something extraordinary to offer to the world and even though some of the traditional cultural traits and patterns are disintegrating under the impact of modern technological civilization, perhaps the future will be benefited by their philosophy and art of health.

The present system is, therefore, presented in the interest of humanity.

Most of the ideas and methods incorporated in this booklet were first presented in different form in lectures at the American Academy of Chinese Culture and the Academy of Creative Education. In presenting this little book to my western readers I want to express my deep gratitude to Mr. James C. Ingebretsen, President of the above-mentioned Academy and Executive Vice President of the Foundation of Social Research, San Jacinto, California, from whom I have learned much that I could not have learned from anyone else. His assistance and insight enabled me to devote much of my time to a thorough study of the Taoist art for health and to the development of the basic ideas and methods which are so fundamental to the Chinese practices I have tried to introduce to the American public in this book. I am also indebted to Mr. and Mrs. Ingebretsen for their careful revision of the original version after numerous teaching experiments at their Academy in the beautiful environment of the San Jacinto Mountains near Los Angeles.

I wish to thank Dr. Judith M. Tyberg, President of the East and West Cultural Center, Inc., in Los Angeles for her courteous permission in allowing me to teach this Glowing Art of Health in her school. I also feel a special debt of gratitude to Mr. Justin Stone, formerly lecturer at U.C.L.A., Japan and India (composer member of A.S.C.A.P.) for his sincere service in correcting my mistakes. His keen interest in Tai Chi Ch'uan, Tibetan Yoga, Taoism, Buddhism Vedanta, and psychology clarified my understanding in this study in the light of Oriental philosophy. Ben Huang, M.A. (Berkeley), my son, has helped me working out some of the illustrations here set forth. I am grateful also to my daughter Nancy Huang for typing the manuscript.

American Academy of Chinese Culture, Inc.
Los Angeles, California
1965

Wen-Shan Huang

SECTION I

SPECIFIC PRINCIPLES UPON WHICH

THE SYSTEM IS BASED.

Good health, the prolongation of life and immortality, have always been the objectives of the Far Eastern people — the Chinese, Indian and Japanese. From the early beginning, the Taoists, who tapped some of the secrets of the universe, knew the function of the human organism and suggested different techniques for the attainment of this objective. It is no wonder that Professor Joseph Needham of Cambridge in his famous book, *Science and Civilization in China,* declared that they had much to teach the world, and perhaps the future belongs to their philosophy.

Indeed, the objects of their philosophy and techniques for the prolongation of life were to become a 'Hsien', or a "True Man" (Chen Jen), which meant that one would go on living forever (Chang Seng) with a youthful body in a kind of earthly paradise. Their practices for Hsien-ship fall into several categories:

1. Gymnastic techniques (physical cultural exercises)
2. Massage techniques (self cultural massage for natural healing)
3. Respiratory techniques (cultural breathing exercises)
4. Heliotherapeutic techniques (the method of wearing the sun rays)
5. Dietary techniques (adequate diets to rejuvenate the human body)

6. Alchemical and pharmaceutical techniques (elixir for the prevention of ageing)

7. Sexual techniques.

Our present system, while allowing the importance of the other techniques for health, chooses to emphasize only three categories, viz: (a) Cultural Physical Exercises, (b) Cultural Self Massage, and (c) Cultural Breathing Rhythms.

In order to grasp the philosophic principles upon which the Chinese traditional culture in general, and physical culture in particular, are based, one needs to understand their organic (or cosmic) philosophy which considers man as part of the living universe.

Each major culture system of the world is based upon certain premises or certain ultimate principles, whose development, differentiation, and articulation makes the total ideology of a supersystem. This is a truism in modern Culturology — a new science of culture. The Far Eastern cultural system, particularly of China, is based upon Tai Chi or Tao as expressed in *I Ching, the Book of Changes:* "One Yin and one Yang is Tao", and Tao is Tai Chi — the Grand Ultimate principle of the universe. In *Shuo Kua, Discussion the Trigrams,* it says: "In ancient times the holy sages made the Book of Changes thus: Their purpose was to follow the order of their nature and of fate. Therefore they determined the Tao of heaven and called it the Yin and the Yang. They determined the Tao of the earth and called it the yielding and the firm. They determined the Tao of man and called it love and rectitude."

Historically, the Chinese and many of the Far Eastern people conceived the entire universe, developed from Tai Chi or Tao, as activated by two principles, the Yin and the Yang, the negative and the positive, and they considered that nothing that exists, either animate or inanimate, does so except by virtue of ceaseless interplay of these two forces. Matter and Energy (Chi), Yang and Yin, Heaven and Earth are conceived as essentially one, or as two co-existent poles of one indivisible whole.[1] In this 'One Law': "Yin activity and Yang activity attract one another. Nothing is wholly Yin nor wholly Yang. Yin and Yang are characterized only relatively; all is Yin and Yang aggregate. Nothing is neutral. Polarisation is ceaseless and everywhere." (See Nyoiti Sakurazawa, *Principe Unique de la philosophie,* Paris. 1958).

With this truism in view Chuangtzu, the chief follower of Laotze, said, "Heaven and Earth and I are of the same root, the ten thousand things and I are of the one substance." Hence, no wonder the Taoist, Neo-Confucianist and even the Zen Buddhist come to the same

[1] Felix Mann, *Acupuncture, the Ancient Chinese Art for Healing,* Random House, New York, 1963.

In bypassing, it may be pointed out that on the basis of the same principle in China, it has been becoming increasingly common to administer anaesthesia by acupuncture. In Peking alone in 1971, 1,200 such operations were carried out. The advantages of the method over drug-induced anaesthesia are considerable: it is cheaper, easier to administer and has no after-effects. It can be administered in a clinic instead of in a hospital.

It may be added that "Acupunctural anaesthesia" (針刺麻醉) has been discovered by China's medical workers. Using acupuncture instead of anaesthetics to induce analgesia is a break-through in surgical anaesthetization. It is a tremendous contribution to the development of medical science.

Two main physiological effects: the analgesic effect and the regulating effect are produced by needling certain points. It is precisely these effects that help increase the patient's endurance to withstand the operative procedure and reduce his sensitivity to pain. It does not need complicated apparatus; it is applicable regardless of equipment, climate and geographical conditions. It helps prevent disorder in the patient's physiological functions during the operation and, after its completion, avoid harmful effects from the use of anaesthetics."

Actually most of the basic principles of Tai Chi Ch'uan and the Cultural Exercise System described in this book have been drawn from the System of Acupuncture.

conclusion that the universe is a super-organism and human being is a micro-organism. But, it must be pointed out that the underlying principle in nature's unique law between the pair of opposites — Yin and Yang — is harmony, balance or equilibrium, or more exactly, the Vital Centre. Where one of the poles predominates, the Vital Centre is lacking. Extremism is not correct because there exists no axis around which the bipolar whole harmoniously revolves. The wrong form which lacks the centre, has no equilibrium. The Taoists, therefore, insisted, "To embrace the Centre and guard the Unity of Oneness, the Heaven and Earth become an organic whole." To gain awareness of this Oneness — the way of the 'Mean' — is precisely man's raison d'etre.

Tai Chi or Tao is the First Principle or basic premise of the Chinese or Far Eastern culture. Every aspect of this culture — art, science, politics, ethics and medicine — has been deeply rooted in this tradition. The secret of the Chinese Health System — physical, somatic, psychological or spiritual — comes from the practice of the principle of Yin-Yang. The task of physical therapy and the aim of any exercise is to keep or restore the physiology of the metabolism in natural equilibrium.

The Nei Jing (Ching) (Chap. 5), a Chinese classic of about 400 B.C., which embodies the whole oriental medical structure, has this to say:

"The Yin and the Yang are contained within the Tao, the basic principle of the entire universe. They create all matter and its trans-mutations. The Tao is the beginning and the end; life and death; and it is found within the Temples of the Gods. If you wish to cure disease, you must find the basic cause."

Felix Mann, an English scientist, adds:

"Not only do they still retain their importance in Chinese medicine today, but the practice and technique built upon that foundation is becoming, to an ever-increasing extent, incorporated into the modern scientific medical curriculum, not only in China and Japan, but in Europe also — in France, Germany, Austria, Belgium, Switzerland, Italy and Russia."2

The monistic conception of the universe — Tai Chi or Tao — as set forth in the *I Ching* and *Tao Teh Ching,* is different from the dualistic conception that is set forth in the works of Aristotle, Descartes and Newton. While dualism sees physical and metaphysical as two separate entities, the Chinese views of Yin and Yang are eternally complimentary and eternally changing. The dualistic conception reigned supreme in Western civilization, dominating the development of modern science. But, with the advent of atomic physics, theories based on the formula of Einstein on the one hand and demonstrable experiment on the other, were seen to negate the dualistic philosophy and the trend of thought since then has led back towards the monistic conception of the Confucianists and the Taoists.

With varying acceptability of statement, monistic and organismic thought run through all modern investigations in methodology and world-view of natural and cultural sciences. The organismic philosophy of Whitehead, the Gestalt psychology of Kohler, the emergent evolution of Morgan, the holism of Smuts, the integralism of Sorokin, the realism of Sellers, and above all, the cosmic field theory of Einstein, point to the same trend. Now, if this thread is traced backwards, it leads through Hegel, Lotze, Schelling and Herder to Leibniz. Leibniz in the 18th century, had studied the doctrine of Neo-Confu-

2 Felix Mann, *Acupuncture, The Ancient Chinese Art of Healing,* London, 1962. Forward by Aldous Huxley, p. 1.

cianism of Chu Hsi, as it was transmitted to him through the Jesuits' translations and dispatches[1].

In this space age, the integration of knowledge for the development of glowing health is absolutely necessary. If humanity mobilizes all its wisdom, knowledge, beauty and especially its reverance for life and 'love energy' — then a most magnificient new era of human culture will certainly be ushered in.[2] As Lawson-Wood has wisely said, "We feel that Western progress in 'Glowing Health Wisdom' could be very much speeded up if only the relatively simple Yin-Yang principle were made more widely known to and understood by the West."[3] It is up to mankind to decide what it will do with its destiny in the future.

[1] See Joseph Needham, *Science and Civilization in China,* Cambridge University Press, Vol. III, p. 261.

2. For the theory of 'love energy' see Pitirim A. Sorokin, *Altruistic Love: A Study of American Good Neighbors and Christian Saints.* Boston: Beacon Press, 1950; *Explorations in Altruistic Love and Behavior* (Symposium). Boston: Beacon Press, 1950; *The Ways and Power of Love.* Boston: Beacon Press, 1952. *Forms and Techniques of Altruistic and Spiritual Growth* (Symposium). Boston: Beacon Press, 1954.

3. Lawson-Wood, *Chinese System of Healing,* London, 1963, p. 5.

SECTION II

ORIENTATION

THE TEN FUNDAMENTAL TREASURES.

This section consists in an explanation of the ten fundamental exercises, or "Treasures", as they are traditionally known in the East. The whole series can be done in five minutes, and should be done once or twice daily. The exercises may be taken independently, or in conjunction with the Cultural Self Massages, Cultural Breathing Rhythms and Tai Chi Ch'uan.

The following are some general notes on the conduct of the TEN FUNDAMENTAL TREASURES:

1. During the exercises, breathing should be natural, but deep breathing by sinking the Chi (or Vital energy, prana: the vital principle in the human body which can be energized by means of regulated breath and meditation for the sublimation of the body and mind) to the T'an Tien (the Vital center or the Field of Elizir, in the terminology of the Taoists) or two and a half inches below the navel (which is the centre of your physical universe) is most desirable. Use the nostrils to inhale and exhale. Always relaxed and harmonious, the tongue should touch the palate.

2. Stand with torso erect, and keep spinal column in the center. Take the position balancing on the opposite legs at an approximate shoulder-width.

3. When the legs are bent in the "riding-horse step", maintain

an erect posture, leaning neither forward nor backward. Reduce the degree of hardship in the first stage of the exercise, particularly in this type of step. Do not pull too low.

4. During the exercise in most postures, the eyes should follow the movement of the hands.

5. The exercises should be practiced slowly and in a relaxed manner. Do not use strenuous force or move too rapidly. No part of the body should be under tension, thereby permitting the Chi or vital energy to reach all parts of the organism.

6. Repeat each exercise or posture ten times or if there is sufficient time, increase it to 20 times.

7. After exercising, a short walk will restore the respiration and muscles to normal condition.

Exercise 1.

"The Change of Sinews". (Yi Chin) (易筋)

Benefits: Breath is the flywheel of life. If one learns to breathe by diligient practice of this exercise, one will be able to balance the Yin-Yang energy of the body and to keep the physiology of the metabolism in natural equilibrium.

1. Stand upright and separate the feet to a distance approximately equal to the width of the shoulders. With the head erect, eyes gazing to the front, keep the mind on the T'an Tien or the 'Vital Center' of the body. Put hands against the thighs, with palms turning downward and fingers pointing forward.

2. Raise the two arms slowly to the chest, breathing in. Push hands forward, with a stretching movement, until the arms are extended, wrists bent, palms pointing forward and fingers upward, breathing out.

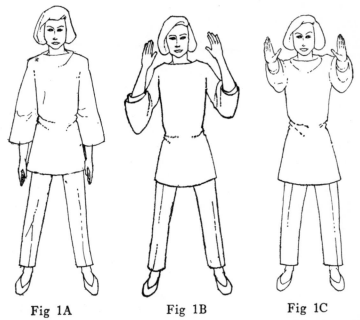

Fig 1A   Fig 1B   Fig 1C

3. While maintaining the stretch, move the hands fully to the left and right with the palms turning upward. At the same time, breathe in and try to visualize the Chi, or vital energy, arriving at the tips of the fingers.

4. Turn palms and slowly lower the hands to the original position with palms facing the thighs. While breathing out, bend slightly at the knees, keeping a straight posture, and allow the hands and arms to swing across each other in front of the stomach. As exhalation ends, swing hands first to the two sides, and then raise hands above the head with palms facing upward, breathing in. While raising hands, return to a standing position from that of the bent knees.

5. Finally, while exhaling, slowly bring the arms and hands with palms in full swing to the sides reaching the thighs. Restore to the original position.

6. Repeat ten times.

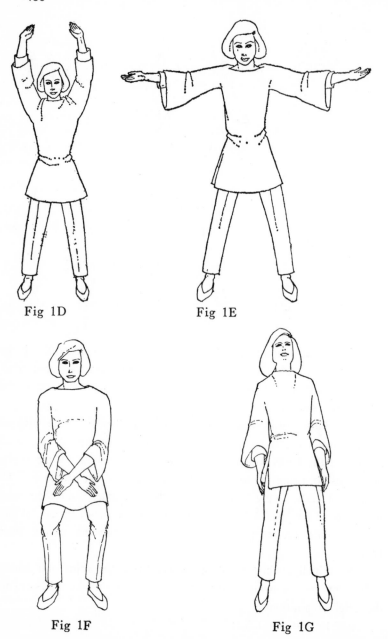

Fig 1D

Fig 1E

Fig 1F

Fig 1G

Exercise 2.

"Uphold the Heaven with Two Hands to Alleviate the Three Heaters." (Liang Sh'ou Toh Tien Li San Ch'iao) (兩手托天理三焦)

Benefits: The purpose of this exercise is to develop the strength-tone of the organism and to harmonize the energy or the Yin-Yang vital force. According to the theory of Chinese Acupuncture, the three heaters have the following functions: the superior heater, Shang Chiao, has the respiratory function; the central heater, Chung Chiao, the digestive function; the inferior heater, Hsia Chiao, the sexual function. It is only through the intermedium of the 'triheaters' that the human organism can absorb and transfer the vital energy necessary to life.[1]

1. Stand erect with feet parallel to each other at shoulders' width and with arms level in front of the abdomen — the fingers intertwined and palms facing upward.

2. Raise the body by standing on the toes, while simultaneously raising the intertwined hands above the head, turning the palms over and again upward and look upward at the back of the palms.

3. While raising body and hands, breathe in, then return to the original position, breathing out. Repeat ten times. (Fig. 2)

Exercise 3.

"The Harmonizing of the spleen and the stomach by raising the hands separately." (T'ao Li Wei Chi T'an Chu Sh'ao) (調理胃氣單舉手)

Benefits: The purpose of the exercise is to harmonize and adjust

---

[1] See Wu Wei-ping, *Chinese Acupuncture*, Health Science Press, England, 1962. Tr. with note by J. Lavier.

Fig 2   Fig 3

the various regions and energy of the body, particularly the stomach and spleen and the energy circulating through or co-ordinating the internal organs. According to the theory of Acupuncture, the Meridian (channel of energy) of the stomach extends a conjunctive channel to the Meridian of the spleen.

1. Stand erect, with arms hanging evenly before the chest, elbows pointing out to the side, fingers opposing each other and palms facing upwards.

2. Turn the left palm and lift it upward above the head with palm facing upward, and eyes following the palm. At the same time the right hand is lowered to the thigh, palm facing downward, with fingers pointing the front.

3. While the left hand is lowered downward to the left thigh, lift the right hand upward with palm facing upward, the eyes following the palm.

4. Return to the original position and repeat the movement on the left side. Count ten. (Fig. 3)

Exercise 4.

"Looking backward for the prevention of Consumption."
(Wu lau chi shang wang hou chiao) (五勞七傷往後瞧)

Fig 4

Benefits: The purpose of this exercise is to develop or strengthen the Meridian of the lungs, which commences at the 'center heater' (the stomach). The pathway extends to the lungs, mounts to the throat, emerges at the sub-clavicular area and becomes superficial at the first point of the Meridian near the shoulder, then running down the arm to the fingers; there the pathway descends the anterior surface of the arm and passes to the bend of the elbow. The looking backward posture is designed also to strengthen and tone the muscles of the chest as well as the neck.

1. Stand erect with hands resting near the thighs, palms facing

inward.

    2.   Turn head slowly to the left and look backward as far as possible, dipping and turning the left shoulder but without twisting the waist, feeling the pull in the muscles over the right chest.

    3.   After returning to the preparatory position, repeat same movement at the right side. Count ten. (Fig. 4)

Exercise 5.

"Opening the Bow to the left and right as if to shoot a hawk.' (Tso yu kai kung szu hsieh tiao) (左右開弓似射雕)

Physical Benefits: The superficial purpose of this exercise is to strengthen the muscles of the shoulders and the arms, as well as to expand the chest so as to increase the active capacity and resiliency of the lungs.

Fig 5A

Fig 5B

1. Stand erect with legs close together.

2. Take one big step to the left, forming a "riding horse step", shifting 70% of your weight to the left foot rooted to the ground and have both feet pointing squarely forward. Simultaneously, cross the arms in front of the chest with right fist inside, the left fist otside, the thumb and index finger of the left fist pointing upward as if holding a bow.

3. Now stretch the left arm straight to the left as if pulling a bow forward, with head and eyes following the arrow, (in this case, the thumb and the index finger). At the same time, the right arm is pulled to the right from the shoulder with elbow staying bent, as if pulling back on the bow string.

4. Return to position 2 and repeat five times.

5. Stand erect and then repeat the movements on the right side, hands and weight reversed. (Fig. 5A and 5B)

Exercise 6.

"Shaking the head and waving the tail in order to get rid of the "Heart's Fire." (Yao tou pai wei chu hsin fou) (搖頭擺尾去心火 **)**

Benefits: This exercise stimulates digestion, circulation, nervous system and glands and also helps to reduce the waist.

1. Stand erect, take a step to the left, then bend knees into a "riding horse step" weight balanced, feet flat, knees above toes.

2. Hold the two knees (or for beginners, the thighs) with palms of the hands, thumbs on the outside of the thighs and fingers on the inside.

3. Holding legs and knees in place, bend the left elbow and twist the torso to the left as far as possible. Return and repeat the same movement to the right, alternating five counts on each side.

Fig 6

4. After coming back to the original position, lean torso backward as far as possible, keeping spine straight and knees and thighs in place with hands. Next, lean torso forward. Repeat back and forth ten times. (Fig. 6)

Exercise 7.

"Holding the fists tightly and gazing with angry eyes in order to increase the strength." (Tsan chun nu mo tsang chi li) (攢拳怒目增氣力)

Benefits: Refreshing and invigorating, this exercise strengthens the metabolism and keeps the vital organs in excellent health. All the movements tend to be 'firm' rather than 'yielding'.

1. Preparatory Posture: Take one big step to the left, bend the knees into "riding horse step". Hold clenched fists tightly upwards at waist level, elbows close to sides.

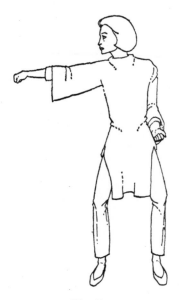

Fig 7

2. With utmost firmness, thrust the left clenched fist diagonally to the front, turning the fist over so it faces down when fully extended.

3. Return to the preparatory position. Repeat the exercise on the right side, alternating five times on each side.

4. Return to preparatory position, thrust the left arm and fist straight out to the left side, turning the fist over the following movement with head and eyes. Repeat the movements on the right side, turning head to right. Alternate, counting five on each side. (Fig. 7)

Exercise 8.

"Abdominal lift for the stimulation of the internal organs."
(Ti tou tzu yin li Tsang Fu) (貼肚自運理臟腑)

Benefits: This exercise has been designed for the stimulation and the strengthening of the internal organs which according to Acu-

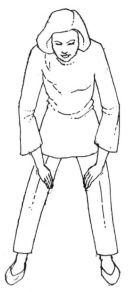

Fig 8

puncture, are divided into two basic categories. The Tsang (including heart, liver, spleen, kidneys, lungs and the heart-constrictor (which is really a function, and not an organ) are those organs which function continually; they are concerned with the circulation of the blood and are Yin in nature. The Fu (including large intestine, stomach, bladder, gall-bladder, the small-intestine and tri-heaters) are those organs of an intermittent physiology; they are concerned with nutrition and excretion, and are Yang in nature.

The exercise may also help to reduce excess weight, abdominal fat and get rid of gas.

1. Take the "horse-riding step" position and press the hands against the thighs, fingers to the rear.

2. Bend head and push forward in a low position. Exhale vigorously and completely. With the breath out, contract the abdominal and gluteal muscles as far as possible. In other words, pull

upon the navel with a strong and substantial effort until the breath is out.

3. Maintain this posture as long as possible, then release the contraction, rise and inhale deeply several times to restore to normal condition.

4. Exert maximum effort, for five or ten counts.

Exercise 9.

"Jump with toes to prevent all kinds of illnesses." (P'ei hou chi t'ien pei ping shiou) (背後七顛百病消)

Benefits: This exercise will keep the body shapely and all the organs in divine health. If practiced daily, the nervous system will ever remain youthful and strong.

1. Preparatory Posture: Stand erect, lower the hands beside the thighs, put weight on toes, bending the knees, heels slightly off the ground.

2. Jump lightly upward, with knees straightening at peak, and bending on return with heels following toes to the ground.

3. Repeat ten times without pause.

Exercise 10.

"To hold the toes with two hands for the strengthening of the kidneys." (Lian shou pan chu ku shien you) (兩手攀足固腎腰)

Benefits: This exercise helps to increase the elasticity of the waist and to start sluggish circulation to the brain. As it will definitely stimulate the kidneys, it helps the body to carry off toxic accumulations and gives the body fresh energy.

1. Preparatory Posture: Stand erect, separate feet at shoulders'

Fig 10

width. Bend arms at waist level in front of the stomach, palms facing the ground.

    2.   While keeping legs straight, bend torso, turn fingers downward and palms facing toes, touching or holding the toes with finger tips.

    3.   Return to preparatory position, repeat ten times. (Fig. 10)

SECTION III

CULTURAL SELF MASSAGE ORIENTATION

"The Initiative Massage", as the Cultural Self Massage is known in the Orient, has been transmitted from ancient times to the present. It has been employed by the Chinese people for more than 3,000 years. Some experts are of the opinion that modern massage is founded upon their system. The most valuable Swedish massage, so admirably elaborated by Henrik Lang (1776-1839), might have been influenced by the Chinese system, which was introduced to Europe by the Jesuits in the 18th century.

Massage, or systematic rubbing of the tissues and muscles of the human organism, aims at the manipulation not only of the head, face, shoulders, chest, abdomen, spine and feet, but also at the toning up of the organs, joints, glands and nervous system for the relief of bodily infirmities and prolongation of health. We often hear of "Russian massage", "French massage", "German Massage", "Swedish Massage", "Japanese massage", and "English Massage", but only the Taoist Massage in China is accomplished by focusing attention on the vital points on the Meridians. According to the concepts of ancient masters in the art of medicine of the Chinese healing system known as Acupuncture, the Ching, or the Meridians, which are in direct correspondence with the energy mutations of the internal organs, are a series of points upon the skin, yet so minute are the Meridians that dissection cannot reveal them. For example, as it has been pointed out by Felix Mann, "the 'heart meridian which is associated with the functions of the heart, runs down the inside of the arm.

Therefore in the majority of heart diseases, particularly in angina pectoris, the pain felt, runs along the course of this meridian."[3]

There are twelve meridians which are: lung, large intestine, stomach, spleen, heart, small intestine, bladder, kidney, circulation — sex (function of circulation and sex), Tri-heaters (function of nervous energy and warmth), gall bladder and liver. The eight channels outside the Meridians have been classified into two groups, according to polarity.[4] First, the channels reuniting the Yang energy are: Yang Wei Mei; Yang channel of the ankle; Yang Ch'iao Mei; channel of the waist, Tai Mei; governing channel, Tu Mei; the above are on the Yang side. Secondly, channel reuniting the Yin energy: Yin Wei Mei; Yin channel in the ankle; Yin Ch'iao Mei; channel of the groin, Ch'ung Mei; channel of the conception, Jen Mei. All the above are on the Yin side.

The pathways of the Meridians are symmetrical and bi-lateral, as are those of the channels, with the exception of the last two channels, those of the Tu Mei (Governor channel) and Jen Mei (Conception channel), which have a single trajectory. The Tu Mei runs along the posterior and the Jen Mei along the anterior median lines of the body. The Chi, or the energy of life, flows through the twelve meridians in a constant flux, and on its unimpeded flow depends the health of the body and organs. And we are indebted to Felix Mann's research — we know that "the arrangement of the meridians follows one of the basic laws of embryology and comparative anatomy, in which it is stated that phylogeny repeats ontogeny; in other words,

[3] Felix Mann, *Acupuncture, The Ancient Chinese Art of Healing,* London, 1963, p. 10.

[4] Wu Wei-Ping, *Chinese Acupuncture,* tr. by J. Lavier, Health Science Press, England, 1962.

the evolution of the animal kingdom repeats, in a certain way, the evolution of the embryo."[5]

The Cultural Self Massage, the oldest form of natural healing used by the Taoists, acts upon every nerve Meridian — the Vital Points in the human body. It promotes better circulation, refreshes weak muscles, prevents adhesions, and helps to harmonize the internal organs through the manipulation of the points upon the skin.

The system of Cultural Self Massage may be divided into two basic types, the local massage and the whole body massage.

While the first type focuses only on a localized area of the body and is used for the relief of temporary pain; the second type pays attention to practically all the important Vital Points of the whole body, and is used in daily practice for glowing health by health seekers, gerontologists, and even to some extent by practitioners of modern Neuropractic.

It is impossible to mention all the Vital Points in the human body, but a careful examination of all the Meridians and Channels (which does not require a great amount of time) will help us to trace their paths into and relationships with the deeper organs.

With regard to the technique of self massage, the palms and tips of the fingers on both hands are used in various ways. Rubbing is usually performed with the full palm of the hand. In general, finger rubbing, which may be firm and rapid, can be applied to arms, fingers, toes, legs, feet and joints. Circular movements on the heart, chest and stomach should be performed with the palm. Vibratory movements of the hands are not required. Whenever pressure is used, the pressure is directed downward.

---

[5] Felix Mann, *Acupuncture, The Ancient Chinese Art of Healing,* London 1963, pps. 15-17.

With all the techniques, the object is to influence the muscles, the deep-lying tissus and the nerve fibers, in order to aid the metabolism, as well as to stimulate the skin to activity. These are simple and can be operated without much experience. In the beginning, it seems as if nothing extraordinary were happening, but as one persists, gradually special results will appear: bright eyes, a clear complexion, a calm disposition.

The study of Cultural Self Massage makes it imperative for the operator to know some aspects of Acupuncture. Those who are philosophically inclined are also highly recommended to go into its theory on which the principles of this type of massage are mainly based.

Anyone, with no more knowledge of acupuncture than is here presented, can benefit enormously by the use of the massage techniques. Nor is it necessary to believe that the theory of acupuncture is valid to reap the benefits of the massage itself. However, it is strongly recommended that those who desire to take full advantage of the suggestions here made should at least become familiar with the general principles and philosophies of acupuncture. Either of the two books mentioned above provide a good introduction and summary.

A. Head and Facial Massages.

Benefits: These combined massages invigorate the nerve center of the cerebrum (Cerebral Cortex), increase the blood circulation and stimulate glandular activity. They keep the face from unnecessary wrinkles, benefit the eyes, teeth, tongue and tonsils, keep the thyroid and pituitary glands in good shape, stimulate the growth of hair and help to prevent colds and strokes.

Head Massage:

a) Place the left palm on the top of the head, and with a rotating movement, rub lightly in a "counter-clock-wise" movement. Change to the right palm and rub in a "clock-wise direction". Count ten in each direction. (Fig. HA; HB)

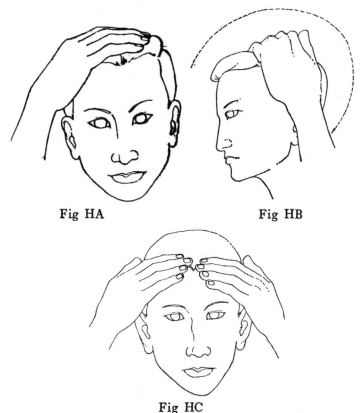

Fig HA   Fig HB

Fig HC

b) As if brushing the hair, use palms of both hands to massage the upper side of the head from the forehead to the termination of the hair on the neck. Repeat ten times. (Fig. HC)

c) Place the fingers of both hands on the forehead and use the thumbs to perform a rotary massage on the two temples (the "Sun

Vital Points") in front of the upper ears. Repeat ten times.

d) Rub palms together until they get warm, then apply the fingers and palms on each side of the forehead and massage from the upper part of the brows down the cheeks.

Eye Massage:

e) Rub the outside part of lower joints of the thumbs until warm, then close the eyes and massage the upper and lower eye lids with thumbs from the inner corner out. Afterwards and while the eye lids are still closed, move the eye balls to the left and then to the right three times, then open eyes widely and turn eye balls both to the left and to right. Three counts. (Fig. EM)

Nose Massage:

f) After warming the thumbs as before, rub both sides of the nose downwards, using slightly more pressure than for the eyes. (Fig. NM)

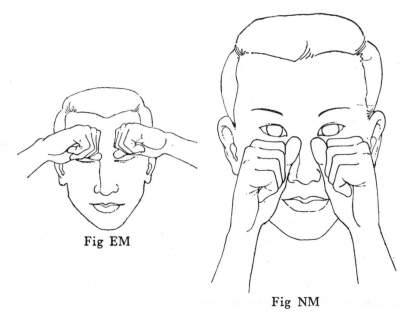

Fig EM

Fig NM

Lip Massage:

g)   After placing the index finger of the left hand on a point midway between the nose and the upper lip, put the index finger of the right hand on a point one-half inch below the lower lip, and rub horizontally ten times.   Finally, shift the index fingers using them to rub the corners of the mouth upward and downward.   Count ten. (Fig. LM a & b).

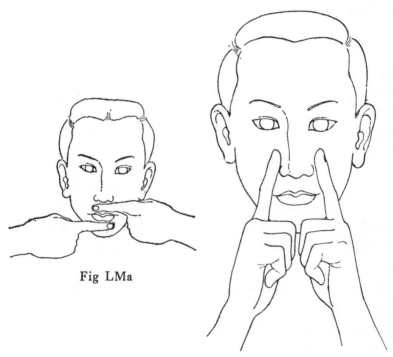

Fig LMa

Fig LMb

Ear Massage:

h)   Place the index and middle fingers of the left and right hands against the ear lobes and massage gently upward and downward ten times.   (Fig. EM)

Knocking the "Heaven's Drums":

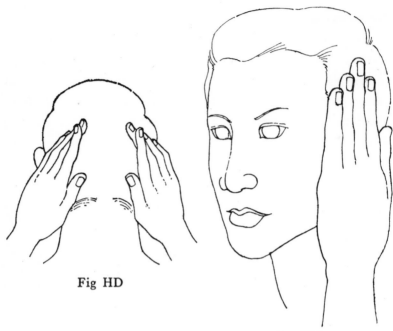

Fig HD

Fig EM

i) Place palms on both ears and put the index fingers *over* the middle fingers. Then knock sharply the back part of the head (cerebellum) by snapping the index fingers off the middle fingers. (Fig. HD)

Tongue and Teeth Massage:

j) Knock lower teeth gently against upper teeth ten times, then massage the palate with the tip of the tongue in a circular style ten times. Swallow the saliva three times and direct the saliva, in your mind's eye, to the Tan T'ien — the Vital Center.

B. The Neck and Shoulder Massages.

Benefits: These massages will keep neck and shoulders shapely and all the neck glands in divine health.

Neck Massage:

    a)   Place the left hand on the right side of the throat with the thumb extending across the throat to the right, and rub the cords of the neck from top downwards. Repeat the massage on the left side of the throat with the right hand. (Fig. NMa)

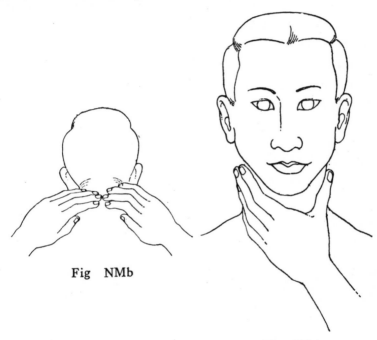

Fig NMb

Fig NMa

    b)   Place the left palm diagonally on the back of the neck and rub slowly toward the left until it reaches the throat. Repeat the same movements with the right palm on the right side. (Fig. NMb)

Shoulder Massage:

    c)   Perform a rotating movement with the left palm on the right shoulder; repeat the exercise with the right palm on the left shoulder. Count ten on each side. (Fig. SM)

C. Hand Massage.

Benefits: According to the theory of Acupuncture, three **Yin** Meridians of the arms running from the breast to the hand are those of the lungs, heart and the heart-constrictor.   The three **Yang** Meridians of the arms that run from the hand to the face are those of the stomach, bladder and the gall-bladder.   Hence, the massage on the hand will definitely stimulate the function of these internal organs.
Massage of Finger Joints:

a)   Place the thumb and index finger of the right hand on the external and internal sides of the thumb of the left hand and massage

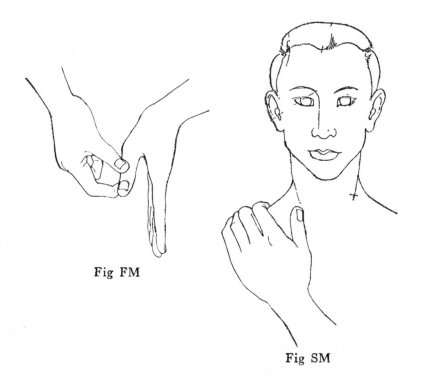

Fig FM

Fig SM

from the thumb nail upward and then downward. Count ten. Repeat the massaging movements on the four fingers. Continue in like manner with the opposite hand. (Fig. FM)

Wrist Massage:

b) Place thumb and index finger of the right hand on the central horizontal lines of the left wrist. Massage slightly on both sides. Repeat movements on the right wrist. (Fig. WM)

Fig WM

Elbow Massage:

c) With the thumb of the right hand on the inner part of the left elbow and the index finger on the bone of the elbow, massage in rotary movements. Count ten. Repeat on the right elbow. (Fig. EM)

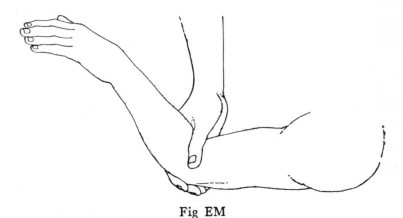

Fig EM

Arm Massage:

d) Rub on the left arm with the right palm running from the

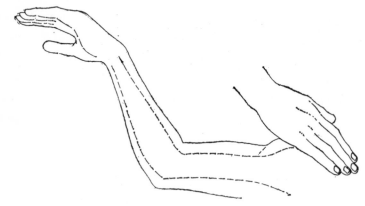

Fig AM

wrist to the armpit and turn round to the shoulder. From there then, massage downward to the back of the wrist. Count ten. Repeat the same movements on the right hand. (Fig. AM)

D. Torso Massages.

Benefits: If these massages are carried out regularly and constantly, the whole body should be strengthened and stimulated. They will help the proper functioning of the respiratory system, cardio vascular system, digestive system, genito-urinary system, and sexual system. They also help to overcome the degeneration of the abdominal organs.

Heart Massage:

a) Put right palm upon the left one on the middle of the chest and massage circularly. Count ten. (Fig. HM)

Navel Massage:

b) Use the left palm to massage circularly on the abdomen within a circumference of about three inches from the navel. Repeat with the right palm and also count ten. The rotation should be first counter-clock-wise, then clock-wise. (Fig. NM)

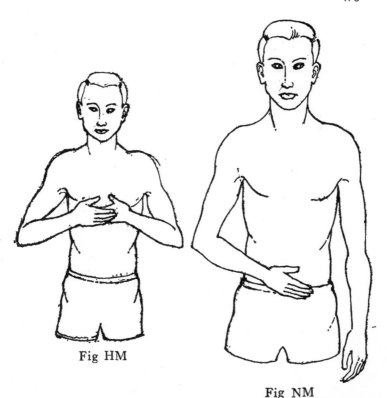

Fig HM

Fig NM

c) Vertical Massage: Put left palm upon the back of right palm, massaging from the upper part of the chest down to the lower part of the navel. Press gently and repeat ten.

E. Spine Massages:

Benefits: This massage will help to invigorate and stimulate the brain stem, which is the core of the brain, essentially an extension of the spine (through which all nerve impulses are channeled).

Coccyx Massage:

a) Place the tips of the two middle fingers of both hands to slide and rub the coccyx (bone) from the lowest point upward and downward within the length of approximately three inches. Count ten. (Fig. CM)

The "Door of Life" Massage:

b) Place the left and right palms on the back at approximately the waist vertebra (opposing the navel on the front) and between the two kidneys, which is named by the Taoists as the "Door of Life". Rub slightly from inside to outside in a circular movement on both sides. Count ten. (Fig. DM)

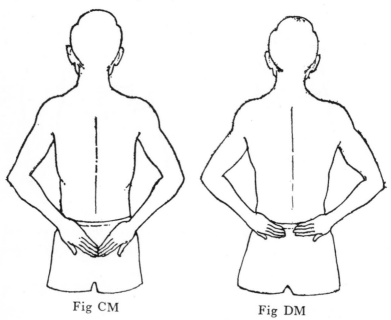

Fig CM   Fig DM

F. Leg, Toe, Knee and Thigh Massages:

Benefits: The massages on the toes, soles, thighs and other areas of the feet will have defintely good reflex action on the functioning of the internal organs, such as heart, kidneys, liver and reproductive organs. From the point of view of Acupuncture, the three Yang

Meridians of the legs that run from the face to the foot, are those of the stomach, bladder and the gall-bladder. The three Yin Meridians of the legs that run from the foot to the breast, are those of the spleen, kidneys and the liver. Hence, the inclusion of foot manipulation, for health's sake, becomes mandatory.

Toe Massage:

a) Place the right thumb on the back of the big toe of the left foot, the index finger on the opposite side, and rub from the tip upward. Repeat the movements on each toe. Repeat on the right foot with left thumb and finger. (Fig. TM)

Sole Massage:

b) Rub vigorously with the right palm on the sole of the left foot. Repeat movements on the right sole with left hand on each side. Count ten. (Fig. SM)

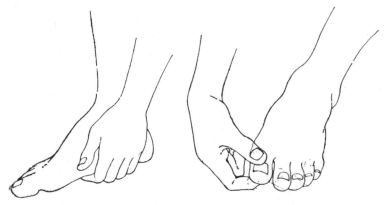

Fig SM   Fig TM

Ankle Massage:

c) Rub up and down on the inner side of the ankle of the left leg with the right thumb with deep stress. Repeat same movements on the right side. Count ten. (Fig. AM)

Knee Massage:

d) The joints of the knees are the supporting columns of the whole body. Massages on the following points are especially important.

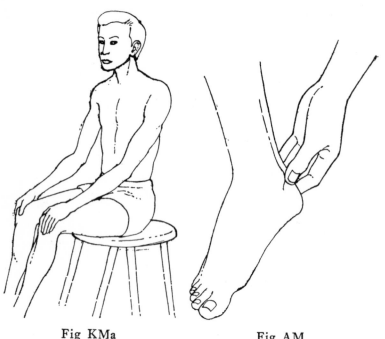

Fig KMa   Fig AM

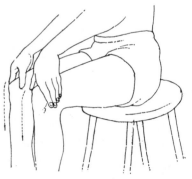

Fig KMb

1.   Place the thumb and index fingers of the left and right hands simultaneously on the knee-cap sides and push down with pressure on the shin-bones, ten times.   (Fig. KMa)

2.   Use the palms to rub the caps of both knees.   Applying the technique of rotation simultaneously is desirable.   Count ten.   (Fig. KMb)

3.   Use circular motion ten times for the calves of the legs (good for stomach).   (Fig. KMc)

Buttocks Massage:

e)   Place the two palms on the outer part of each thigh near the knees and press upward along the back of the thigh to the point of the buttocks from where rotate downward along the side and front. Count ten on each side at the same time.   (Fig. BM)

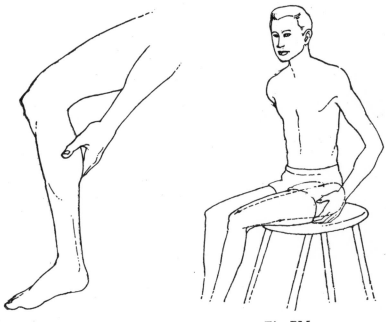

Fig KMc   Fig BM

SECTION IV

THE CULTURAL BREATHING RHYTHM

ORIENTATION

Cultural Breathing Rhythm is the great art of health. From the earliest ages in China, the art of breathing for health has been a synthesis of physical and spiritual aspects.

Indeed, people, since the earlier Chou dynasty (ca. 1027 — ca. 221 B.C.) in China, were captivated by the concept that through their techniques of breathing it was possible to achieve a material immortality and rejuvenation and to arrest the process of aging — even to return to the physical condition of a young organism.

Laotzu, who lived and wrote in the sixth century B.C., wrote:

"Tao gave birth to one; one gave birth to two; two gave birth to three; three gave birth to the multitude of things which attain the state of harmony when the opposite elements of Yin and Yang are mingled in a well-balanced manner.

"The spirit of life is immortal and may be compared to the mysterious productive power which forms the base of the universe. It is imperceptible, and its usefulness is inexhaustible."

After the Chin (221 — 206 B.C.) and Han (205 B.C. — A.D. 220) dynasties, the Taoists, the followers of Laotzu, formulated their theory of immortality. Some of their techniques for the prolongation of life, as has been described in the first section, were considered as the best method of improving health. Modern breathing exercises, the heritage of the Taoists and the Buddhists, differ not dramatically from the exercises of the past. Fundamentally, they are rooted in tradition. Even today the most ancient techniques can be practiced with great profit as timeless and universal observations about the aims and methods of cultivating health.

Although there are many sects and methods of metitation as well as breathing exercises known in China, India and Japan, the most popular and well-known schools are those of Ch'an (Zen) School and Tibetan Yoga among the Buddhists and the 'Nei Kung' ('inner efficiency') or 'Chi Kung' ('inner attainment of breathing') School of the Taoists. With regard to the former, besides the Ch'an School, there are the Pure Land School and Tien T'ai School, which also give a series of practical instructions regarding the mind. And in the latter, the Taoist method, although usually regarded as mysterious, tries to control the breath (the Chi, or Prana, or Vital Energy) and circulates it through the psychic pathway ('nadi') known as Meridians and Channels (Ching and Mei). Both the Buddhists and the Taoists emphasize the training of the mind, as the Sutra says: "Just by mind control, all things become possible to us", but from the objective point of view, the Buddhists' aim is "dyana-samadhi" or "Complete Enlightenment" which is supra space and time, the Absolute, the Nirvana, while that of the Taoists is the prolongation of life or the unifying with Tao.7

---

7 There is a Taoist motto which goes: "Lien Ching hua ch'u, lien Ch'i hua Shen. Lien Shen fu hsü, lien hsü ho Tao." Through compounding sperm (Ching), the breath (Ch'i) is transformed; through compounding the breath, the spirit (Shen) is transformed. Thus Ching, Ch'i and Shen are most fundamental elements in the process of meditative breathing. Hsü means nonbeing, or nothingless. The transformation of hsü finally leads to the processes of self-realization — the unifying with Tao (the ultimate of the universe). See Chang Chung-Yuan, *Creativity with Taoism*, A Study of Chinese Philosophy, Art, and Poetry, The Julian Press, Inc., New York, 1963, pp. 135-158, for further explanation of this motto.

In this age of gerontology and psycho-cybernetics, it is the art of cultural breathing of the Taoists that justifies the attention of modern man. The exact technique of their exercise will be described later, but some of the main characteristics may be given as follows:

A. In the exercise, one needs to imagine or visualize that there is such Chi (breath, vital energy, vital principle, prana or even light)[8] in the body that can be directed to go in regular lines (the psychic pathways of energy such as the Yin-Yang Meridians and Channels described above). In the long run, through long visualization, meditation, contemplation as well as auto-suggestion, the extension of conscious control over the function of the central nervous system is possible.[9]

B. What we call "Chi" in this particular exercise may not necessarily mean the air that we breathe through the nostrils. Many theories have been advanced in regard to this type of Chi, but no unified conclusion has been reached. The traditional Taoists' explanation, which may not be strictly scientific, is this: "The foetus in the womb does not breathe through nostrils, but its inner Chi circulates by rising up to the spine and head and then descending to the navel; this is called foetal breathing. At birth (after cutting navel-cord), this circulation ceases and is replaced by respiration through the nostrils. Therefore, after a long meditation, the practitioner can make use of the circulation of the vital principle to restore the foetal

8 The 'Light Method' is used by some Taoist Schools. See *The Secret of the Golden Flower, A Chinese Book of Life,* tr. by Richard Wilhelm, with a European commentary by C. G. Jung. Harcourt, Brace and World, Inc., New York, 1931.

9 For the Law of Suggestion, see Rammurti Mishra, *Fundamentals of Yoga:* Julian Press, 1959, N.Y., ch. 2

breath."10   In other words, the Taoists believe this type of Chi is the
"Primeval Chi" or the "A Priori Chi" (the respiration of the embryo
in the womb).   They further believe that a return to the foetal circulation is possible by these methods of breathing practice.   Some
prefer the use of the "Light Method" in which one must concentrate
and visualize the movements of the Light, a Yang element, from the
"Third Eye", (the middle point between the two eye-brows — also
known as the upper Tan Tien), to go along the pathways of the
energy.   However, the Chi, according to our point of view, cannot
and must not be isolated from the breath, which is the essence of life.

C.   Eventually, after a certain time of practice, say about six
months or one year, a particular sensation of heat is generated
inside the abdominal area (belly) or a sense of dynamic vibration
begins to start in the same area and circulates around the head and
along the Meridians (Ching) and Channels (Mei).   When this result
is attained, good health and longevity can be reached.   Yin Shih Tsu,
an expert in this Method of Meditation says, "The cause of this vibration is very profound and is not easily explainable.   Most probably,
with free circulation of the blood and an accumulation of (psychic)
force in the belly below the navel, this concentration of strength causes
the movements which produce the heat."11   However, we know that
vibrations bear no definite relation to the efficiency of meditation or
breathing exercise.   One should not be impatient in desiring quick
results.

Of all the arts of exercise for health, breathing is the typical
expression of ancient and modern man.   The ancients believed the
perfecting of the spirit could be attained by mastering the matter,

10 Charles Luk, *The Secrets of Chinese Meditation*, Rider, 1964, London, p. 175.

11 Charles Luk, op. cit., p. 175.

and glowing health and longevity comes from the Chi being able to circulate (or communicate) freely through all the psychic pathways of energy. As moderns, we would like to point out that glowing health comes from the perfect harmony of the Chi, or vital energy or prana in the human body — the restoration of the metabolism in natural equilibrium. Hence, the Cultural Breathing Exercise as a system of healthy training is highly recommended.

POSTURES TO BE TAKEN IN THE
CULTURAL BREATHING RHYTHM

There are three types of postures that could be taken selectively for practicing these exercises in accordance with the need and inclination of the practitioner. They are:

Posture I. Standing Posture, The Three-Circle Style.

Separate the two feet, shoulders wide, with tip of toes of both legs curving inward to form a circle, legs slightly curving, spinal column straight, chest hollowed. Raise arms to shoulder level, with elbows slightly down, fingers opposing each other as if to grasp a ball with a distance of about one foot. Head should be upright with imagination to hold the heaven, eyes half closed or gazing at a target. The mind and brain are in a state of stillness.

The so-called THREE-CIRCLE STYLE consists of: 'foot circle', 'arm circle', and 'hand circle'. The circular feet aims at the uprightness of the spine and the stableness of the legs; the circular arms and hands aim at the strengthening of the function of breathing so that the breath or vital energy can circulate directly to the tips of the fingers.

In general, the aim of this style is also to strengthen the muscles of the legs, waist, arms, so that they may increase their degree of elasticity.

In the beginning, you may take the standing posture two or three minutes, and gradually increase to ten minutes. If tired, use auxiliary exercises such as Massage or Tai Chi Ch'uan to adjust the body.

The benefit of this style for the practitioner is that in exhalation, the Chi can be directed to the middle of the soles, while in inhalation, the Chi is drawn to the Tan T'ien and ascends to the crown.

Posture II. Siting Posture, The Lotus Style And The Ordinary Sitting Style.

The LOTUS POSTURE consists in the placing of the left leg over the right leg and then the right leg over the left leg. The head and spine should be erect.

Fig SIA

However, for elderly people, if they find the first style too difficult to follow through, they may take a natural sitting position or ORDINARY SITTING POSTURE. Sleeping posture may be taken by old people.

Prior to the taking of any of these styles, it would be advisable to take the Ten Treasures Movements aiming at the activation of the body. In the sitting posture, the nose, tongue and the navel should be in a vertical line so as to maintain the uprightness of the body.

The chief merit of the posture is to help the breathing or vital energy to sink to the Tan T'ien. With the palms folding each other before the abdomen, the mind easily concentrates on this Vital Center without any distraction. While meditating for the purpose of 'satori" (spiritual awakening or enlightenment) or aiming at the prolongation of life, both the Zennist and the Taoist usually prefer the famous Lotus posture.

The ordinary sitting posture may be easily taken by elderly or weakened people without hardship or numbness. Therefore, it is also considered as one of the best ways for beginners in breathing exercise.

The sleeping style is good for those who are in the process of recuperation from ailments. One may lie down with face facing upward, feet straight, toes upright, hands closing to thighs. Use pillows to raise the head, concentrate your mind on the Tan T'ien.

To sum up, the sitting and sleeping postures have long been used for meditation and may be taken with benefits, while the standing posture is a new style helping the circulation of both breathing and blood to move freely.

FUNDAMENTAL PRINCIPLES OF
CULTURAL BREATHING RHYTHM

Principle I. Internal Tri-Harmonies.

This sub-section is an attempt to expound the general principles on which this type of exercise is based, something of the procedures that it involves, and some of the ways in which it can be expected to have considerable results. A process that produces results, the principles of which we do not fully know and understand, is apt to be labeled as metaphysical, or even mystic. As a Westerner said, "Once it is understood, we call it science."

The principle of Tri-Harmonies concerns three aspects:

(a) The Harmony of the Mind and the Yi (imagination, consciousness of will);[12]

(b) The Harmony of the Yi and the Chi (breath, prana or vital energy); and

[12] The so-called Yi in Chinese can be rendered into English as Idea, Consciousness, Will or Imagination. Here, we prefer to use the term "Imagination" which is the expression of the "new brain" in the cerebrum or cerebral cortex, the seat of mental activity, voluntary action and the senses. It controls not only the activities of the mind and body, but also transforms the natural pattern for the purpose of self therapy and the strengthening of the body and the mind. In his "Psycho-Cybernetics: the Principles of Cybernetics as Applied to the Human Brain", Maxwell Maltz says: "Your nervous system cannot tell the difference between an imaginative experience and a "real" experience. In either case, it reacts automatically to information which you give to it from your forebrain. Your nervous system reacts appropriately to what 'you' think or imagine to be true." (Maxwell Maltz, *Psycho-Cybernetics, New Technique for Using Your Subconscious Power;* Wilshire Book Co., Los Angeles. California: 1963, p. 29.)

(c)   The Harmony of the Chi and the strength.

The following interpretation is in order:

(a)   The "Harmony of the Mind and the Yi" is actually a psychological process in which the mind and the imagination are identical.   Direction and control of the Mind and the Yi as a unit are essential steps towards good mental exercise.   In other words, we must have confidence that the various parts of the body can definitely be transformed or controlled in accordance with the imagination or the will working through the Chi.

(b)   The "Harmony of the Yi and the Chi" is also a psychological process in which the Chi (breath) should be led or directed by the Yi, or imagination, to descend or ascend along the psychological paths of energy known as Ching and Mei (Meridians or Channels, to be itemized later) in the body.

(c)   The "Harmony of Chi and Strength", the principle of which is that in the process of exhalation and inhalation, the Chi must be led to descend and ascend in the body, and strength has to be used to contract or expand the abdomen in accordance with the breathing.   However, the so-called strength is a psychic force or "heat current" that moves along the circulation by one's idea or imagination. It has nothing to do with strenuous physical force. Due to the rhythmic movements of the abdomen, the diaphragm and the internal organs are activated simultaneously.

Principle II.   The Relaxation Of The Body And The Firmness Of The Yi.

According to this principle, people with emotional problems must be trained to overcome them in order to live a relaxed life.   For this purpose, the first condition is to cultivate the capacity of adjusting oneself to unavoidable stress of life by relaxing or loosening the body — including the muscles, shoulders, chest, abdomen, the limbs, as well as the mind itself. On the other hand, the Yi, the idea or imagination which leads the Chi to circulate, must assert a certain sense of firmness. With relaxation of the body, the blood circulates freely; with firmness in imagination, the Chi can be directed to creative good health and prolonged life.

Principle III. The Harmony Of The Shen And The Mei.

"Shen", which is often rendered as "Spirit", is normally defined as an abstract term embracing thought and consciousness and all the manifestations of life and movement. Gandhi once attempted to describe "spirit" in terms of "light", and Betrand Russell said: "The life of spirit centers round impersonal feeling". The Taoists always mentioned that Ching, Chi and Shen are the Three Precious Treasures.[13]

Mei, according to the theory of Acupuncture, are conjunctive channels which, along with Meridians (Ching), form a continuous circuit in the body. The pathways of the Meridians are symmetrical and bilateral, as are those of the channels, with the exception of the last two channels, those of Tu Mei (Governor Channel) and Jen Mei (Conceptional Channel), which have a single trajectory. Tu Mei runs along the posterior, and the Jen Mei along the anterior median lines of the body.[14]

[13] In Chang Chung-Yuan's *Creativity and Taoism,* we read: "The basic theory of this Inner Elixir School, as it is known, is that the inner elixir is compounded through Ching (essence), Chi (breath), and Shen (spirit)... Ching, or essence, in its material form is sperm. Therefore, Taoist meditative practice draws its power through the spine and is said to commence from the Gate of the Tail. Sperm provides the vitality of the human body, maintain-

ing energy and life. But Ching cannot be complete without an understanding of its immaterial, primordial aspect. In this light it is not sperm at all, but an invisible, ungraspable cosmic force that derives something outside the universe, such as the sun and the moon. It is said that through man he takes in this cosmic force for the compounding of the inner elixir.

As for Ch'i, breath, it is, in one sense, the physical effort of the beginning practitioner. who inhales and exhales, moving his diaphragm up and down. But when the practitioner achieves embryo breathing he is said to be in a state of total extinction, or cessation. It is the primordial beginning of the universe. In man it is referred to as breathing without breath. This is called embryo breathing or primordial breathing. From it man draws the invisible ungraspable force of the universe for compounding the elixir.

The third principle, Shen, refers to both Shih Shen, ordinary consciousness, and Yuan Shen, or spiritual consciousness. The former is man's senses, perceptions, thoughts, feelings and the like, which are obtained at birth or afterward. The latter is the spiritual consciousness existing before one is born. As soon as man is born, it becomes invisible, covered by man's ordinary consciousness. It is believed that through meditation man once again reveals this spiritual consciousness and eliminates its ordinary consciousness. What is this primordial spiritual consciousness? It is power of the power that permeates and pervades the whole universe." (Chang, op. cit., pp. 135-136.)

14 See Figures 1, 2, 3 and 4.

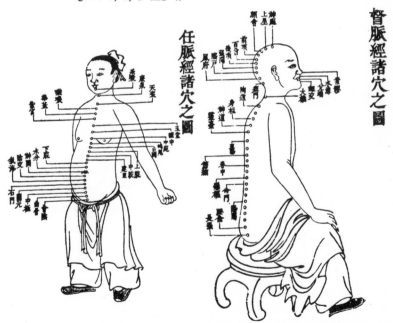

Diagrams showing the Vital Points along the Tu Mei and Jen Mei in Chinese. (See p. 466)

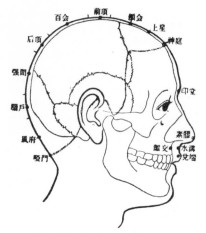

Fig 1. Tu Mei (Governing Channel) (1)

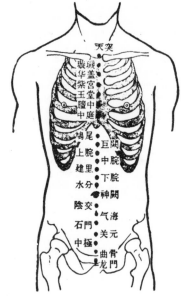

Fig 4. Jen Mei (2) a channel passing down the front of the body to the genital region (huei yin).

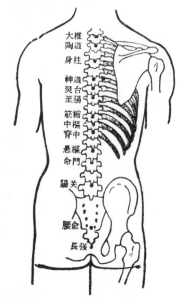

Fig 2. Tu Mei (2) a channel going up the spinal column from the base of the spine to the top of the head and over the head to the upper lip.

Fig 3. Jen Mei (Conceptional Channel) (1)

Based on the "Acupuncture" The Chinese Medical Institute, Shanghai

As the Chi or vital energy is to be directed to go cyclicly along the channels (Mei, particularly the Tu Mei running along the posterior, and the Jen Mei along the anterior,)* the Shen or spirit must be incorporated or identified with the flowing of the Chi inside the Mei. Eventually, when one arrives at the highest stage, the attention may be concentrated on the Mei — the psychological pathways of the Chi — only, rather than the Chi.

Principle IV. The Concentration Of The Yi (Idea or Imagination) On The Tan T'ien (Field Of Elixir).

This is also considered as a basic principle of this art, for in order to get more benefit from it,the traditional way was to concentrate the Yi (idea or imagination) on the central point — which in this case is the Tan T'ien (Field of Elixir) — the centre of the physical body and the "Sea of the Chi", about two and one-half inches below the navel.

YANG*	YIN*
Channel reuniting the Yang energy:	Channel reuniting the Yin energy:
Yang Wei Mei	Yin Wei Mei
Yang channel of the ankle:	Yin channel of the ankle:
Yang Ch'iao Mei	Yin Ch'iao Mei
Channel of the waist:	Channel of the groin:
Tai Mei	Ch'ung Mei
Governing channel:	Channel of conception:
Tu Mei	Jen Mei.

* See Wu Wei-ping, *Chinese Acupuncture,* tr. by Philip M. Chancellor: Health Science Press, Rustington. Sussex, England. 1962, p. 17. See also, Felix Mann, *Anatomical Charts of Acupuncture Points,* Medidians and Extra *Meridians:* William Heinemann Medical Books Ltd., London, 1963.

The concentration of the Yi on the Tan T'ien is the basic art through which the mind is to attain the state of stillness. Working up to a point where one can attain complete concentration, or even relaxation, can be done in a relatively short period of time.

THE METHODS OF CULTURAL BREATHING RHYTHMS

There are many important methods and techniques that should be stressed and remembered in the practice of this exercise. We can now start with the course of practical experimentation, which would mean in practice that breathing exercises might again become a living art of health without mystery. The following formula should be adhered to:

Basically, the general method can be classified into two types:

(a)   Natural Breathing — When exhaling, the abdominal cavity, with the direction of the Chi by the Yi downward from the crown to the Tan T'ien, is to be contracted inward. While inhaling, the breath is drawn inward through the nostrils and descended to the Tan T'ien by expanding the abdomen.

(b)   Unnatural (reversed) Breathing — In exhaling, the Chi (a posteriori) should go upward through the nostrils, but the Chi, a priori, (in the lower part) ought to be lowered down to the Tan Tien, and the abdomen is contracted inward.

Method I.   Long Breathing.

(a)   Natural breathing is adopted.

(b) Use the nostrils to breathe, close mouth with tongue touching the palate.

(c) When exhaling, imagine the Chi is descending from the crown along the forehead where it is branched into the cheeks and enters the palate where they merge and join the tip of the tongue, the ending of the Jen Mei, from where it further descends to the Tan T'ien.

(d) The abdomen is contracted inward through the direction of the Yi.

(e) Immediately after the exhalation, use the nostrils to inhale deeply into the Tan T'ien and the abdomen is to be expanded outward.

(f) All breathing should be long, slow and harmonious. Continue this rhythm for three breaths, then proceed to Method II.

Method II. The Microcosmic Orbit — The Small Yin-Yang Cyclic Breathing. (Latent Breathing).

(a) Basic Idea — This method, a latent breathing, is technically known as MICROCOSMIC ORBIT, OR THE SMALL YIN-YANG CYCLIC BREATHING. The exhalation is Yin, while inhalation Yang. The Chinese conceived the organism, as a small universe, that is activated by two principles, the Yin and the Yang, the negative and the postive. These two forces, by virtue of ceaseless interplay, are the two co-existent poles of one indivisible whole. The function of this exercise is to maintain or restore the dynamic equilibrium of the Chi (vital energy) in the human body. The purpose in this stage of breathing exercise is different from the first one — Long Breathing — in that it aims not only at the cultivation of the Chi but also attempts to utilize the Chi for the strengthening of the central nervous system and to restore the equilibrium of the metabolism of the physiology.

(b)   The unnatural (reversed) method of breathing is used.

(c)   The "Process of Directing the Chi to the Tan T'ien" —
When you are exhaling, the tongue is touching the palate. Imagine
the Chi is descending to the Tan T'ien and the abdomen is expanded
outward.

(d)   The "Process of communication between the Jen Mei
and the Tu Mei". — After exhaling, inhale gradually through the
nostrils.   The abdomen, following the inhalation, is drawn inward.
The tongue is touching the palate which is the end of the Tu Mei,
while the tip of the tongue is the station of the Jen Mei.   Because of
the meeting of the tongue with the palate, the two Meis begin to communicate with each other.   Starting from the Tan T'ien and arriving
at the Hui Yin (the vital point situated midway between the reproductive organ and the anus), the Chi goes upward along the coccyx,

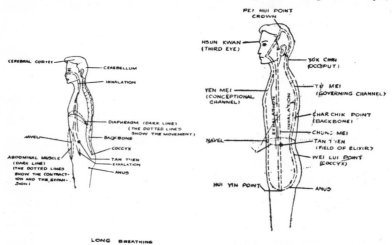

Fig CH1

Fig CH2

backbone and the occiput (the so-called "Three Gates) in the Tu Mei (Governing Channel) to the Pei Hui vital point (crown or cerebral cortex). While descending from the forehead and branchng out along the cheeks, the Chi again merges at the tip of the tongue, connecting with the Yen Mei. Technically speaking, this is what is called the SMALL YIN-YANG CYCLE meaning the breathing (consisting of one exhalation and one inhalation) has circled the upper part of the body in a small circle. Through the function of suggestion, the Chi is led by the Yi (idea or imagination) and the two channels (Meis) of Jen and Tu are thus connected with each other.15

Method III.   The Macrocosmic Orbit — The Great Yin-Yang Cyclic Breathing. (Harmonizing Breathing).

(a)   Basic Idea — The chief significance of this method is to enlarge the scope of the cyclic movement of the Chi from the upper part of the body down to the soles in order to cultivate the Chi beyond the state of "Latent Breathing" described in Method II.

(b)   In exhaling, while the tongue is touching the palate, direct the Chi to descend to the Tan T'ien with abdomen expanding outward.   Again, sink the Chi downward to the Point of Hui Yin (the midpoint between the anus and the reproductive organ) where it is branched out and imagine it to go further downward along the two legs, passing the knees and through the big toes to the middle of the soles (Bubbling Well Points).

(c)   In inhaling, while the tongue is touching the palate, con-

<hr />

15 What the Taoists called the passage of the three gates by the Chi is the most difficult process to be attained.   One's success in the art of "Inner Efficiency" (nei kung) depends very much upon this task.   Obviously, it takes time and patience to attain this very important objective.

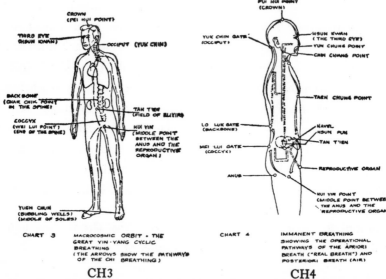

CHART 3 — MACROCOSMIC ORBIT - THE GREAT YIN-YANG CYCLIC BREATHING (THE ARROWS SHOW THE PATHWAYS OF THE CHI BREATHING)

CHART 4 — IMMANENT BREATHING SHOWING THE OPERATIONAL PATHWAYS OF THE APRIORI BREATH ("REAL BREATH") AND POSTERIORI BREATH (AIR)

CH3   CH4

tract the abdomen inward gradually, and raise the Chi upward from the Bubbling Well Points (soles) to go through the thighs meeting at the anus. Again, "raise the anus", leading the Chi to ascend along the spinal cord by passing the three gates — coccyx, backbone and occiput — arriving at the crown (cerebral cortex), from where it is directed imaginatively to descend to both cheeks, merging separately at the tip of the tongue, then the Chi joins hand with what is exhaled. The whole process is known as "The Great Yin-Yang Cyclic Breathing". 16

16 It may be added that in the practice of this process, an additional pathway may be taken by those who are matured enough. The pathway is: When the Chi, by visualization, has reached the middle point between the shoulders, from where it may branch out to go through the shoulders and the elbows, it finally arrives at the tips of the middle fingers. Turning around the tips, it is led to the palms, wrists and armpits from where it is directed back to the midpoint between the shoulders along the spinal cord, where the two branches merge as a unit again. Moreover, it is led imaginatively to go through the occiput. When it reaches the level of the two ears, it is branched out to go around the ears and merged at the former point from where it ascends to the crown.

Method IV. Immanent Breathing.

(a) Basic Idea — This is the highest method in the practicing of cultural breathing, which cannot be ascertained or realized without a few years' continual practice. This type of breathing has its aim in utilizing the "Real Breath" (known as Foetal-Breathing), which is the root of nature in human beings and an important secret of the Taoists for the prolongation of life and rejuvenation.

In addition to certain particular techniques that will be described later, all the previous three methods can be employed simultaneously or alternatively. After a certain period of intensive training, one may experience a sense of vibration or a heated sensation (the circulation of the "breath" as a heat current) accumulated around the Tan T'ien from where it flows freely along the Channels (Mei) and the Meridians (Ching) According to many experts, this kind of force, if attained, seems to be very powerful and can raise the body upward (Levitation) spiritually. As the *I Ching, the Book of Changes,* believes SHEN (Spirit) to be supra Time and Space and is the fifth dimension, it is advisable to find the way to embark on a crash program of research on the true scientific basis of it. Nowadays the para-psychologists believe the sixth sense cannot be denied, even though there is no physio-chemical explanation for the process. We are assured that the human body is not a physio-chemical complex but something more, something beyond that. Hence we may probably say, "Where there is will, there is "Shen" or spirit".

(b) The concrete method of Immanent Breathing is to mainly use Methods I and II as ways of exhalation and inhalation. After practicing about ten minutes in the highest stage, one suddenly feels that the Mind-Body is vibrating when a sensation of HEAT gathers in the T'an Tien in the abdomen, which momentarily descends to the pathway of Hui Yin, from where it branches out imaginatively and arrives at the Bubbling Well Vital Points (soles). With inhalation, this "Heat-current" seems to ascend upward along the coccyx (backbone), and occiput arriving at the cerebral cortex (crown). The mass of the Heat-Current is so great that the whole body seems to have been raised altogether. When this state is attained, it is considered as the expression of the "total communication" (passage) of all the Chi-Mei's in the organism.[17]

(c) The sensation that may be actualized comes from the practice of techniques of "the Concentration of the Mind in the Tan T'ien", and the "Harmonizing of the 'Real Breath' ", but for the purpose of intensifying the result, certain minor techniques are also very beneficial. They are:

(1) In the use of the Method of the great Yin-Yang Cyclic Breathing, one must keep the mind in stillness, shuting the mouth and harmonizing the breathing, in order that the "Harmonizing Breathing" and the "Harmonizing Mind" be merged as a unity, and the "Dynamic" and "Static" may attain a normal equilibrium.

(2) In addition, one may use the technique of "Counting (such as 1,2,3,4.........10 up to 100) to attain the highest degree of stillness (concentration). Next, use the technique of "Following the Breath" to adjust the exhalation and inhalation until the sensation of breathing seems to be discontinued. This is known as the technique of "Discontinuing the Breath".

(3) Furthermore, in order to see whether the phenomenon of breathing complies with the eight criteria of "naturalness, slowness, delicacy, harmony, stillness, continuity, depth and length", the technique of "INTROSPECTION" is available. After the introspecting of the breath, try to focus your mind or imagination in the Tan Tien

---

[17] The so-called "Five Communications" will be itemized in a later sub-section.

for a moment, and then, you may take the step of "Stilling the Breath". Now, outwardy, the activities of exhalation and inhalation seem to have attained the state of discontinuity (Stop), but practically and imaginatively, you have to use your navel to breath, that is the foetal breathing considered by the Taoists as "REAL BREATHING". Arriving at this stage, with all kinds of distraction avoided, the mind and brain would come to a state of quietitude — the merging of the dynamic and the static, the harmony of the mind and breathing. This is the realization of the aim of Immanent Breathing — the "Real Breath", the Spiritual Awakening and the "establishment of the destiny".

(4)   After the exhaustion of the above techniques, however, the technique of "Drumming and Stimulating" may be constantly practiced with tremendous benefits, according to which the Chi is directed and visualized to be moving cyclically inside and around the navel, first clock-wise and then counter clock-wise, for 36 counts each turn. At the beginning, it appears that what is revolving continually is the Chi only, but after a certain period, you may experience a brilliant light — pearl like — circulating around the area of the Tan T'ien and finally around the whole body along the pathways of energy, emitting an aura outside the head or the torso. This stage has sometimes been referred to as the 'spiritual bath.'

(5)   With the realization of this stage, technically speaking. when your mind or imagination reaches the tips of the fingers, the fists, the soles, etc., your Chi (or what the Tai Chi Chuanists call "INTRINSIC ENERGY") reaches with it too. In fact, the T'ai Chi Ch'uan, the eminent Chinese Health Exercise-Art — a slow, soft, continuous, circular, dynamic and static, long and effortless exercise, cannot be practiced with success without the accomplishment of this "INNER EFFICIENCY" (Nei Kung).

THE STAGES IN THE APPLICATION OF THE FOUR
METHODS OF CULTURAL BREATHING EXERCISE

Stages	Methods	Operation of Breathing	Chi (breath) & Yi (Idea or Imagination)	Results
1	Long Breathing	Breathe with nostrils, mouth Eyes slightly open, concentrate imaginatively on the Upper Tan Tien (the Third Eye), or gaze at a distance.	Relax whole body. Natural breathing. Use imagination to lead the Chi or breath.	Spiritual. stimulation and physical comfort.
2	Microcosmic Orbit, or the Small Yin-Yang Cyclic Breathing (Latent Breathing)	Tongue touching palate, raising anus. Use unnatural method of breathing. In inhalation, contract abdomen, while in exhalation, expand it	During exhalation, imagine that the Chi descends from the crown to the Tan Tien. In inhalation, breathe with nostrils. Direct the Chi to Tan Tien and thence to Hui Yin from where turn upward through cocyx, and occiput to crown. Passing cheeks to connect it with tongue.	Help to overcome indigestion, panting, etc.

| 3 | Macrocosmic Orbit, or Great Yin-Yang Cyclic Breathing. (Harmonizing Breathing) | The art of breathing, same as Stage II. In exhalation, imagine as if flying downward. In inhalation, flying upward. Same should be applied in II. | During exhalation, imagine that the Chi descends downward from the crown by passing the chest (middle Tan T'ien), the lower Tan T'ien (Vital Center) through Hui Yin to soles. In inhalation, imagine the Chi to go upward through spine to crown. | Strengthening nervous system. |
| 4 | Immanent Breathing | All methods in Stages I, II & III may be used. Breathe in accordance with different techniques described in text. | "Real Breath" or "Foetal Breathing" — the highest aim. | Help to prevent all ailments, prolong life. |

TEN FUNDAMENTAL POINTS FOR SUCCESS
IN CULTURAL BREATHING RHYTHMS

Because breathing exercise could be the most significant event in a man or woman's life, it is important that the points for success be properly noted. The vital information and advice give you guidelines to worthwhile leisure-time activities.

(a)   Learn about the function and structure of your organism, observe the principles upon which the Breathing Exercise are based. "Know thyself" and discipline thyself.

(b)   Understand the need and value of relaxation and stillness (quietude) in modern technological civilization. Activity combined with quietude are features which add greatly to the control of the body of awareness through vital or cultural breath.

(c)   An exercise which claims such benefits affecting body, mind and spirit simultaneously, must embody a right attitude, and particularly, a right living. Hence, it is necessary to (1) appreciate and practice a harmonized diet: (2) recognize the value of early to bed and early to rise; and (3) develop a self-discipline for the practice of high morality and the actualization of "absolute love" for an "organic humanity".

(d)   Realize and have absolute confidence that Cultural Breathing Exercise is the need for the accomplishment of mental therapy and glowing health.

(e)   Observe that at the end of all victory over circumstance, one must gradually develop the one universal remedy for overcoming laziness, that is *persistence* and *patience.*

(f)   Accept all the challenges and face all difficulties in the

process of training and experimenting in the breathing exercise. The
sensations of heat, coolness, numbness, vibration, are the natural products signifying the phenomena of the circulation of the Chi and its
struggle with sickness. Continue to concentrate your mind on mental
and emotional stability, do not expect quick results.

(g) Learn to cultivate the Chi without inserting force and tension by practicing the Long Breathing. After a certain length of
time, say about three months, begin to practice the Microcosmic Orbit
or Small Yin-Yang Cyclic Breathing with intensive effort. After
another three months you may take up the Macrocosmic Orbit, or
Great Yin-Yang Cyclic Breathing. The practice of both Orbits may
take about five to eight minutes. One may repeat each Orbit three
times but not more than nine each time, depending on the physical
condition and patience of a practitioner.

(h) Try to practice stage by stage. The Preparatory stage is
to cultivate the Chi, while the Transitory stage is to start the Chi to
circulate through the whole body according to your will or imagination
with a view to harmonizing it with the mind. The highest stage is to
actualize the principle of the "harmony of the Shen (spirit) and Mei
(channel)" in order to utilize the Chi in restoring the Yin-Yang
equilibrium in the physiology of metabolism and in maintaining Glowing Health.

(i) After the Exercise, try to take up the system of Self Massage, massaging the head, face, ears, eyes, knocking the teeth, stretching the legs, etc.

(j) To work without weariness, with easy proficiency, and
especially "to be in harmony" with the Chi, the Shen and the Mei,
are goals everybody desires. Finally, do not forget that the main objective is the attainment of the 'Five Communications' (passages),
which consist of: The Communication of the Chi, the Communi-

cation of the Heat, the Communication in the Anterior, the Communication in the Posterior and the Communication in the Whole Body, (Total Communication or Passage). When no obstruction is to be encountered, an appropriate maturity level has already been attained.

BENEFITS OF CULTURAL BREATHING EXERCISES

In fulfilling the fundamental points or conditions for success mentioned above, we are convinced by experience of centuries that the following benefits may be the results:

(1) The Improvement of the Process of Metabolism.

With the intaking of a great quantity of oxygen, this enhances tremendously the working of the cerebrum and the metabolism of billions of nerve cells.

(2) The Strengthening of the Muscles.

Because of the great effect of the exercises on digestion through the contraction and expansion of the abdominal cavity, it naturally strengthens the development of the muscles.

(3) Adjusting the Function of the Nervous System.

There is consistent interrelationship between the physical conditions of the brain and the qualities of consciousness. With an imaginative force directing the operation of the Chi circulating along all the pathways of energy, particularly the spine and the brain, it would be hard to imagine that there are no good consequences for the functioning of the nervous system.

(4) Massaging the Internal Organs.

With the rhythmic movements of exhalation and inhalation, the massaging effect on the diaphragm leading to the electrochemical activity in the specific organs, such as the heart, lung, bladder, kidneys, the intestines, is by its very nature not a mysterious and unexplainable phenomenon.

(5) Cultural Breathing Exercise is a "must" for all types of Oriental Exercises.

There are many types of Oriental exercises such as Yoga, Judo, Karate, Shao Lin Ch'uan, and particularly Tai Chi Ch'uan, that can be practiced by every one for different reasons at different times, depending on the needs. But at all times, none of them would have the ability to enable people to produce stamina and endurance, sense of well-being and mental balance, without resorting to Chi Kung — the "Inner Efficiency" through abdominal type of breathing as expounded in the above section. The Chinese system of Tai Chi Ch'uan is a dynamic system of Health Exercise-Art, the purpose of which is to activate the human organism for the cultivation of physical, spiritual and mental well-being. All its postures have to be done in slow, circular, gentle, rhythmic and graceful movements which have to be coordinated with the internal breathing rhythms. The entire structure, both in the manner of moving and the form-pattern is regulated by the principle of Tai Chi and the negative and positive forces of Yin and Yang, which is the Chinese philosophy of the interplay and harmony of the opposites. However, the Cultural Breathing Exercise is the core or kernel of this or other eminent Oriental exercises. Hence this exercise is particularly recommended to those who have learned the other types of exercise.

(6) Scientific Explanation of the Benefit on the Nervous System Through Operation of Cultural Breathing Rhythms.

According to modern practitioners of the Cultural Breathing Rhythms, the achievement of the so-called "spiritual bath" or the attainment of the experience of a 'flash of light' takes approximately one hundred days, practice. The circulation of the Chi in the body is, of course, purely imaginary for the beginner. However, after a certain time, one can with concentration send his idea to any chosen spot. In the Taoist work, as pointed out by Chang Chung-Yuan, "during this training period the chief task consists in stimulating the heart current by sending the genuine idea to unify heart and kidney. In the Taoist phraseology, this is to compound the mercury from the center of the heart and the lead from the center of the kidney into the elixir of life. . . . Thus the polarities of Yin and Yang are unified and the Golden Flowers bloom. The blooming of the Golden Flowers is due to the union of Yin and Yang, and the union of Yin and Yang, in turn, is initiated by the concentration on the genuine idea."[18]

From the scientific point of view, it appears that the effect of action along the meridian channels or nervous system is connected with the increase of electro-negative (Yin) or electro-positive (Yang) charges affecting colloidal structures.

Western science already established in 1933 that four main factors are able to disturb or alter colloidal equilibrium, namely, *Physical,* such as light, heat, sound, rays, currents, etc.; *Mechanical,* such as puncture, friction, pressure, etc.; *Chemical,* such as acids, arsenic, tar, paraffin, etc.; and *Biological,* such as microbes, parasites, sperm, etc. In these four main factors, we can find sufficient evidence to account for nearly all kinds of effective action at the Meridian points. But not quite all. We owe it to A. Korzybski to recognize a fifth factor — a potent factor, the semantic, which enables us to effect colloidal equilibrium.

In fact, all thinking is accompanied by energy currents of electric-wave nature, and experiments seem to indicate that such currents can and do effect both organic and inorganic material outside the skin.

[18] Chang Chung-yuan, *Creativity and Taoism: A Study of Chinese Philosophy, Art and Poetry.* New York: Julian Press, 1963, p. 156.

What is now required is sufficient investigation and experimentation to give understanding of the energy manifestation accompanying "intention" and "visualization", which will lead to the periodical control of that energy.[19]

Thus, from the point of view of science, we may assume that concentration, or sending one's idea or imagination to a certain spot of the meridian channels may have the effect of stimulating the nervous system in that region. In order to illustrate this point scientifically, we are also indebted to Chang Chung-Yuan, who, on the basis of the evid-

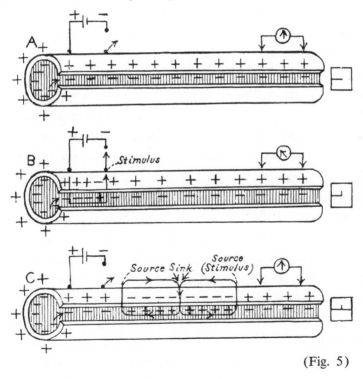

(Fig. 5)

[19] Credit is due to Marshall Ho'o, President of the National Tai Chi Ch'uan Institute, Los Angeles, California, for the above information and research.

[20] Figure 5, The Initial change of electrical current in nerve fiber.

ence advanced by Ernest Gardner in his *Fundamentals of Neurology,* has this to say: "According to modern neurology, nerve fibers are considered as hollow tubes, normally having a positive electrical charge on the outside and a negative charge on the inside surface. When a stimulus is applied, the charge is reversed in a small region. The outside, which was originally positive, becomes negative and the inside, formerly negative, becomes positive. This region of reversed polarity, as indicated in Figure 5,20 then moves along the tube, reversing the charge immediately ahead of it as it moves, and allowing the charge behind the movement to revert to normal. The charge of electricity is called a potential. When a stimulus is applied, we say the resting potential is reversed."

In Figure 5, taken from the *Fundamentals of Neurology:* "It illustrates the initial change of electrical current in a nerve following stimulation. At "A" we see the fiber as a tube, with interior exposed. Electrical charges both inside and outside are indicated. At the left end an electric circuit is attached to provide a mild shock. At the right is another circuit to record the results. At "B" the stimulus is applied and the charge begins to reverse, as shown by the arrow near the left end. At "C", after the charge has been reversed, the nerve impulse is propagated and moves down the fiber. As the impulse moves, it stimulates the region ahead of it and thus continues independently after the original triggering stimulus has ended."

"What makes the impulse repeat itself and flow as a current is simply the artificial stimulus. Thus one single shock applied to a nerve fiber creates a self propagating current and reverses the entire electrical activity both inside and outside the nerve. This phenomenon initiated by an artificial stimulus is produced by a psychic stimulus in meditative breathing when the well-trained practitioner sends the genuine idea to a certain nerve center. It would be logical to think this psychic stimulus applied to the nerve fiber would also create a self-propagating current and involve a change of electric charges. Furthermore, when the practitioner constantly sends the genuine idea to the nervous system, it moves on unceasingly; a tremendous change in the electrical charges is effected and the current flow is greatly increased. As the operation in the serious practitioner goes on month after month, and year after year, the emergence of "lightning and thunder" within his nervous system will be the natural outcome. Therefore it does not surprise us to learn that when the Taoist master reaches the highest level of meditation the "dragon" is revealed and the "thunder" is heard. Here symbolic language is used to describe a physical phenomenon. Whether the practitioner's way of initiating an electric current has the same value as the method of the electro-therapist would be worthwhile studying. It is obvious that what the Taoist calls the controlled course is the path of the sympathetic nerve. When the electric charge works on the sympathetic nerve, the healing of the inner organs will naturally follow, since heart, stomach and the other inner organs are closely connected with it. Figure 1 also from *Fundamentals of Neurology* by Ernest Gardner shows the relationship between the inner organs and the sympathetic nerve system."21

In ancient times, the purification of one's body by the utmost quiescence through the Breathing Rhythms has been interpreted by the Taoists as the manifestation of divine power revealed in man. "But in the light of modern neurology", as it has aptly been pointed out by Chang Chung-Yuan in the above passages, "these apparently miraculous revelations that emerge from a very high state of concentration (which functions as the psychic stimulus) may be interpreted

21 Chang Chung Yuan, op. cit., pp. 157-161.
22 Chang Chung-Yuan, op. cit., pp. 162-163.

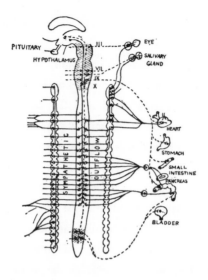

(Fig. 1)

as the physical phenomenon of depolarization of electric charges."22
It, then, appears that besides the physical, mechanical, chemical, biological as well as semantic factors that stimulate the points in the
meridian channels, the psychological factor — psychic stimulus —
working through the Cultural Breathing Rhythm can, no doubt, enforce
the electric capacity of the current, which circulates over the entire
body.

中華文化與太極拳

——在中國太極拳研究會五十八年第一次講演會講辭——

主席，各位先生：兄弟今天能有這個機會與各位見面，共同研究中華文化與太極拳這個問題，內心覺得極為高興，極為榮幸。這樣大問題，當然不是一二小時所能講解明白的。我這裡對於中國文化與其說是要分析其內容，不如說是要簡單地，握要地指出其全貌。我想自五四運動以來，國內研究文化問題的學者均從方法論上着眼，所以所得到的結論，往往突過前人，有特殊的創獲。胡適之先生民六由美歸國，發表中國哲學史一書，分析各家學說，極為精闢，名重當世。他當時所採用的方法，也即是經驗主義或實驗主義的方法。這種方法在科學上自然有極大的貢獻，不過採用這種方法所得到的結果，可惜往往是零碎的，片段的，也就是諺語所謂「只見樹木而不見森林」。目前西方研究文化的學者，除却窄而深的專門研究之外，似乎特別注重「體系的方法」(Systematic approach)，而其目的不是要指出文化的片段，而是要表現文化的全貌(Configuration or Gestalt)。這種方法在晚近二三十年間，由物理學開始應用，後來進到生物學，心理學，現在則更為歷史學，社會學和文化學所採用。當代的文化形態學者，社會學者，文化學者例如斯賓格勒（Spengler），湯恩培（Toynbec)，素羅金 (Sorokin)，克魯伯（Kroebcr）等，就是因為採用這種方法，洞流索源，明體達用，使我們對於世界文化的類型及其興起和沒落的全貌，有較深刻的瞭解。

我在拙著「文化學體系」一書上，也就是採取這種方法，對於世界文化的上層體系，分成「冥觀的」，「實感的」和「中庸的」三種基本類型。根據「兩極概念」(Polar Concept) 來看，冥觀文化是偏向精神主義和唯心主義的。歷史上，印度敎，佛敎，道教，原始的基督教大部是走向這一路。第二種實感型則偏向物質主義和唯物主義。現代西方四百年來的文化，可以說是走向這一路的。數千年來，中國文化雖然也具有不少冥觀文化與實感文化的特質，但因為它自堯舜禹湯文武以至周公孔子乃至孫中山，即倡導以中道或中庸法則做根據——所謂「唯精唯一，允執厥中」——這是「唯中論」的精義之所在，故中國文化的優勢類型，實在可說是屬於中庸文化的。

中道法則，應用到文化體系上，可以使它擷取「冥觀」與「實感」文化體系的精華，馴至可以造成「動的均衡體系」。我覺得，由於中華民族近年來對于文化的重估及覺悟到履行中道法則之重要，故這種中庸文化體系不難融會中西，逐漸完成文化的新均衡。亦惟如此，我們才能以自己的力量，拯救世界於水火，脫離人類於浩劫，從而建立民主的、倫理的、科學的、會通的整合世界文化體系。

我在上述一書內，對於這種理論已有比較詳細的分析，此處因時間所限，未便詳談。總之，中華文化的前途自然寄於復興運動之上，而中華文化復興之大道就是要切實踐履中道法則，在政治、經濟、社會、法律、藝術和科學各方面務求折衷至當，不走極端。

談到太極拳，大家都知道太極拳的哲學實以「周易」、老子「道德經」、慧能的「六祖壇經」為根據。因此我曾大胆地斷定太極拳係根據中國文化的基本哲學或中道文化法則組織而成——一方面是藝術，而另一方面也是科學，猶之乎印度瑜伽之同為藝術與科學一樣。

中國文化的基本哲學與最高法則，最早還是見諸「周易」。易文言說：「乾元用九，乃見天則。」天則就是現象的法則。易傳說：「易與天地準，故能彌綸天地之道。」易又說：「一陰一陽之謂道。」道就是宇宙萬物根源的總稱，乃由陰陽構成。道有時稱為太極，因為太極生兩儀……。故宇宙的第一原理也就是「

太極」。易說：「易有太極。」太極便是「大一」或「太一」。易繫辭傳說：「天下之動，貞乎一者也」。這「一」可以說是宇宙的根本原理。太極是「自存」的，絕對的，永久的、無限的。現象的宇宙，只是太極外表的表現罷了。

宇宙複雜的現象，變化萬端，其間有沒有法則可尋呢？當然是有的。周易一名而三義，就是說明現象是有法則的。分開來說：

其一是「簡易」。簡易就是說宇宙中有簡單的普遍原則。宇宙中本來有兩類現象，即是乾與坤、陰與陽、剛與柔。沒有乾坤就沒有易，所以說：「乾坤毀則無以見易。」沒有　陽，就沒有生生」，「孤陰不生，獨陽不長」，沒有「剛」「柔」，就沒有變化。「剛柔相推而生變化」，這是簡易的原則。

其二是「變易」。易傳說明宇宙是一個「變」的過程，所以易經叫做「變經」，英文譯易經為Book of Changes，也就是表達變的意義。人類萬物，由自然現象以至文化現象，時刻在變，不惟年變，兼又日遷，有如逝水，涉足長流，前水已非後水。易傳說：「天地變化，聖人效之。」「變動不居，周流六虛，上下无常，剛柔相易，不可為典要，唯變所適。」（易傳繫辭下），因此斷定「神無方而易無體」，「生生之謂易」。易的八卦就是聖人用各種符號來說明宇宙各種變象的模式。

其三是「不易」。一切變動，均依照一定的模式或法則表現。這些法則在今天自然科學所已發現的，有所謂「萬有引律」，有所謂「相對律」，有所謂「統一場」，在文化科學上有所謂「內變律」(Law of Immanent Change)、「有限律」(Law of Limit)、「進化律」(Law of Evolution)、「循環律」(Law of Cycle)等等。但是周易則歸納各種事象，演成以下幾種法則；而太極拳也是按照同樣的法則而組成的。試繹如下：

（一）兩極交泰的法則：儒家和道家的許多道理，淵源于易經。「道」，依照老子所說，是先天地生的東西。「有物混成，先天地生，寂兮寥兮，獨立而不改，周行而不殆，可以為天下母，吾不知其名，字之曰道，強名之曰大。」（道德經廿五章），而易傳則斷說「一陰一陽之謂道。」可見道或太極是體，陰陽是用。古人發見這種真理，完全依憑直覺或妙悟法，而不是靠理性法（數學或理則）或實驗法。由于先賢的超人的智慧，我們今日乃知道宇宙一切生生不已的現象是有兩方面的，是相對的。其見于自然者就是陰與陽，光與暗，熱與冷，動與靜，向心力與離心力；其見諸人類者，為男與女；見于數學與理則者為正與負，然與不然；其見于道德者為善與惡。現代物理學已給易經這一個中心理論，給予證明。例如從前認為原子是宇宙極微的基礎，現在物理學家把牠裂分後，知道當中有陽電和陰電，叫做電子（Electron）和質子(Proton)。電子繞着質子或原核而旋轉，正如行星之繞太陽而旋轉一樣。最近物理學更發明電子也可分為陰陽（負和正）兩面。這與周易所發見的真理，畢竟符合。這種「陰陽互動的法則」，西方叫做「兩極化法則」（Law of Polarity）。陰陽為什麼會互動？老子說：「反者道之動」。易說：「剛柔相摩，八卦相盪而生變化」。但兩極的動不是矛盾的動，因易傳說：「萬物睽而其事類也。」易睽卦象傳曰：「天地睽而其事同也，男女睽而其志通也，萬物睽而其事類，睽之時用大矣哉。」正義說：「睽者乖異之名。」萬物雖乖異或對立，但「天地是交泰的」，「陰陽是互濟的」。惟有交泰和互濟，才能構成兩極交泰法則。

太極拳是宋代張三丰根據這種法則而組成的。關于張氏的生平，各人的考證，不一其說，這裡可以置之不談。本來周濂溪（敦頤）（一〇一六——一〇七三），在宋時就已根據道家陳摶（希夷）之說，傳下來一個「太極圖」——用來解釋宇宙生化的原理，謂「太極」由「無極」而來，因此太極拳譜亦有「無極而太極」一語。依周氏的說法，「太極」是大而無外的東西，太極動而生陽，動極而靜，靜而生陰。陽即物體的動，陰即物體的靜，一動一靜，相互為根，即一陰一陽的互涉，由「無極而太極」（也就是同于德國大哲萊布尼芝（Leibnitz）所發見的「零與一」

之哲學。這種哲學或符號與今日電子計算機所用的符號相同,其原出自周易,此處未便詳說。太極拳作者把這種理論採取過來,認爲「陽」是「實」,「陰」是「虛」,太極拳的全部姿勢,只是陰陽虛實,互相爲用,相反其實相成。所以太極拳理論家王宗岳有「動靜之機,陰陽之母」的說法。可見太極拳的組成是以易的第一種法則——「兩極交泰」——爲根據的。

（二）「循環往復的法則」:這種法則,西方叫做「輪化或循環法則」(Law of Cycles)或「生滅法則」(Law of Growth and Decay)。循環往復或生,異,住,滅的現象,見諸自然世界的,有晝與夜,寒與暑,生與死,見諸文化世界的有文化之興起和沒落。依照這個法則講,宇宙的一切東西,由人類及其文化以至太陽系,乃至整個或無限的宇宙現象,其變動均莫能逃離這個法則的支配。易傳說:「日中則昃,月盈則食,天地盈虛,與時消息。」易傳又說:「日往則月來,月往則日來,日月相推,而明生焉………。」易乾卦卦辭:「乾、元、亨、利、貞」,而貞下起元,皆表現此一法則的義諦。由此便可明瞭,這種法則的意義是什麼。

太極拳祖師張三丰,王宗岳根據這個法則,所以創造出太極拳的架子,由「太極拳起勢」,以至「合太極」,循環往復,如環無端,一手一太極,所謂「往復須有摺叠,進退須有轉換」,即指手臂相沾,互相翻覆。在「行功心解中」,說到行功,則說:「行氣如九曲珠,無微不到。」至于道書上所稱之「小周天」,「大周天」,也不離循環法則。在太極拳的應用上,所以說:「收即是放,放即是收」,這也是循環不斷的現象,可見太極拳的組成,顯然是以周易的第二個法則做根據。

（三）「有限的法則」或「反的法則」:這個法則,英文叫做Law of Limit 或Law of Reversion。哲學上則多用希臘文Enantiodromia一字,表示事物發展到了一定限度時,必囘到相反的地方。易傳說:「復其見天地之心乎?」「終日乾乾,反復道乎?

」「亢龍有悔，盈不可久也。」「无往不復。」這是此種法則最好的說明。太極拳作者根據這一法則，所以說一切動作，「有上即有下，有前即有後，有左即有右」。又「放」到了極度必須收，「收」到了極度必須放，虛到了極度必轉實，實到了極度必轉虛，虛實相生。可見動作到了極限，必須回復到相反的方面。這種現象由太極圖看來，尤其明白。圖包括陰陽兩面。白的部分表示陽，陽由中心產生，產生以後，由擴大而增進，直到限度，以圖的上部之直線做代表。到了最大限度時，則反而為陰，陰由中心產生，直到最大限度，以下部直線做代表，因而陽由陰產生出來。如此循環不已，以至無窮。這代表着兩種法則，即循環法則與有限法則。可見當代的直線進化說，(Theory of linear evolution)所稱的「永遠進步和發展」之不可能，而太極拳動作都採曲線，是很有道理的。

　　（四）中道法則：中國人向來認定由堯、舜、禹、湯、文武、周公、孔子傳下來的十六個字的心傳，所謂「人心唯危，道心唯微，唯精唯一，允執厥中」，就是我們的道統。其實允執厥中這個中道法則，在周易發揮得最透澈，最實際。所謂中，易傳分別為空間之中，時間之中，人間之中，適中。而中庸則說：「中也者，天下之大本也，和也者，天下之達道也，致中和天地位焉，萬物育焉。」又說：「致廣大而盡精微，極高明而道中庸。」老子亦說：「多言數窮，不如守中。」佛家亦主張中道，凡事以道德為主，不走極端。我們因此可斷言：中道乃中國中庸文化體系所由建立的最基本的文化法則。太極拳作者以執一守中為根據，所以張三丰論十三勢說：「十三勢者，掤、擴、擠、按、採、挒、肘、靠、此八卦也。進步，退步，左顧，右盼，中定，此五行也。掤、擴、擠、按，即乾，坤，坎，離四正方也。採、挒、肘、靠，即巽、震、兌、艮，四斜角也。進，退，顧，盼，定，即金、木、水、火、土也。」十三勢是太極拳的基本動作，向愷然氏對此解釋得很好，他說：「十三勢以中定為主，掤，擴，……等十二勢爲輔，有中定後一切勢皆不能離乎中定。每一虛實，皆先有中定，而後有變化，處處有虛實，即處處有中定，蓋法無定法，而一切法皆中定中出，法遍周身，中定亦遍週身。」這是確話。

我們所以斷論，太極拳作者在整體上，以中道法則做根據，所以在身法方面，王宗岳第一便標示出：「尾閭中正神貫頂」。尾閭與脊骨（神經中樞）有關聯的關係，爲元氣升降之要道，故須中正，與玉枕垂成直線，方爲適宜。又說：「立如平準」「不偏不倚」，因爲立身中正，如天秤之不偏不倚，無前傾後仰，左歪右斜之勢，然後身法可立。第二，他又指明『立身中正安舒，支撐八面』，倘立身偏倚，不守中定原則，則精神立現渙散，安能各方兼顧。縱使「運動時身體轉換甚繁，不免因擴大收放，腰之上而稍有偏倚，但腰以下至尾閭一段，則無時不須中正。此段如不中正，則將發生彈性之根據失去，全身一切蓄發均不可能矣」（郭連蔭，太極拳譜語）。又陳長興謂「惟有五陽駢五陰，陰陽無偏稱妙手。」因陰陽配合得中方稱妙手，其餘只是軟手、硬手、散手、好手，均不合乎中道使然。孫祿堂氏精太極，八卦，形意，謂「內家之技擊，必求其中，太極空中也，八卦變中也，形意直中也」，亦同此理。中庸之道，精一執中，蓋惟能中，所以能立於不敗之地，偏者遇之，靡不挫敗。站在中道立場，不求勝，而天下莫能勝，太極拳之大用在此。

（五）天人合一的法則：太極拳作者謂太極拳的目的在給「天下英雄豪傑，延年益壽，不徒在技藝之末」，所以我們提出「道技雙修」一語，這是很重要的決策。人類壽命，據科學家言，將來可以達到三百歲，現在印度習瑜伽術者往往可以達到百九十歲。普通人士，現今亦有達到百歲者。故我以爲練太極的人士，第一步應該以達到百五十歲爲目的，最低亦應達到百歲。如何才可達百歲或以上，我以爲單是靠技還是不夠，進一步必須向道的方面講求。修瑜伽學者向不把能習得各種身法算做成就。反之，

「親證現量，可能成爲障碍。若惟求此等成就，祇能成爲一個專家，依然是一個凡夫，惟自證實際，方是究竟目的。」（引自軍荼利瑜伽一書）。瑜伽之道，據我所知，在哲學與科學方面，力求自性眞智之貫澈，而歸于「一」。太極拳作者亦認爲太極拳之眞義，「無形無象，全身透空，忘物自然，西山懸磬，虎吼猿鳴，泉淸水靜，翻江鬧海，盡性立命」，可見習拳之最高境界，確實進到與儒、釋、道之聖道合而爲一，打破了我與宇宙分立之二元論，做到與「太空同體」，「天地並立」（無我）。這種境界也就是依于天人合一的法則而來。天人合一的法則，易傳曾揭其公式：「立天之道，日陰與陽，立地之道，日柔與剛，立人之道，日仁與義」。易的全部總綱，其實不外指示天人合一的法則，故又說：「易之爲書也，廣大悉備，有天道焉，有人道焉，有地道焉，彙三才而兩之，故六；六者非它也，三才之道也」（易傳繫辭下）。宇宙本爲一大有機體，人不過其中的一小部分，故老子說「人法地，地法天，天法道，道法自然」。自然即陰陽之常。「一陰一陽之謂道」，誠性存存，道義之門。人的心性，就是自然之質與能的活動的中心，如能還歸于一，與道合體，達到「我即宇宙，宇宙即我」，那就是修道的最高境界。張三丰云：「學太極拳爲入道之基。」又說：「學者須于動靜之中，尋太極之益。」這是關鍵的啓發與指示。我們如能以中庸「誠者天之道也，誠之者人之道也」，「至誠之道，可以前知」，由人道以達到天道，則乾以易知，坤以簡能，萬變雖殊，而歸于一。「一」就是「道」，也就是「太極」。這與瑜伽學者以「卡華利耶」（Kaivalya）爲覺之境界相同。「卡華利耶」乃是脫離一切障碍，得大自在之謂，佛謂：「把幕一層一層揭開，然其後還有一層一層的可以發見。」（Veil upon veil shall lift, but still veil upon veil will be found behind）。到了這種道功完成，我們不但致人生于康樂延年之完善境界，抑亦「與天地合其德，與日月合其明，與四時合其序，與鬼神合其吉凶，先天而天弗違，後天而奉天時，而況于人乎，況于鬼神乎」。莊子說：「天地與我並生，萬物與我爲一」，如斯而已。所以我認爲，「道技兼修」，有其必要及可能，這在做過道家靜坐與內功者，都會有深入的洞見。「技」僅是達到「道」的橋樑或方便，若執技爲道，兩皆失之。

以上所說，僅是個人對于中國文化與太極拳的關係之臆測，粗疏簡陋，自知不免，還請各位先進大德，多多指敎！謝謝！

參考資料

黃文山著：文化學體系（台北中華書局印行，一九七一年第三修正版）

Wen Shan Huang, New Perspectives on the Processes and Fundamentals of Chinese Cullure. Chinese Cullure, Vol. IX, No. 3, Sept. 1968

Wen-Shan Huang, I Ching or the Book of Changes and Tai Chi Ch'uan, Chinese Culture, Vol. X, No. 4. 1964.

I. K. Taimni. The Science of Yoga, The Theosophical Publishing House, Wheston, Ill, U. S. A.

R. G. H. Sue, The Tao of Science, an Essay on Western Knowledge and Eastern wisdom, The M. I. T. Press, 1964.

Wei Tat, An Exposition of thn I-Ching, Institute of Cultural Studies, Taipei, 1970.

東西壽命學合論

一、緒　言

　　人類自遠古開始，舉凡傾向哲學思考的先知先覺，免不了對生命和生存的基本問題，不斷地找求答案。所謂基本問題，第一是宇宙的創造或進化，其究極原理是什麼？第二、我們怎樣可以獲得體格上，精神上的長期的健康，俾能從事於最後眞理的探討？

　　由對後一問題的追求，在東方和西方文化的演進過程中，乃產生「壽命學」的研究。西方人說，「人乃萬物的尺度」，而「死是人的尺度」。東方人說，「人生五福壽爲先」。但是爲什麼有生必有死？人們最多可以活多久？生與死，壽與命，確是人生最高最大的問題。

　　在中國古人看，「人生七十古來稀」，但由於時代與思想進步，今人則又倡言「人生七十方開始」。原始民族在舊石器或新石器時代，平均的壽命，大約不過二三十歲。二十世紀七十年代的今日，西方衛生進步，美國男子平均已可達七十歲，女子可達七十二歲。「百年乃人壽之大齊」，筆者相信，我們如果努力探討「壽命學」，一方注重於形體與生命之延長，一方注重精神與心性之修養，則每個人即在二十世紀末期，平均或可達百歲。到了二十一世紀及以後，人類能夠去取自然，括囊無咎，則平均由百歲以至百五十歲，乃至二、三百歲，由不可能者成爲可能，不可有者成爲可有，或非絕對不經之談。

　　「長壽」旣爲人類共同蘄求的生活最高目的，但如何才能夠長壽？由於東西學人治學態度的不同，因而對於「壽命學」研究的方法，遂致釐然各別。西方先進國家，近三四百年來，治學方法，注重實驗，生命科學遂跟着科學與醫學之發達，一日千里。美、英、德、法、俄各著名大學，近年來盛設「壽命學」（Gerontology）講座，或倡導建立「壽命學學院」（Institute of Gerontology），其目的在研究吾人一生之內部變化， 討求內部變化之法則，以期延長人類之壽命。成績雖未臻至高境界，但千里之行，已起於足下了。東方文化以中國及印度爲代表，二者數千年來治學方法，重直覺及理性而絀實驗，對於「壽命學」之研究，集中「從內築基」，故中國有性命學之產生與煉丹術之成立，視「百歲爲夭」。印度則有瑜伽健身術，大要基於瞑想，集中內視、求我之眞正形式，視我爲遍在，遍能與遍知，以期達於至道至聖至神。此與儒家道家天地與我並生，萬物與我同體之「天人合一」或「自然有機體論」之人生觀，實有異曲同工之妙。而其對於維持「生命力」與「生存能」課題之探究，亦有獨到之處。當今太空時代，東西空間隔離，經已打破，而「萬教歸一的大同宗敎」，也跟着科學的演進，而逐漸形成，故東西壽命學，實有綜合探究之必要，因作「東西壽命學合論」。

二、西方壽命學支配年齡的科學的研究

「壽命學」或「老年學」（Geriatrics）乃是西方新興的科學之一種。

壽命學的目的，一方在延長人的壽命，一方在改進人的生命。通常認衰老與疾病是同義的，但壽命學者指出衰老與疾病乃是兩種純然不同的歷程。個人不論有沒有疾病，衰老歷程在個人的生命中，却不斷地在進展當中。

許多醫生揚言，心疾和癌症乃是今日死亡的最大原因，但到底必有可以克服的一天。 然我們要問，到了那時 ， 人類壽命會不會大加延長？羅安琪加省大學分校醫藥學院壽命學敎授高乃曼（Ralkh Goldman）博士謂在美國裡，上述二種疾病，爲引致半數死亡的因素，但假使這些疾病可以消除，每人平均年齡之增加，

也不會超過八年半。高博士所以說，與其專門依賴消除疾病去延長生命，不如進一步注意我們爲什麼會衰老？惟有如此，我們才可以支配衰老的歷程。他似乎在說：「我命在我，不在於天」。高氏同時又說，我們縱能消除一切疾病，但對於現在的平均壽命的延長，最多不能添增十五年。

倫敦大學的甘福（Alex Comfort）博士爲當今英國壽命學的領袖。他說，在疾病消除的領域，「遞減囘復的法則」經已發生效力。在美國白人當中，大家講求衞生，對營養不斷改進，疾病已受到控制。當二十世紀開始時，男子平均年齡不過四十六歲，現在已增到七十歲。然而依現在情形看，人體等於一架電視機，牠的部份總有缺點，到了缺點太多，整個機器便告毀壞，無法修理。因此，甘福氏認爲現在醫學上雖能製造人爲器官，或把器官移植，但到底不會對於平均壽命，作無限的延長。

所以目前的壽命學者，都兢兢業業地企圖發見支配衰老歷程的普遍方法。然而現在沒有任何科學家，知道這種方法是什麼。依照目前說明衰老歷程的性質之各種學說看，不同觀念雖然具有各自的價值，但許多學說，現仍在實驗室試驗當中，還須若干時間，方能談到實用的價值。無怪乎許多人對於利西安（Ponce Le Seon）的「靑春永在說」，及其他科學家對於猴子內分泌器官的移植法，都還在懷疑之列。

總之，西方科學家多少年來，已不斷注意控制壽命的可能性之問題。直到今日，他們還承認沒有成功。然而當代壽命學者並沒有放棄他們的目的，而不往前追求，往前探討。"不問收穫，只問耕耘"，這是科學家的眞精神之所在。

三、西方壽命學的目的——延緩衰老

人生爲什麼會衰老？其原因何在？壽命學者研究衰老歷程，相信今後當可一步一步地認識身體變遷的原因。人身由細胞組成，科學對於細胞衰老，已有相當認識。今後對牠們變遷的原因，倘有更正確的了解，則由細胞形成的身體之衰老歷程，自然可望加以延緩。

三十年前，康奈爾大學的麥琪（Mac Kaye）博士對老鼠及其他低等動物作過無數實驗，發見老鼠的幼年期，可加控制，使到這種期限與生命的期限延長。到了把老鼠的幼年期可以和緩之後，牠便由成熟而趨入衰老。經過這樣的試驗，證明老鼠的年齡，可受控制，且能比普通的壽命延長一倍。

麥琪博士的方法非常簡單。他把飼鼠的吃料，減少一半，便可把幼年期延緩，到了通常吃料恢復以後，老鼠的身體變遷，便一如從前，由成熟而趨於衰老。波利磨大學的壽命學教授巴魯思（Charle H. Barrows）採取海上的微小動物而加以實驗，發見牠們衰老歷程，除所吃的物料之外，受溫度影響甚大。把水的溫度降低，對於那些動物的老年階段，有重大影響。科學家因此相信如果人們深知食料和溫度對人的衰老歷程上發生何種影響後，則身體的變遷，當一樣地可以控制或延緩。

現在的壽命學者相信每個細胞的遺傳質料，叫做 DNA 的，可以受到環境的影響。他們說，只要深知 DNA 的結構，便可改變一個細胞由幼年到成熟以至衰老的歷程，進一步更可控制衰老。現在的科學家，所以有些集中研究 DNA 的歷程，有些則專心研究環境對於 DNA 的影響，以及這種影響對於衰老的關係。

羅安琪加省大學醫學院的華爾福（Roy L. Walford）教授在另一方面指出人們到了年老之後，細胞的 DNA 往往發生突變，而這種突變，是反身體的。如果對於這種機械，能夠了解，則控制衰老，當有可能。其方法在減少這種突變，或在未變之前，加以修理，以便防止其發展。

根據滿地可大學實驗醫藥和手術學院的報告，顯示出人類總有一天可以免除受到常態的衰老歷程的支配。（見大英百科全書一九六六年年鑑醫藥條）。該學院的主任施易（Hans Selye）早就說，鈣的分播在身體內發出混亂，實為衰老現象的許多原因之一種。紐約大學醫藥中心的德遜（Meyer Texon）教授指出普通認爲血管硬化，由食物、年齡、性別、種族、藥物、酵素、緊張、脂肪及其他疾病所形成，但他認爲血管硬化乃由支配血之流行的液質動力學之基本法則造成。該法則謂流行的速率越大，靜的壓力越低。如果這個法則是對的，醫學界必須在理化方面，找出支配人血流行的方法，方能對於年齡衰老之原于血管硬化者，予以控制。

社會環境對於衰老當然有其影響。思波利維打醫院專研究衰老問題的索巴爾（Harry Sobel）教授指出我們沒有出世以前已受到環境的影響。例如母親的營養如何、她服食何種藥物、她的情緒如何，對於未出世的孩兒，均有影響。癌症可以減少人們的壽命至數年或數十年之久，其產生當然與環境的因素有關係。較次的環境影響，如宇宙的輻射線，空氣與水之染污等等對於衰老有沒有影響？如果是有的，則對牠們的控制，當然可以延長壽命，並改進其品質。蘇聯壽命學者高維治（Georgi Gurvich）謂長壽的秘訣，在排除個人的憂慮，增進個人的快樂。他說，蘇聯自革命後，把階級社會的一切社會紛擾消滅。失業、飢餓、貧窮、壓逼都不存在，所以嬰兒的死亡率大大降低，成人平均的年齡亦大大增加。社會文化的循境因素對於衰老的關係（縱使沒有以上的例子），似亦不應忽視。中國古諺謂「憂能傷人」，而處世則要「清風明月，忘懷富貴」，誠哉其言。

美國朱思丹研究基金的朱思丹（Johan Bjorksten）博士在另一研究領域，說明化學品如食物、菸草、污染、及其他原料，進入體內之後，如何可以增進衰老。同時他又指出許多「分子」在體內往往互相「橫結」，結果便把分子對身體的利益取消，同時又把細胞的機械阻碍着，這便使細胞一方進入沒落，一方又減少應付壓逼的能力。如果這種學說是可以證實的話，科學家的工作，在如何應用酵素來把「橫結」的歷程加以解除，這也許是對衰老醫治的方法之一種。

統而言之，今日的科學家預料人類的生命總有一天可以控制，使到幼年期延長以後，其成熟期與健康期可以有六十年至七十年之久。但一般來說，西方壽命學者直至今日，認爲我們在經常生活中，可以靠自己努力控制衰老的歷程，其主要關鍵不外三種。第一種是精神。「精神建造人的身體」。如果個人的精神萎弱不振，身體的特質也與之相應。如果人格是偏向振作的、奮鬥的、冒險的，身體也就跟着活潑、剛健、快樂。「天行健，君子以自强不息」，實有至理。第二種是營養。根據醫學家實驗，要延長壽命，不但要適宜的食料，最要緊的還是食料不要過量。「甘、脆、肥、濃、乃腐腸之藥」。古人的格言，在這裡一樣用得着。第三種是運動。運動對於全身的器官及系統均有益處；而適宜的運動尤其可以培養精神，增强心力，延長壽命。所謂「流水不腐，戶樞不蠹」，信然。

以上所述，僅點出西方壽命學者由實驗而得到的結論之發端。茲再述東方壽命學的梗概，以資比較。

四、東方壽命學畧論

東方壽命學當以中國道家的性命學、印度的瑜伽學爲主要。

中國古代壽命學，實爲最高最大的學問。其注重物質元素，認爲是壽命之基礎者，始於洪範。其以陰陽剛柔，推論宇宙人生之變化者，始於周易。易繫辭言：「生生之謂易」，由此可見古人注重變化與壽命之關係至大。至於陰陽兩極之法則，尤爲中國醫學不祧之宗，且具有絕大科學價值，這是毫無疑義的。孔子說：「未知生，焉知死」，由此亦可窺見他對於生命的關懷。然而先秦思想，足以啓發二千餘年來中國性命學之研究，而貢獻特大者，當推老莊。老莊的自然主義，以養生盡年爲要道。老子主清靜無爲，貴柔不爭，虛心實腹，無知無欲，和光同塵，長生久視，早已指出壽命之途逕與方術。莊子尤肆言養生之道，注意緣督爲經，吐故納新。「在宥」言廣成子自云修身千二百歲，而形未嘗矣。華封人云:「千歲厭世,去而上僊」。大抵莊子之學。在於與大化冥合,天人合一。其著作中如'養生主','大宗師','達生'各篇,包含世界壽命學的理想,多不磨之眞理,歷久而常新。彼嘗謂郭子玄所謂「同天人,齊萬致,萬致不相非,天人不相勝,故曠然無不一,冥然不在,而玄同彼我,則眞人之至德也」。'大宗師'反復申言此意,明道(原理)之玄於天地上古之先,見獨(絕對)之入於不死不生之境,玄冥而無形,參寥而廣遠,疑始而莫知其所自萌,死生存亡,通貫爲一體。(參見吳康、老莊哲學、商務)。這種理想,實多與現代科學之新發見相密合。新的有機體論說明人身由元子構成,人身之元子與宇宙之元子一致。人死後,元子不滅,復歸於宇宙。莊子所謂始卒若環,是謂天鈞。所謂一死生,泯物我,通造化,本末相同,終始一貫。此當爲近代自然有機體論之先河,而又是壽命學之最高境界。故其理想不特與最新之科學一致,且與印度之瑜伽學,亦多密合。

道教本由老莊之自然主義發展而來,其理想境界,以長生不老爲目的。一部「道藏」,其中雖多迷信之說,但撮其精要,則以發明養生長壽之秘訣爲關鍵。(看日人伊藤光遠著,「養生內功秘訣」,另近人所編「養生長壽秘訣」叢編等書,均台北自由出版社出版,可參考。)道家以及其後道教對於養生長壽方法之發明,實可代表中國長壽學之全部份或大部份,其方法有七:

一、吐故納新的呼吸法;

二、服食日華的太陽療治法;

三、熊經鳥申的運動法;

四、燮理陰陽的房中術;

五、服食丹藥的仙道法;

六、辟穀寡食的養生法;

七、自我療治的按摩法。

要之、道家或道教內功煉丹之術,以「精」「氣」「神」爲人身三寶。至其修命之方,則又有所謂「移精補腦法」(英國科學家李約瑟著的「中國的科學與文明」，首卷由本人譯述行世。台北商務，一九七二年初版。他在第二卷中，批評此法，認為無科學價值。）「煉精化氣，煉氣化神之法」，以及「煉心法」、「煉形法」、「服氣法」、「胎息法」、「導引法」（即上述之呼吸法），「按摩法」、「無漏法」、「先後天交煉法」、「陰陽雙修法」等，其中幼稚可笑之點雖多，但也有許多仍與科學之說密合。自從德人衞禮賢譯述道教的「金華要旨」（The Secret of Golden Flower, A Chinese Book of Life, translated by Richard Wilhelm, English Tr. by Cary F. Baynes, N. Y）一書，復經心理學大家榮格（C. G. Jung）作序發行後，煉丹導引之術，經已流入歐美，頗能引起西方人之注意。我們認為道家壽命之學，如果能排除一部份幼稚的迷信思想（如「服食丹藥，以求長生，多為藥所誤」，這與西方之服食幻想藥（LSD），也許同樣無用。又如房中術如不在燮理陰陽，敦睦夫婦，而流為旁門左道之採補術，則亦毫不足道），披沙鑠金，自有可取之處。日人伊藤光遠謂「當今世界各國，對於「壽命之學」之研究，無不全力以赴。而人類的壽命，亦復因而在日漸長加中；由於各國國民平均年齡之逐漸提高，足為證明。如能更從事提倡此煉丹內功運動，則「百歲壯年」「百五十歲的老年」的美夢，當是件很容易的事」，或非無所見。

閒嘗思之，竊以為道家對壽命學最大的貢獻，蓋為太極拳之創作。相傳太極拳創自張三丰眞人，但亦有謂出自河南陳家溝者。陳家太極拳本為楊家太極拳之所自。大抵陳家太極拳淵源於王宗岳。王著「太極拳論」，首述「無極而太極」之說。可見太極拳的根本原理，除以易家陽陰剛柔相濟，老子專氣致柔之原則為依皈外，要以宋儒所解釋之太極圖為主要。朱彝尊考證出濂溪之太極圖說，本於道家的無極圖。太極圖說明宇宙萬物生成之次序，無極圖是道家用以講丹法，後來更應用於太極拳。太極圖最上為無極而太極。次二為陰陽配合，陽動陰靜。次三為五行定位，五行各一其性。次四爲乾道成男，坤道成女。最下爲化生萬物。無極圖由下而上。初一爲玄牝之門，次二爲鍊精化氣，鍊氣化神，次三爲五行定性，五氣朝元，次四爲陰陽配合，取坎塡離，最上爲鍊氣還虛，復歸無極。（參看劉百閔，羣經肆言）（又關於鍊氣化神等方法，可看近人王先青著，養生新論，台北版）。輓近太極拳專家董英傑等，均注重鍊精化氣，鍊氣化神，鍊神還虛之術。可見太極拳除外形外，實以玄功爲其爲精要。近來太極拳已流傳美國，明智之士，視爲壽命學之要道，可惜多數人只懂得太極之形，至能眞心一意，同時從事內功修養者，爲數甚少。今後如何可以扭轉這一形勢，其責任應落在中國知識份子的身上了。此外有可注意者，却爲趙中道氏傳出之「太極尺」，目的注重鍛鍊先天氣功，而以「動」，「挸」，「搖」，「抖」，「靜」爲不易之秘訣。趙氏詩說：『度過百年十五春，筋強骨壯滿精神，勞動教授先天術，人人鍛鍊健康身，』而方法則甚簡單，收効亦極宏速，老少易學，大可以爲太極拳之補充。（看程達材著先天氣功太極尺及功法圖解等書，香港太極柔術研究社出版。）

其次，佛家視人生與痛苦俱來，深信空諦，故以涅槃寂滅爲究竟。心經謂：「無無明，亦無無明盡，無老死，亦無老死盡」，並認「色即是空，空即是色」，故能「遠離顚倒夢想」，禪家則倡見性成佛，本來未嘗有肉身不壞，長生不死之說。然而「無量壽佛」，佛到底與天地合一，同其永在。中國禪宗的修養方法，特別是禪定宗，與道家修養方法，印度瑜伽學有許多相通之處。定境成熟，對於健康身心，却病延年，當然有其特效。故禪定之業，與東方壽命學，有密切關係，這是筆者所深信而不疑的。

東方壽命學，除以道家性命學，佛家禪宗爲主流而外，當以印度之「瑜伽學」爲最重要。印度史前期的祺達（Gita），根本就是一部瑜伽的精神訓練之史詩，把行動、知識和崇拜綜合在一起（參看程兆熊譯「博伽梵曲」，香港鵝湖出版社印行）。祺達瑜伽，不是逃離人生，遺世獨立，而是一切生命之精神化、神聖化。佛陀在二千五百年前，已受到它的影響，而在佛滅後這二千餘年中，瑜伽在印度傳統文化上，仍佔最高位置而未嘗間斷。

印度現代大哲奧魯賓鐸 (Sri Arobindo) 在少年時期，本來受學英倫。歸國後，經數十年之努力，把古代瑜伽綜合起來，倡導「整合瑜伽學」(Intagral Yoga)，追溯瑜伽的淵源，由祺達以至烏賓曉諦 (Upanishad)，再由烏賓尼曉諦以至吠陀(Veda)經典本身。所著「神聖的生命」(Life Divine)，把印度的古代的精神生活與現代的精神生活，打成一片，聯成一氣，尤值得萬分注意。

許多宗教家把瑜伽學(The Science of Yoga) 與宗教視爲同體，這是錯的。瑜伽無疑幫助一切宗教家去從事瞑想，然而瑜伽不是宗教。牠包括一切科學，而又超乎一切科學。牠具有研究精神力的特獨的方法，爲其他科學研究所不及。

筆者相信瑜伽就是印度的壽命學，而也與道家的性命學，佛家的禪定學一樣，同是東方智慧的結晶。我們把牠應用來治療一切體質的和精神的疾病，當然不會發生任何損害。有如一切科學，牠也是思想的分析和綜合之結果。進一步，瑜伽也可以說是支配心靈的科學，若從實際的觀點看，我們可以把它區分爲以下八個體系：

（一）戒律（Yama）——A戒暴行、B戒殺生、C戒盜竊、D戒淫邪、E戒說謊。這是支配心靈的體系。

（二）精進(Nijama)——修行必須誠意專精，謹守成規。這是達到支配心靈底目的之體系。

（三）調身（Asana）——練習各種姿勢，增強肌肉、神經、骨骸、內臟、四肢及各部的機能。這是採用各種姿勢，以達到支配心靈的狀態之體系。

（四）調息（Pranayama）——練習呼吸控制，使血液得以適當循環，並使血氣充沛。這是支配「生命能」的體系。

（五）攝心（Pratyahara）——控制情緒，摒除雜念。這是鬆
　　　弛一切器官，把意識撤離的體系。

（六）凝神（Rharana）——集中精神，用志不分。這是把意
　　　識集中在身體的某部份之體系。

（七）入定（Dhyana）——淨化心靈，片念不起，而入于定。
　　　這是對身體作永恒的暗示之體系。

（八）三昧（Samadhi）——達到證悟本性，以至天人合一之
　　　最高境界。這是創造一切意志力和意識力之體系。

由於以上八種體系組成的瑜伽「壽命學」——也可說是超壽
命學，便有下列八個步驟：

一、以決定的意志，去支配心靈，這是第一個步驟。

二、依據嚴格的規則，達成決心。這是第二個步驟。

三、練習自己的身體，達成堅定的姿勢。這是第三個步驟。

四、實行和練習支配呼吸技能，這是第四個步驟。

五、把意識能從對外的接觸撤離，使與最高的意識證同，這
是第五個步驟。

六、把心靈集中身體的一部份或特殊的「靈球」（Cakras）（
共有七個）或肢體，乃至集中整個身體，這是第六個步驟。

七、在心靈集中後，對身體發出強有力的暗示，要暗示什麼
，這就靠自己的意向而定。要寒如冰，熱如火，隨意所至，均可
達成，這是第七個步驟。

八、經過長期的練習，意識心靈，自能跟着意識命令而轉進
，這是第八個步驟。

瑜伽學者相信在最後境界，自然而然地感覺到最高意識的存
在，且能與最高意識合而為一。「你將感覺到宇宙就是你，你就
是整個宇宙」。由於自身受心靈的支配，進一步便是覺悟、圓滿
、自由。瑜伽學者指出由感官而獨知的宇宙，只是宇宙的四份之
一。其潛藏未知的部份，則屬於神的層面。故瑜伽學所感知的乃
是一個永久的不死的世界。

其在中國，易文言曰：「夫大人者，與天地合其德，與日月合其明，與四時合其序，與鬼神合其吉凶」。又曰：「聖而不測之謂神」。老子：「治人事天莫若嗇。夫唯嗇，是謂早服，早服謂之重積德。重積德則無不克，無不克則莫知其極，可以有國，有國之母，可以長久。是謂深根固蒂，長生久視之道」（道德經長生章第五九）。又說「死而 不亡者壽」（第三十三章）莊子則說：「指窮于薪，火傳也，不知其盡也」。薪喻形體，火喻精神。以指折薪而燃之，則薪有盡時；薪雖有盡，而火終無窮極。蓋形體有時而盡，精神（生主）如能凝而不發，則永可長久長存。所以他主張「外天下」，「外物」，「外生」，「見獨」，「無古今」「物物而不爲物所物」，「然後能入于不死不生」。此種超絕空時而一切爲「神」之境界，最後或與瑜伽之發見——悟——互相印證。這也許是東方壽命學的最高境界——無限之時，謂之「無量壽」，無限之光，謂之「無量光」，無量壽無量光，已超出科學的範域以外了。

結　論

東方文化發展許多以精神支配物質，以意識支配肉體的方法；其目的，無非養性修道，使人格昇華，登峰造極，而壽命乃爲其修養之最高境界。其所採取之方法，爲直覺與理性，與實驗無涉。

西方近代文化，因生物學及醫藥科學之發達，對於人生衰老之歷程，與如何克服衰老現象，使能返老還童，青春永駐亦多簇新的發見與了解。循此以往、克服死亡之年齡線，增長老年之健康線，自當可能。其所遵循的方法，則爲觀察與實驗，而非直覺。

然而西方人士，特別是知識份子，在壽命學方面，現已逐漸接受東方之觀點與方法，對於東方的「心靈科學」、「心理治療」，痛下功夫，而對於禪那，瑜伽、太極拳、靜坐，以及針灸學等等之研究與學習，尤在風靡一時，幾有取原有的宗教崇拜而代之槪。惟東方一部分文人，晚近服膺「賽因斯」（科學），對於東方最高最精之壽命學，却早已置之腦後。今者，太空時代來臨，東西文化融貫之機會在望。東方聖人、西方聖人，此心同、此理同。詩云：「高山仰止，景行行止。」雖不能至，心嚮往之。吾人旣對於西方的老年學，旣已不斷採取與涵化，而對於東方最高智慧之壽命學，豈可視若敝屣？作「東西壽命學合論」竟。

參 考 書

Nathan W. Shock, Trends in Gerontology: Standford University Press, Standford, California, 2nd ed. 1957.

Nathan W. Shock, A Classified Bibliography of Gerontology and Geriatrics, and a Supplement One, 1949—1955.

Rammurli Mishra, Fundamentals of Yoga, New York: Julian Press, 1959.

I. K. Taimni, The Science of Yoga, Wheaton, Ill: The Theosophical Publishing House, 1967.

Chaudhuri, Haridas and Frederic Spilgelbreg, The Integral Philosophy of Sri Aurobindo, London: George Allen & Unwin, 1958.

John C. H. Wu, The Golden Age of Zen, Taipei: National War College, 1967.

Wei Tat, An Exposition of the I - Ching. Taipei: Institute of Cultural Studies, 1970.

易學叢書（精裝十七冊）台北廣文書局主編（一九七一年）

禪學大成（全六冊），台北中華佛教文化館（一九六九年）

麥惠廷：瑜伽對人類的偉大貢獻，香港上海印書館（一九六七年）

蕭天石：道家養生學槪要，台北自由出版社（一九六三）。

張起鈞：老子哲學，台北正中書局（一九六九、三版）

南懷瑾：禪與道、台北眞善美出版社（一九六八）

APPENDIX I

ON LONGEVITY

Wen-Shan Huang

In this paper, I want to develop and present the problem of
longevity as seen by the West (represented by the U.S. and Soviet
Union), India, and China. Based on my theory of the Integral Culture
of the West and the East, I finally want to introduce my program for
the prolongation of life for modern men and women.

In the West, there has been a long history of medical studies and
the science of health. However, due to the limit of time, I will only
state the recent acts and developments in the study of Gerontology.
For India, I will present the theories of yoga and how to live to be one
hundred years or more. As to China, the emphasis will be on the Tao
of Longevity as seen by the Taoists.

I. A Brief Review of the Recent Developments of Gerontology in the U.S. and Soviet Union

First, an exciting improvement in America's health in the
last decade has been reported by the National Center for Health
Statistics, a government agency. Few deaths from heart disease
have made a significant contribution toward increasing the life-
span of women by four years and men by nearly three years.
This was reported also by the Census Bureau in 1977.

The longer life expectancy — up to 81 years for women
and 71.8 for men living between now and the year 2050 — will
make the median age of the current population from three to
eight years older than expected only 20 months ago.

Second, Gerontology, the scientific study of the aging
process is one of the most important frontier areas in current
biochemical research. A report on the revolutionary scientific

discoveries now being made about aging and dying, and their explicit promise of a vastly extended life span — without old age is found in Albert Rosenfeld's work *Prolongevity* (Alfred A. Knopf, N. Y. 1976).

The gerontologists and the futurists believe the day is coming when we're all going to be able to live forever. That day, Saul Kent believes, may come as early as the middle of the next century. An expert on life extension, he believes immortality will become possible once scientists finally crack the body's DNA code and perfect genetic engineering techniques to control the human aging process. That kind of breakthrough would totally revolutionize almost every aspect of the way we think and the way we live. (Reported by William Overend: "The Future Stakes When Man will Live Forever", L. A. Times, July, 1977).

In any case, because the older explanations of aging leave so much still unexplained, interest in the avant garde view has been growing in research laboratories all over the world. This view has been summarized by Rosenfeld in the following quotes (Rosenfeld, 1977, 13-17):

1. "That there does exist within ourselves an identifiable "clock of aging," a genetically determined program which dictates that all will age and die, and the rate at which this will occur;

2. That we have an excellent chance of discovering the location (there may be more than one) of the 'clock of aging', as well as the nature of its operating mechanism — and how to interfere with them to our advantage;

Issued in May 1979

3. That, moreover, all this can begin to happen, not centuries from now, but now if only the research can be carried out.

4. That senescence may thus be started on its way to obsolescence."

Hence, according to the prediction of gerontologists:

"Within the next decade or so, we will see the proving-out of some of the potential anti-aging substances known at this time, as well as others yet to be discovered. Thus human beings who are very young today may hope that, if they remain in reasonably good health . . . . . they may become the first people in history to have their lives extended by artificial means to 200 or even 300 years."

Already boasting many of the oldest people in the world, the Soviet Union is showing new interest in the scientific possibilities of even more dramatic longevity.

According to a recent report, Dr. L. Sukharebsky, director of the Public Institute of Juvinology, told a Russian interviewer, "Scientists believe that the human being can live not just 100 years, but 400 years or even more."

There is frequent mention of the fact that there are about 19,000 people in the Soviet Union (total population 254 million) who are 100 years old or older. By contrast, there are about 9,400 centenarians in the United States, out of a total population of 214 million (Fisher 1977; Marx 1978).

II. The Studies of Gerontology in India

Gerontology in India and China is an ancient science. Since time immemorial, man in these two countries have sought ways and means to conquer death. Before reviewing the study in

China, let me state very briefly the Great Systems of Yoga in India. One of the greatest modern Hindu philosophers, Sri Arobindo, had already synthesized the Ancient Yoga systems into a single system which he called "Integral Yoga", in his "Life Divine", which integrated the ancient Hindu spiritual life and modern spiritual life into a wholeness. Suffice it to say Yoga is gerontological science and yet it is also a super-science. It has its independent method of research which cannot be compared to modern science.

What is Yoga: A world view, a Weltanschaung comprehending reality in its totality providing both metaphysics and practice. Yoga is based on sources traditionally considered authoritative, among them chiefly Patanjali's Yoga Sutras, the Bhagavad Gita, the Yoga Upanishads, and Shiva-Samhita (Wood 1954: 15-37)

Patanjali's systematic instruction for practical training for a healthy body, dating back to at least 300 B.C., is given in the "8" limbs of Yoga.

1.	Yama, five abstentions	} Ethical
2.	Nijama, five observances	
3.	Asana – Balanced Posture	
4.	Pranayama – Regulation of Breath	} External
5.	Pratyahara – Withdrawal of Senses	
6.	Dharana – Concentration	
7.	Dhyana – Meditation	} Internal
8.	Samadhi – Contemplation	

On the ethical aspects, Yoga is rooted in morality, which is in turn rooted in brotherhood or, a feeling for others. On the external steps, the first is right posture; the second, right breathing, and the third, control of the senses. Finally, there come the three internal steps, which are concentration, meditation, and contemplation. Contemplation opens the door to intuitive knowledge and many other powers – including supernatural powers. It is assumed that when one is established in these practices, one will be the master of his mind and this mastery will open a new, eternal and happy world for himself (Mishra 1959: 237-238). But it must be pointed out that the miraculous powers achieved by yoga practicers is viewed with skepticism by modern observers.

Finally, according to the instruction of yogi, the secret of longevity may also be based chiefly upon discretion in the choice of food and drink, and a hopeful, optimistic outlook on life; and so gluttons, drunkards, the idle, the dissipated, and the lazy, cannot reasonably hope to attain full ages. Time of Death is called Kaala. To go beyond time is to go beyond birth and death; to attain immortality. The Yogis believe that when you detect Death, restrain your breath in Sushumma; Death will run away from you. That is how you should get over death and enjoy good health and prolong life indefinitely.

III. The Tao of Longevity in China

In Western science, as it has been pointed out in the first section of this paper, an expert on life extension believed that immortality will become possible once scientists finally crack

---

1.   It is interesting to point out that according to Richard Leake and R. Levin that witers such as Lgmunh Freud and Konrad Loreny see man as a blood stained fighting animal. On the contrary, the evidence shows that early man (who lived in million years ago) was primarily non-aggressive, like the big apes of today, People of the Lake Mankind and its Beginnings by Richard Leakey and Roger Lewin (Ancliory Double-day: illustrated).

the body's DNA code and perfect genetic engineering techniques to control the human aging process. A longtime student of the *I Ching*, Kenneth L. Phillips, has come to see that the structure of the *I Ching* is comparable to the process by which genetic information is passed on from a living cell to a new, forming one. The architecture of the *I Ching*, with its sixty-four hexagrams, is similar in structure to the genetic code of DNA, which consists of 64 different arrangements of bases, which later direct the formation of basic proteins and determine which types of cells develop. And the *I Ching*, or the "Book of Changes", provides the development code for all changes that are continally happening in the universe, from the level of molecules to that of social groups (Phillips 1957:330). If this theory is finally accepted, modern science should expect, then, to be able to discover the code of DNA — the key for human immortality in the future.

Besides Buddhism, Confucianism and Taoism have evidently drawn their sources from the *I Ching*. But all of them are usually considered as three united religions in China, since all of them emphasize meditation and a philosophy embracing the mind, body and soul. The studies of the three religions pay much attention to Longevity, but their attitudes are different. The Buddhist accept the idea of fate (t'ien ming) and that chance and prayer alone determine whether death occurs a little earlier or a little later. On the other hand, Confucianists, as seen from the *I Ching*, believe that there exists the law of cycle in the universe; human beings cannot escape the determination of life and death. The Taoist attitude is totally different. It assumes that people can do something actively and successfully about their life-span. So wrote Sun I—K'wei in his *Ch'ih Shui Hsuan*

Chu (The Mysterious Pearl Discovered in the Red River, finished in 1596, same year that saw the publication of the greatest of all treatises on pharmaceutical natural history, the P'en Ts'ao Kang Mu of Li Shih-Chen): 'One cannot entirely attribute events to fate, on the contrary, man can act in such a way as to conquer Nature.'

Further, a phrase, "Returning to the State of infancy," was found in Lao-Tzu's *Tao Teh Ching,* written in the 4th century. It was one of the most ancient slogans of Taoism and the methods were elaborated upon more and more as the centuries went by; the fundamental idea of reversion to youth in the attainment of longevity, because of continual rejuvenation – worked for by means of hygiene and other physiological techniques.

Lao Tzu said: "The Sage is not sick, being sick of sickness, That is the secret of health." (ch. 70)

With this concept in view, the Taoist aspirant for material immortality or "Hsienship", (仙道) was prepared to undergo a considerable amount of training during the medieval age in China.

In the third millenium B.C., Huang Ti, the Yellow Emperor, who is believed to have lived before Lao Tzu, developed a system of curative and preventive medicine based on the technique of acupuncture, massage, herbs, and breathing. According to history, he became an immortal. The medical techniques which he originated were codified as the first Chinese medical book, *Nei Ching,* probably in the Han Dynasty. The theory of Yin Yang expounded in this book has remained the dominating principle of Chinese medicine to the present day (Huang-Ti, Nei Ching Su Wen, 1972 trans. Ilza Veith,).

P'eng Tzu, who reportedly lived to be 800 years old, the oldest man in Chinese history, used Huang Ti's exercise system, called Tao Yin — the use of proper breathing techniques to regulate the metabolism of the body, and so attained longevity. Confucius refers to him in the *Analects,* edited by his disciples. (Leggie 1960) Chuang Tze, the chief follower of Lao-tzu has said:

> "When man breathes in and out, or inhales and exhales in order to release the old air and take in the new, man hibernates like a bear and stretches his neck like a bird. He is really striving for longevity. Such a man indulges in breathing exercises in order to develop his physique, wishing to live as long as P'eng Tzu." (Chang 1963: 130)

In the later dynasties following the Chou, the Chinese practices for longevity and immortality developed further into several categories (Needham 1956:II, 23-156):

1. Respiratory techniques
2. Heliotherapeutic techniques
3. Gymnastic techniques
4. Sexual techniques
5. Alchemical and Pharmaceutical techniques
6. Dietary techniques

Taoism thus has a strong conviction that "The Destiny of myself depends on me and not upon Heaven." And thus, the Taoists problem lies mainly in how to preserve life and avoid harm and death (Huang 1974: 96-99).

The existence of two parallel traditions in Chinese alchemy practiced by the Taoists for the attainment of longevity are the so called "External Tan" (Elixer for longevity by taking drugs or medicines), and the training of the "Internal Tan" (the nourishment of the Chi). There are thousands of books in the Tao Ts'ang (A.D. 1190-1445) discussing the techniques.

A treatise fundamental to the nei tan (Internal tan) system appears in the Yun Chie Chi Ch'ien (雲笈七籤), collected in 1019 A.D. This is the Yan Chi Lun (Discourse on the Primary Vitality and the Cosmogonic Chi), written by an unknown writer in the second half of the 8th century. The precise techniques involved:

The manuals of the immortal (hsien Ching 仙經) says: 'One's life-span depends upon himself. If one can conserve the seminal essence (精) and obtain ch'i, one may obtain longevity without end.' And they also maintain the form (hsing) without (harmful) agitation, restore the mind (hsin) to ataraxy and peace. That is how longevity can be obtained. The fundamental root of the life force and life span is set in this Tao. Although a man practices respiratory exercises (hu hsi 呼吸), gymnastic techniques (tao yin), charitable acts (修福), initiating or assisting works of public benefit (hsin yeh), and the consumption of exalted medicines (elixirs), it will profit him nothing if he does not know the Tao of Primary unity (yun ch'i chih tao 元氣之道). He will be like a tree with fine branches and luxuriant foliage which yet has no proper roots, and so cannot endure. Is he not like a man who enjoys the pleasures of music, dancing girls, and all imaginable gastronomic joys the whole night through? They will profit him nothing.

This is evidently a criticism of those who practice many auxiliary techniques while ignoring the principle of counter-current flow (tien tao), the enchymoma produced from secretions made to follow courses opposite to the normal. A little later we read more of this:

The mannuals of immortals say: "One Yin and one Yang constitute the Tao. The three primary (vitalities) and the union of the two components: that is the enchymoma (san yan erch ho wei chih tan (三元二合謂之丹) ...... and these manuals also say: 'The Tao of Yin and Yang is the prizing of the seminal essence and the saliva. If these are well and truly guarded, then longevity will be obtained."

This is a good example of the eleventh century theorizing. It includes the basic ideas (a) that three primary vitalities have to be recreated within the body, (b) that a 'union' or reaction is necessary to form the enchymoma which does this, (c) that the reactants are Ch'i or juices in the body, (d) that in order to induce the geriatrix reversal effect, the secretions must be made to proceed in directions opposite to those in which they normally flow, and (e) that when they reach their extreme points, both topographically and quantitatively, they undergo a change of sign, Yang into Yin, Yin into Yang (Lu 1973: 78-83).

Thus, what the physiological alchemists were talking about, essentially, was rejuvenation, and they believed that by their techniques they could 'make all things new.' However, we may judge their physiological theories now. According to Lu Gwei-Djen, "there is no reason for doubting that, under appropriate conditions, they could perform miracles of restoring physical and mental health. Alchemy, in spite of its medieval character, and its use of ideas and practices so unfamiliar in the West today, was in a real sense akin to the optimistic and experimental outlook of modern science, especially biochemistry, endocrinology, and geriatrics."

It must be remembered that since the appearance of the *Nei Ching* of Huang ti and the Tao Tek Ching of Lao-tzu, the

Chinese people have paid much attention to the problem of how to preserve health and how to attain material immortality. In the *Nei Ching,* amazingly enough, an entire chapter is devoted to the circulation of the breath. The author correlates the normal and the abnormal functioning of the inner organs to the circulation of the breath. The basic principle of circulation is related to the fluctuations of the Yin and Yang forces, and the transformations of the energies symbolized by the five elements.

The eminent physician Hua Tu (華陀) of the Han Dynasty (206 B.C.-A.D. 220) modelled his system of exercise for physiotherapy after the movements of the bear, the deer, the monkey, the tiger, and the bird. It has been widely practiced by the common people century after century. 〔長壽修行法，眞善美出版社，臺北，參看程家鼎（時修）華陀五禽之戲，（同上）〕。

Besides the medical people, Bodhidharma, (or Ta Mo in Chinese) arrived in China during the Liang Dynasty (A.D. 506-56) from India, where he was the 28th Patriarch of Zen; while in China, he became the First Patriarch. He was deeply influenced by Yoga and the theory of Hua Tu, who emphasized the five essences of (1) spirit, (2) bone, (3) strength, (4) Chi, and (5) L'agnent. in man. Tao Mo thus created the Shao Lin System of Martial Art and wrote a book called *Yi-Chin Ching* (易筋經) introducing the Nei Kung exercise known as the Changing L'agment The latter consists of three series, altogether 24 styles of exercises. Along with this there is the Sitting Pa Tuan Chin, meaning 'Eight pieces of silk'; also called 'Pa Kua Hsin Kung', (八卦行功) particularly recommended by Li Ching Yuen (李青雲), a man who lived for 250 years in modern China (he died in 1930). It can be included into the Nei Kung (內功)

or Chi Kung (氣功) category for the training of the Chi, or energy, as an aid to all kinds of martial arts.

At the end of the Sung Dynasty (about 1300 A.D.), Chang San-feng (張三丰), a Confucianist-Taoist had succeeded in revolutionizing the Shao-lin System (少林拳) into Tai Chi Ch'uan (太極拳) by basing his principles on the I Ching and the Tao-Tek Ching. It is the most important training for the holistic health in order to help people to nourish the Chi and the cultivation of the body. As Joseph Needham, the author of the famous *Science and Civilization in China* has pointed out, nothing better shows that the theory and practice of the Taoists was one facet of the whole organic character of Chinese thought, which did not suffer from the typical schizophrenia of Europe, the inability to get away from mechanistic materialism on the one hand, and from theological spiritualism on the other. Here lies the value of Chinese martial arts and Nei Kung or Chi Kung for Longevity.

IV. Conclusion-A Program for Longevity

After reviewing the theories and practices concerning Longevity in the West and East, in this final summary, I would like to suggest my Integral Theory of Longevity, based upon my own studies and personal experiences. Few gerontologists, even among the avant garde which Strehler symbolizes, would predict the outright abolition of death. But many would certainly go along with the more modest forecast that old age, with all its attendant aches and ills, may well be abolished and the life span extended, perhaps for a substantial number of years. The teachings of Sri Aurobindo, the integrator of East and West, are the inspiration of this paper. His Vision of a Divine Life on Earth and his sayings; such as "The Knowledge that unites is the true knowledge", and the guiding torchlights. However, I have to admit that an Integral Theory of this nature will only be tentative and partial.

I.   To begin with, my program for the Tao of Longevity is based upon three general principles:

(1) The Pinciple of Organism — If the philosophical concept of the atom was essential for the construction of Newtonian science in the 19th century in the West, the philosophy of organism is essential for the construction of modern science — the 'new physics' in its present form (Capra 1975:330).

The organismic world view (and life view) stemmed from ancient and medieval China and it was transplanted to Europe in the 17th century by Leibnitz. From the writers of the I Ching to Lao tzu and to the Neo-Confucianists, they all believed that the Tao of Heaven, Earth, and Man is identical. They all belived that the Tao of Heaven, Farth, and Man is identical. They adapted Ataraxy as the dominant attitude and set up the highest possible standard for mankind. With Leibnitz as fore-runner in recent times, organism has been expounded by Whitehead in philosophy, Sri Aurobindo in Yoga, Sorokin in sociology, and Kroeber in anthropology (Needham 1959:505).

According to the idea of the Chinese, the universe is a vast organism, and the human body is a small one. As a logical consequence, in the Chinese system of exercise, such as Tai Chi Ch'uan, Pa Kua Ch'uan and Hsin I Ch'uan, attention is paid not to the limbs or a single organ, but to the integral whole — physical and spiritual — that is the human organism.

(2)   The Principle of Holism — The increasing momentum for the actualization of the Principle of Holistic Health in all areas of life in modern times reflects the wide-spread reawakening awareness that to be a human being means to be at one with all aspects of the cosmic organism. Problems, diseases, and disharmonies do not occur in a vacuum unrelated to the events, attitudes, thoughts, feelings, activities and changes forming the total environment in which they occur. To be holistic is to realize and experience that mind, body, and spirit are so interrelated as to truly be one (Cohen 1977:8). In other words, this principle is a non-fragmentization of the whole. Hence in the Chinese exercises for longevity, emphasis is laid on both the dynamic and static. The slogan: 'In the extreme of dynamic in the body, it turns to static. In the extreme of static, it again turns to dynamic. Dynamic and static are unitary.

(3)   The Principle of Yin-Yang — According to the I Ching and the Nei Ching, Life manifests itself as dynamic equilibria of Yin and Yang, the two polarities of a unitary Vital-Force or Energy (Tai Chi), in ever-changing pattern complexities, and complexes of patternings. The life of an organism depends upon the free flow of this force, and a proper balance between the two polarities. If the equilibrium is upset or the flow restricted, the organism is sick; balance and free flow must be restored. The reestablishment of balance is accomplished by discharging excess accumulations, by stimulation of polarity in deficiency by dispersing obstructions, and by sealing the avenues of wasteful escape of Vital-force or Energy. In the system of Tai Chi Ch'uan, for example, attention is particularly paid to the generation of intrinsic energy and the equilibria of the Yin and Yang forces in the human body (Huang 1974:86).

II.   On the practical aspect, I would like to emphasize the following three points:

(1)   Ethical View. Based upon the above world and life views my Integral Theory is rooted in morality and that in brotherhood and 'Love-energy'. We are to be at peace with the world, even if the world is not at peace with us. At the same time, we should also return to the Median Way, or the "Law of Chung Tao" (　中道法則　). Aristole's 'doctrine of the Golden Mean' proposes that moral virtues lie in the intermediate state between the extremes of excess and deficiency. Confucius advanced a generally similar concept (Siu 1957: 123; Huang 1971). This should be our rule for a healthy life.

(2)   Purification of the body and spirit. Using the method of weekly fasting to flush dangerous and damaging poisons and toxins from the body is advocated by Buddhists and Paul C. Bragg in his "The Miracle of Fasting: Proven Throughout History for Physical, Mental and Spiritual Rejuvenation." Furthermore, in order to live in agelessness, we should also use a similar method for mental and spiritual purification that the greatest spiritual leaders have used throughout the ages in all civilizations.

(3)   Diet. In the realm of diet, I would like to advise everyone to eat lightly and to eat a well balanced and nutritious diet. Get rid of 'dead foods' (i.e. artificial sugar, liquor, cigarettes, coffee, fat meats, salt, etc.) and take mostly 'organic foods' (i.e. fruits and vegetables, etc., etc.) if possible.

V.   Exercises and Meditation

(1)   As for exercise, I like to advocate that for people who do not participate in regular athletics, it is best to do Tai Chi

Ch'uan (and Chi Kung) regularly. The fundamental principles of this eminent Chinese art and science, as has been pointed out in the above already, are based upon the I Ching and Lao-tzu.

Its postures and movements are devised to stretch, particularly the legs, and turn the body — the centripetal axis — right and left to between 90 and 180 degrees, and occasionally, completely around in a circle. All movements are zigzagged forward, backward or crosswise, alternately shifting and balancing the body on one leg by bendingone and straightening the other. The mind will thus be conditioned to relax and will consciously direct each movement. The body will be disciplined to follow the commands of the mind and made as flexible, supple, and agile as a youngster's, preventing it from becoming stiff and rigid. Each movement is also synchronized with slow, deep abdominal breathing in order to activat the involuntary msucles of internal organs, *reburbish* blood and oxygen, and accelerate the upward flow of blood from the feet and legs to the heart via the Tantien (丹田) (the blood cistern located just below the navel) (Liu 1975). It is the circulating center of the Chi leading to all the meridians and channels, as explained in Acupuncture.

(2) With regard to meditation, Dr. Hu Shih, the authority on Chinese philosophy, has pointed out that the Chinese type of meditation is diametrically opposed to Indian meditation, where the mind tries to avoid the external world, ignores outside influences, aims at intellectual understanding, and seeks to unite with the infinite. In contrast, Chinese meditation works with the aid of external influences, operating in the world, emphasizes quick wit and insight, and aims at self-realization. This was the meditation taught by early Buddhist masters like

Hui Yuan, and it became a major tradition in Chinese Buddhism. But from an objective point of view, I would like to say that the Buddhists' aim is "Dhyana-Samadhi" or "Complete Enlightenment," which is supra space and time, transcendental, the Absolute, the Nirvana; while that tof the Taoists is the prolongation of life, or the unifying with the Tao (the law of the universe).

For our present purpose, the Taoist type is highly recommended. Of course, those who aim at Samadhi and the concept that the knower, knowledge, and known become one, the Zazen is preferable.

After all, meditation on the psychological side is an experience that may curb and still the oscillations of the mind. It brings mental peace. On the physical side, it has the power of healing by the process of "Kuang Shuang", (觀想) or "suggestion", or "biofeedback" in modern psychological terms. Also, it leads to warmth, heat, purification by Yang fire, enlightenment, and transfiguration. It helps to prolong the body's anabolic process of repair and growth, and to reduce the catabolic or decaying process. A reversing and rejuvenation of the human body are thus possible.

(3) Another type of Nei-Kung or Chi Kung (the author also calls it 'Tai Chi Kung') exercise, a supplement to Tai Chi Ch'uan and Taoist meditation, which has been mentioned above in this paper, may be re-emphasized again.*

Li Ching Yuen, the oldest modern man who lived in China from 1678 to 1930, as reported in the New York Times, told the secret of his longevity. He related that an old Taoist monk, who was 500 years old, taught an exercise called 'Pa Ku Hsin Kung' (actional exercise of the eight Trigrams') to him. He did these everyday for 120 years. "They are very effective, if done regularly, correctly, and with sincerity." (Liw 1974:45-59) In reality, it combines forth of Wai Kung (外功) (external merits) and Nei Kung (內功) (internal merits) together.

Hence, along with Tai Chi Ch'uan and the Taoist meditation, this system along with the others such as the "Changing of Liagaments & Self Massages", may be taken as auxiliary techniques for longevity as well. Finally, let me quote Lao-tzu to end this paper:

"Can you control your mind so that it never strays from the way of Tao? Can you control your breathing so that it is soft and gentle like a newborn baby?

Can you purify yourself so that you are perfect? Can you love all the people, rule them, and remain unknown? And do so without interference?

Can you play the same role always?

Give birth; provide' nourishment, do this without being possessive. Give help without obligation. Lean without dominating.

The world will follow, without fear of evil, serene, peaceful, secure, one who follows the great symbol of Yin-Yang.

The Book of Tao, Key to the Mastery of Life,
translation by Frank J. Mao Hovec, Peter Pauper Press, New York, pp. 28-29, 32.

*   Nei Kung (內功) or Chi Kung (氣功) (The art of Inner Cultivation, in not a martial art nor meditation. Its origin may be traced to Huang (Ti)-Las (tzu) (黃老) for thousands of years. At present I want to treat it as an independent discipline such as Acupuncture. It would help us to produce radiant health, greatly increase mental power, and to transcend the ego and merge with the Tao. Its techniques may include three main aspects: (1) The Breath or mental Exercise (神經運動); (2) The Internal Tsang Exercise (內臟運動); and (3) The Hormone adverse current Exercise (內分泌逆流運動), etc, etc. For details see the authors Coming book: The Fundamentals of Chi Kung (Taoist Yoga), to be published in the near future.

BIBLIOGRAPHY

Capra, Fritjof
1975 The Tao of Physics, Berkeley: Shambhala.
Chang, Chung-Yuan
1963 Creativity and Taoism. New York: Julian Press.
Chen, Harold A.
1977 Medition for Healing. Alburquiee: Sun Books.
Fisher, Dan
1977 Soviets, Aim for Lifespans of 400 Years. *L. A. Times* July 10.
Huang, Wen-shan
1971 System of Culturology. 3rd ed. Taipei: Chung Hua Books.
1974 Fundamentals of Tai Chi Ch'uan. Hong Kong: South Sky Book Co., 2nd ed. 3rd ed. 1979.
Huang-ti, Nei Ching Su Wen
1972 The Yellow Emperor's Classic of Inernal Medicine, Trans. Ilza Veith. Berkeley: Univ. of California Press.
Leggie, James
1960 The Chinese Classics. Hong Kong Univ. Press.
Liu, Yan Ting
1975 A Review on Wen-Shan Huang's Fundamentals of Tai Chi Ch'uan 2nd ed. Hong Kong: South Sky Books. unpublished manscript.
Liw, Da
1974 Taoist Health Exercise Book. Quick Fox. Inc.
Lu, Gwei-Jen
1973 The Inner Elixir (Nei Tan); Chinese Phychiological Alchemy in Changing Perspectives, in the History of Science, Essays in Honor of Joseph Needham, ed. by Mikulax Teich and Robert Young, London: Heinemann.
Mar, Henry
1978 In the Bottle Against Old Age, Plenum Press. Revised Edition.
Mishra, Rammrali S.
1959 Fundamentals of Yoga. New York: Julian Press.
Needham, Joseph
1956 Science and Civilization in China Vol. 2. Cambridge: Cambridge Univ. Press. Vol. 3.
Phillips, Kenneth
1975 Western Science/Eastern Wisdom, a Review of Fritjof Capra, The Tao of Physics. Berkeley: Shambhala. pg. 330. in Parabola, Myth and the Quest for Meaning. 1 (1): 99-102, 1976.
Rosenfeld, Albert
1977 Prolongevity, the Extension of the Human Life Span. *Futurist,* 11 (1): 13-17.
Siu, R. G. H.
1957 The Tao of Science. Mass: MIT Press.
Wood, Ernest
1954 Great Systems of Yoga. New York: Philosophical Library.

APPENDIX II

CONDENSED TAI CHI CH'UAN, A REVIEW

I

Tai Chi Ch'uan is finding an increasing number of adherents in the West because of its ability to promote physical fitness and self defense capabilities as well as spiritual and mental powers.

It has been gradually perfected over its 3,000 years of history in China. Based upon Taoism, I Ching (Confucianism), and Zen, it sums up the whole philosophy of its country. The objective of Condensed, or Simplified, Tai Chi Ch'uan is the promotion of health and the prevention of illness. It is founded upon the Yaung (Ching-fu) structure. Comparatively, the new system is easier and quicker to learn. Because the Condensed Tai Chi Ch'uan is brief and easy to learn, one can easily make a good habit of this exercise and incorporate it into one's daily routine.

Based on traditional experience, it is possible to teach a person the Condensed Tai Chi Ch'uan in one hour. In contrast, it takes three months to learn the entire series of movements involved in traditional Tai Chi Ch'uan.

Condensed Tai Chi Ch'uan was originated by a committee in 1954. It published its ideas in the *Athletic Magazine,* which were well received by the public.[1]

II

Tai Chi Ch'uan is *erroneously* called both "Long Ch'uan and "13 Postures." These two names actually refer to two separate sets of Tai Chi Ch'uan. The first set, called "13 Postures" (十三勢), is much shorter than the long second set, called "Long Ch'uan (長拳). In "Tai Chi Ch'uan Theory", it says: "Long Ch'uan is similar to Long River and Great Sea, which are running continuously without ending."

The name "13 Postures" originated thus: According to ancient legend, the "13 Postures" includes "Five Elements (actions) and Eight Trigrams (八卦)". The Five Elements are "Gold, Wood, Water, Fire, and Earth" which are similar to Tai Chi Ch'uan's Five Modes of Steps. The Eight Trigrams are Chien (乾), Kun (坤), Kan (坎), Li (離), Sun (巽), Chen (震), Tui (兌), Ken (艮), which are similar to Tai Chi Ch'uan's Eight Modes of "Hand Methods."

Now we may thus understand: Tai Chi Ch'uan has Five Modes of Steps. They are: Advancing, Retreating, Look to the Left, Look to the Right (These are similar to Eye Sights, and may be called 'step methods'), and Central Equilibrium ("Chung Ting") (中定). There are Eight Modes of Hand Methods: "Ward Off" (掤), "Pull Back" (攦), "Press Forward" (擠), "Push" (按), "Pull Down" (採), "Bend Backward" (挒), "Elbow Stroke" (肘), and "Shoulder Stroke" (靠). They are performed in eight directions: East, West, South, North, Northeast, Northwest, Southeast, and Southwest. These eight directions with the Five Steps are called "13 Postures."

Now, the sequence of the "13 Postures" is thus:

5 Steps — Advancing, Retreating, Look to the Left, Look to the Right, Central Equilibrium (Gold, Wood, Water, Fire, and Earth.)

8 Directions

4 Sides (East, South, West, North) — Peng (掤), Lu (攦), Chi (擠), An (按) = Chien (乾), Kun (坤), K'an (艮), Li (離).

4 Corners Northeast (東北), Northwest (西北), Southwest (西南), Southeast (東南) = Pull Down (採), Bend Backward (挒), Elbow Stroke (肘), Shoulder-Stroke (靠) = Sun (巽), Chen (震), Tui (兌), Ken (艮).

13 Postures

(1), (2), (3)

Note 1 — "Tai Chi Ch'uan Theory" was written in the Chien Lung Period of the Ching Dynasty by Wang Tsweng Yueh. It is in the famous Tai Chi Ch'uan Classics.

Note 2 — Compare p. 90 of Huang's *Fundamentals of Tai Chi Ch'uan,* 3rd ed., to this chart.

Note 3 — Look to the Left (左顧), Look to the Right (右盼), are Eye-Sights. They are considered as "Modes of Steps."

III

The comparison and contrast of the original Tai Chi Ch'uan with the Simplified, or Condensed, Tai Chi Ch'uan may be said thus:

(1) Both Condensed and traditional forms of Tai Chi Ch'uan are based on the Yang (Ching-fu) structure. Therefore, their structure and motion are basically similar.

(2) Some of the main points of physical posture (i.e. "Lowering the shoulders and hanging the elbows"), important psychological points (i.e. "Spiritual collectivization and Thought Centralization"), important motion points (i.e. "Upper and Lower parts coordination", and the "Distinguishing of Substantiality vs. Insubstantiality") are similar.

(3) In training the body, one can achieve the same results of promoting health with either form.

(4) In view of the 'principle of Self-Defense', they are different, as shown in the following chart:

	Condensed Tai Chi Ch'uan	Original Tai Chi Ch'uan
Actional Aspects	From simple to complex, and from easy to difficult	From complex to simple, and from difficult to easy
Posture Aspects	Shorter, two repetitions to and fro	Much longer, repetitions: 5 routes, to and fro
Learning & Teaching Aspects	Explanation and Chart are less detailed, more convenient for training, and self-taught.	More detailed Charts and explanations concerning the foundation of learning Tai Chi Ch'uan. For those students who learned traditional form first, and learned simplified Tai Chi Ch'uan as advanced training.
Self Taught Aspects	Lack of Principle	Has the principle of self taught: "To overcome motion by tranquility; To conquer hardness by softness."[2]

IV

"We sincerely hope that our "Theory of the Integral Tai Chi" would give the world a new creative idea, and a fresh dynamic approach to the basic problems of health as well as civilization. This philosophy of life is, after all, an all-embracing synthesis in world thought such as integrates the highest cultural values of East and West. It lays the foundation of the art of integrated living which aims at the unity of mankind – the collective community of Tatung "The Great Harmony" (大同) – in the sense of Confucius."[3]

According to this "theory", it includes the "Song of the Whole Reality and the Great Function of Tai Chi Ch'uan." This song explains the training method of the structure of Postures of Tai Chi Ch'uan. It includes the Reality and its Function. The Reality means the Chuan's main body, while the Function indicates the Application of the postures. Its main body includes the "13 Postures" – Peng, Lu, Chi, An, Tsai, Li, Chou, Kou, Advancing, Retreating, Look to the Right, Look to the Left, and Central Equilibrium ("Chung Ting"). The Method of Application is the martial art technique of the whole postures in practice, including the summarized principles of the Reality and Function. The whole Song includes all the aspects of Tai Chi Ch'uan.

However, despite the advantages of briefness and ease of learning, there are many Tai Chi Ch'uan masters who believe the Condensed Tai Chi Ch'uan to be an incorrect method. They believe that Tai Chi Ch'uan moves "cyclically, endlessly, and ceaselessly, like a slow motion picture." These masters all adhere to the traditional long form. Master Wang Yin-Ning and General Kuo Chi (王延年、郭岐) of Belgium teach a long form that was based on Taoism, Huang Ting Ching (黃庭經). This form includes the Song of the Reality and the Function.

Professor Cheng Chia Yuan (程家鼎), teacher of Martial Arts at the University of Oriental Studies, Los Angeles, and editor of the 2-volume *Chinese Kung Fu Source Book* (Vol. I — *Tai Chi Ch'uan*: Vol. II — *Five Animals' Games*), promotes the original form of Tai Chi Ch'uan, dating back 3,000 years. T. M. Sze (施調梅) of Taipei has recently published a very fine book concerning traditional Tai Chi Ch'uan, entitled *Tai Chi Ch'uan Geneaology, the Inner and Outer Kung Study* (太極拳譜，內外功 研幾錄).

As mentioned earlier, both forms achieve similar results of promoting health and well-being. The form one chooses therefore depends on one's outlook and time.

Condensed Tai Chi Ch'uan —
the whole Terminology of the Structure

First Set

1. Commencement

2. Wild Horse divides its Manes
   a. Left Style
   b. Right Style
   c. Left Style

3. White Stork Spreads its Wings

Second Set

4. Brush Knee and Twist Steps
   a. Left Style
   b. Right Style
   c. Left Style

5. Play the Fiddle

6. Repulse the Monkey 例撞猴與 '例捲肱' 同
   a. Right Style
   b. Left Style
   c. Right Style
   d. Left Style

Third Set

7. Left, Grasping Bird's Tail

8. Right, Grasping Bird's Tail

4th Set

9. Single Whip

10. Wave Hands Like Clouds
    a. Takes 1st Open Cubic Step
    b. Takes 2nd Open Cubic Step
    c. Takes 3rd Open Cubic Step

11. Single Whip

5th Set

12. High Pats on Horse

13. Kicks with Right Sole

14. Strikes Ears with Fists

15. Turns Body, Kicks with Left Foot Upwards

6th Set

16. Left, Creeps down, Stands indepently
    a. Left, Creeps down
    b. Left, Stands indepently

17. Right, Creeps down, Stands indepently
    a. Right, Creeps down
    b. Right, Stands indepently

7th Set

18. Fair Lady Throws at Shuttle, Left & Right
    a. Throws at Shuttle (1), and (2), Left Style
    b. Throws at Shuttle (3), and (4), Right Sty.

19. Needle at Sea Bottom

20. Fan Three Back   與 '閃通臂' 同

8th Set

21. Turn Body, Strike, Parry and Punch

22. Apparently Close Up

23. Cross Hands

24 Conclusion

(FOOTNOTES)

1. Ching, Ku-Lui (editor), *Athletic Magazine,* Shanghai Educational Publication, 1954.
2. This relates to ·the system of Sun Tzu, a famous military strategist who lived 2,500 years ago. His book, *The Art of War*, is famous.
3. Huang, Wen-shan. *Fundamentals of Tai Chi Ch'uan,* 3rd ed., South Sky Book Company, Hong Kong, 1979.

BIBLIOGRAPHY

Ching, Ku-Lui (ed.), "Condensed Tai Chi Ch'uan", *Athletic Magazine*, Shanghai, Shanghai Educational Publication, 1954.

Chang, Wen-Yuen, "The Common Sense of Tai Chi Ch'uan, Questions and Answers", *The People's Physical Education Publication,* Shanghai, 1960.

Chong, Y. N., *Illustrations of Tai Chi Ch'uan Simplified,* (Chinese-English), 1st. ed., Hong Kong, 10,000 Miles Book Store, 1978.

Lee, Yang-An, *The Essense of and Condensed Tai Chi Ch'uan,* Hong Kong, Unicorn Press, 1965.

APPENDIX III:

HIGH BLOOD PRESSURE AND ISOMETRIC EXERCISE

According to Mr. Edward L. Lai of Taipei, "high blood pressure is a disease which kills people silently." In the preliminary stage, it has no apparent phenomena. But when it enters a later and more serious stage, it easily leads to what the Chinese call "chung-feng", which means a disease hitting with "wind', i.e. hemorrhage, or the 'breaking of the brain', or heart attack. Many people who had been struck with 'chung-feng' suddenly, suffered from such symptoms as paralysis and the immobilization of the heart and/or brain.

Mr. Lai wrote an article that appeared in the China Central Daily. He wrote:

Two years ago, I was struck by an article called "The Muscle Movements to Lower Blood Pressure." Skeptically, I tried the technique for five weeks. Beyond my expectations, my blood pressure became much lower. After half a year, the disease was gone and I was normal.

Confident in the result of this therapeutic method, I introduced it to some of my friends. Everyone has had the same positive result.

Later, Mr. Lai wrote a report describing the movement:

Everyone who practices this exercise must first stand still. Maintain normal breathing. The whole body — head, neck, breast, shoulders, back, the four limbs, eyes, and the face — must first be relaxed.

Next, tighten or tense up the whole body, gaze straight ahead, and centralize the head over the body. Hold this position for six counts. (1, 2, 3, 4, 5, and 6). Then, relax. Repeat two more times for a total of three times. Perform this procedure three times a day, just before each meal (breakfast, lunch and dinner) for a total of nine times. Try this continuously for five weeks and note the result.

Three months later, I happened to be in New York City and remembered this movement was originated by Dr. Broino Kiveloff, Director of New York Infirmary. I visited him. He was very gracious and was glad to show me the movement. He said that his exercise was conceived as a service of a doctor for humanity and he wished no payment or tuition. He stated that there was no need to buy drugs and yet this movement attained the same end. It attained good results and aided human welfare. This was his motive of social service and spirit.

(Incidentally, in a personal letter to me (11/9/80), Mr. Lai told me that he had had high blood pressure for nearly three years. After practicing this technique, good results had come indeed. Everyone who had tried this method (at least 4 or 5 hundred people) received the same good results. Further, these people refrained from smoking and drinking. Salted foods were limited.)[1]

---

1. One out of every third adult in this country is suffering from cardivascular disease. Heart disease kills one million people a year in the U.S. Heart disease may be included Coronary arteriosclerosis, angina pectoris, cardiac failure, myocardial infraction, dizziness, headache, palpitation, dyspnoea, hypertension, hemiplegia, thromboangiitis obliterans.

附錄 IV

我怎樣治好高血壓
不服藥物而行肌肉運動的新發現

本文作者前國立西北大學校長，本年已屆八十高齡，於七八年前，患高血壓症，瀕臨危險邊緣，經仿用此法，五星期後，血壓開始下降，以後繼續如法運動，至今血壓正常，健康良好。

高血壓症是在現代國家很流行，而又為殺人不見血的疾病；尤其是中年以上的人，幾乎人人都有被它侵害的危險。

那種疾病初起時，每每被一般人所忽視；因為它無顯著的象徵，亦不引起若何不能忍受的痛苦。它也因此而不大為患者所察覺。自信健康無問題的人，更不願常請醫師作「體檢」。

然而，一個患高血壓者，一進入嚴重狀況時，就可引起中風，或腦充血，也能導致糖尿或心臟等許多老年人易患的疾病。到了那個時候，不但患者措手不及，恐怕醫生也有愛莫能助之感。

在我青年及壯年時期，我的血壓是低於一般人的。醫師為我檢查身體時，認為那是好的象徵，幾乎一致向我「道賀」，可是我始終知道高血壓的危險性；因為我的父親和祖父，都是在老年時因患中風而死亡的。後來，我又看見幾個中風的友人，有的半身不遂，腦筋失靈；有的纏綿床第，飲食維艱。他們那種痛苦不堪的情形，提高了我對血壓和胆固醇的警覺。

血壓和胆固醇的升高，不但會引起上述那些病症，而且可以導致心臟的衰弱和突然的死亡。大約六七年前，一位為我檢查身體的醫師，忽然查出我的血壓增加，幾已瀕臨危險的邊緣。我便遵照醫師指示，立刻戒酒、戒鹽，並服用降低血壓的丸藥。想不到，我的體質竟不能接受那一類的丸藥。每一服用，它就引起我的遺傳性的頭暈及吐嘔。而且，那種丸藥並無根治的效能；一旦停止服用，血壓立即恢復原狀。我於是改用中國人的土方，把山楂熬成飲料，每天喝一、二小杯，又聽故友薛光前兄的介紹，服用中藥杜仲；過了一年，兩者都未發生任何效果。我便對我的健康問題發生了一點憂慮。

今年五月，我偶然在一美國銷行甚廣的醫藥衞生雜誌PREVENFION看見一篇「你願意每天花一分鐘去減低你的血壓嗎？」我因爲這個題目很動人，登時把全文讀了兩遍，還照着它所指示的，把那個所謂ISOMETRIC EXERCISE的肌肉運動，試行了幾次；隨着天天如此練習。我當時雖仍半信半疑，但五星期後量血壓，居然發現它有下降的趨勢。我初讀那篇文章時，我的血壓是190－90；那自然是太高；醫師認爲只要低的數字不超過九十，還是不會發生危險的。我在實行那肌肉運動的第五星期，即查出低的數字已由九十降到八十七；我便知道這種治療是有效力的。我的信心增強以後，我便不斷的每日作此運動三次，也不斷的查出我的血壓高的數字和低的數字同時逐漸下降。

從今年五月到十一月，我的血壓可以說是直線下降。高的數字是190－180－170－160；低的數字是90－87－85－83。我於十一月初返台省親，又連續量了幾次血壓；最後的紀錄是140－80這對一個中年人或老年人都是很正常的。我平日對寫作的態度一向很嚴謹；尤其是涉及歷史或學術性的。以我一個不懂醫藥的人，苟非自身有此六個多月的實際經歷，決不敢隨意作此有推介意味的報導。現在我就要談到這個肌肉運動治療的本身。它是極輕便而極簡單；人人可以一學即會。而且隨時隨地都可練習。任何人只要有恒心、有毅力，天天行之，一個月後便可見功效！而且，花費的時間很少，每日三次，總計不過一分半鐘。這是初聽起來，不大容易使人相信的。

我現在再進一步的作簡略說明；凡練習此項肌肉運動者，首須全身鬆弛而直立，兩手下垂，十指伸張而不可握拳；然後用力使全身緊張，包括頭、頸、胸、背、四肢、雙眼及面部，同時口叫一、二、三、四、五、六後，即將全身鬆弛。如此一緊一鬆，反覆三回，即告結束。每日照此方式練習三次，最好每餐之前行之三次合計不過一分半鐘而已。

當然，如果有人親身示範，五分鐘內應可學會，自比書面說明更易使人明瞭。但此項運動既極簡單，讀者如將此文多讀一遍，亦必可於一刻鐘內照行，不至有何困難。惟正在服用降低血壓丸藥者，暫時不可立即停止丸藥，只可逐漸減少，以求兩種治療法之協調和比較。如有懷疑之處，不妨與醫師商談。

此種肌肉運動之新治療法，乃美國三位專家，包括一位名醫，偶然發現。那位名醫因見若干向他就診的老年人，步履維艱，又不能作任何健身運動，藥石既已無靈，只好讓他們一試肌肉的一鬆一緊。不意他們練習了五星期後，個個恢復兩腳行動的機能。他再叫那些病者繼續做下去。不出兩月，不但個個足疾消失，行路正常，而且個個的血壓都跟着降低。

他於是和其他二專家研究其中奧妙；一致承認這是治療高血壓的新發現。於是他們一面發表那篇論文，一面把那方法推行於其他患高血壓者。推行雖還不廣，但至今沒有發生相反的結果，或有甚麽不良的副作用。至於上面所講的口叫「一、二、三、四、五、六」，正是要全身緊張時調劑呼吸，也有一點「練氣功」的作用。

據這三位專家的看法：凡作此肌肉運動而將血壓降低者，降低以後，仍應繼續行之，以求血壓正常化的永恒。即目前無血壓問題之人，如願行此肌肉運動，亦可防止血管硬化，而使血脈流通。

　　身體肥胖之人，如能於戒煙酒，慎飲食之外，行此肌肉運動，必可如一般人一樣的減肥通血，延年益壽。深盼讀者切勿忽視血壓問題而致血管硬化、心臟衰退。一個國家的富強康樂，須賴有心身健康的國民。我們對自己，對國家，實都負有增進個人健康的責任。（文於一九七八年）

註：患高血壓的人宜減少食鹽。

BRIEF MAXIMAL ISOMETRIC EXERCISE

IN HYPERTENSION

BROINO KIVELOFF, M.D.* AND OLIVE HUBER, Ph.D.†
New York, N.Y.

ABSTRACT: Brief, maximal isometric exercise of six seconds' duration, repeated three times daily for five to eight weeks may be associated with lowering of the blood pressure in hypertensive patients. In 8 subjects with hypertension there was a decrease of 16 – 42 mm Hg in systolic pressure and 2 – 24 mm in diastolic pressure. In 5 subjects receiving a constant dosage of hypotensive drugs, there was a decrease of 4 – 28 mm in systolic pressure and 2 – 14 mm in diastolic pressure. In 2 subjects previously treated with hypotensive drugs in whom isometric exercise was substituted for the drugs, normal blood pressure was maintained for eleven months.

Observations on animals, including humans, as they awaken from sleep indicate that brief maximal isometric contraction effects muscular and circulatory conditioning. To ascertain whether a simple regimen of either localized or extensive brief isometric contraction can promote improved circulation, we carried out short-term and long-term studies concerning the effect on blood pressure and pulse rate.

MATERIAL AND METHOD

Subjects

Twenty-two subjects (15 with high blood pressure and 7 with normal blood pressure) were tested in 5 groups as follows:

3 subjects (controls) with normal blood pressure (ages, 22, 27 and 59).

4 subjects (controls) with normal blood pressure who performed the isometric exercise (ages, 38, 43, 67 and 67).

8 subjects with elevated blood pressure who performed the isometric exercise (ages, 57, 58, 61, 63, 64, 65, 67 and 72).

5 subjects with elevated blood pressure, taking hypotensive drugs, who performed the isometric exercise (ages, 55, 55, 56, 58 and 58).

2 subjects .with elevated blood pressure whose hypertension had been controlled by hypotensive drugs, who then substituted isometric exercise (ages, 30 and 40).

Method

Isometric contraction consists of stiffening of the muscles without moving the joints. If practice is needed, initiation can be facilitated by forceful contraction of the fist, followed by contraction of the upper-extremity muscles; then the lower-extremity muscles are contracted isometrically, followed by the

*   Chief Physiatrist, Department of Physical Medicine and Rehabilitation of the New York Infirmary, Stuyvesant Square and 15th Street, New York, N.Y. 10003.

†   Professor Emeritus, Department of Physiology and Health, Hunter College of the City University of New York.

muscles of the buttocks, back and neck. Next, all the foregoing muscles are contracted isometrically, simultaneously. The greater the mass of muscles contracted isometrically and simultaneously, the more extensive are these exercises. Normal breathing is maintained throughout.

For maximal isometric exercises the subject assumes a relaxed standing position with elbows and knees partially flexed about 10 degrees. The muscles of the neck, extremities, abdomen and buttocks are isometrically exercised for brief periods. Agonist and antagonist muscles harden simultaneously, without any change in muscle length. Electromyography shows that muscles and their antagonists, when contracting simultaneously, develop potentials similar to those in muscles contracting against maximal resistance.

RESULTS

The subjects (volunteers), while breathing normally, underwent maximal isometric exercises of the muscles of the extremities, buttocks and abdomen, as well as overall extensive isometric exercises for periods of 30, 10 and 6 seconds each, in 32 experiments. Systolic and diastolic blood pressures (mm Hg) were measured separately in the last two seconds of isometric exercise.

All systolic blood pressure readings increased (Table 1). In 20 of the 32 experiments, the increase in diastolic pressure was greater than the increase in systolic pressure; in 7 the increase in diastolic pressure was less than the increase in systolic pressure; in 3 there was no difference between the increases; and in 2 there was a decrease in diastolic pressure. The 2 cases of decreased diastolic blood pressure — also associated with the largest increase in pulse pressure — represented the second and third experiments in the same subject, without intermittent rest. Pulse pressure decreased in 20 cases; in 3 it was unchanged; and in 9 it increased (Table 1). In all experiments, blood pressure readings returned to resting values within 90 seconds after cessation of isometric exercise.

In isometric exercises maintained for 60, 30, 20 and 10 seconds, all pulse rates increased. The extent of increase varied directly with the mass of muscle involved. Recovery occurred within 90 seconds, taking longer with increased duration of exercise and increased muscle mass.

The fact that isometric exercise is accompanied by an increase in pulse rate, an increase in diastolic blood pressure, and dilatation of the pupils of the eyes is suggestive of increased activity of the sympathetic nervous system.

In the long-term observations, all control and experimental subjects were volunteers and maintained the same occupation, activities, and nutritional levels throughout the study period. All blood pressures and pulse rates were recorded at the same time of day for each subject. Blood pressures and pulse rates were determined weekly with each subject in a relaxed, comfortable sitting position.

Each subject, breathing normally, performed maximal extensive, simultaneous isometric exercise of the muscles (agonists and antagonists) of the extremities, neck, abdomen, and buttocks for 6-second periods, repeated three times at intervals of a few seconds, three times a day (in the morning, afternoon, and evening), for five to eight weeks.

Results indicated that isometric exercises did not change the blood pressure nor the pulse rate in persons with normal

TABLE 1
Immediate Effects of Brief Isometric Exercise upon Blood Pressure

Isometric Contraction		Change in Blood Pressure (mm Hg)		Change in Pulse Pressure (mm Hg)
Muscles	Time (seconds)	Systolic	Diastolic	
Abdomen & buttocks	30	+ 16	+ 24	− 8
Right hand	10	+ 2	+ 4	− 2
Forearm & hand		+ 2	+ 8	− 6
Right arm & right leg		+ 10	+ 10	0
		+ 12	+ 12	0
Both legs		+ 10	+ 20	−10
		+ 12	+ 20	− 8
		+ 12	+ 22	−10
		+ 14	+ 12	+ 2
Abdomen		+ 8	+ 14	− 6
Abdomen & buttocks		+ 10	+ 8	+ 2
		+ 14	+ 6	+ 8
		+ 16	+ 18	− 2
		+ 18	+ 22	− 4
Extensive exercise		+ 22	+ 28	− 6
Right arm	6	+ 14	+ 8	+ 6
		+ 12	+ 16	− 4
Right leg		+ 10	+ 18	− 8
Both legs		+ 8	+ 22	−14
		+ 4	+ 16	−12
		+ 8	+ 18	−10
		+ 10	+ 26	−16
		+ 24	+ 16	+ 8
Abdomen & buttocks		+ 8	+ 18	−10
		+ 10	+ 24	−14
		+ 14	+ 12	+ 2
		+ 14	+ 26	−12
		+ 17	+ 20	− 3
		+ 17*	−12	+ 29
		+ 29*	− 8	+ 37
Extensive exercise		+ 24	+ 24	0
		+ 32	+ 24	+ 8

* Taken in sequence on the same subject without rest.

blood pressure. There was no difference in standard deviations as compared with controls not performing isometric exercise. However a definite decrease in systolic and diastolic blood pressures was evident in persons with elevated resting levels of blood pressure, after a regimen of isometric exercise during a period of 5-8 weeks. Pulse rate changes were not significant when compared with those of controls. Extensive isometric exercise lowered systolic, diastolic, and pulse pressures significantly as indicated by standard deviations (Table 2). In 2 subjects with elevated blood pressure that had been reduced by isometric exercises, an increase in systolic and diastolic blood pressure occurred when isometric exercise was discontinued.

After isometric exercise, subjects who were taking a constant dosage of hypotensive drugs demonstrated a decrease in systolic, diastolic, and pulse pressures. Pulse rate changes were not significant.

Two subjects had previously been treated with hypotensive drugs. When the blood pressure had been brought to a normal level, drugs were abandoned and an extensive isometric regimen was substituted. Both subjects showed a decrease in systolic and diastolic pressures and have maintained lowered blood pressure for 11 months to date without benefit of drugs (Table 2).

After long-term isometric exercises, subjective results were reported by participants. A feeling of fitness was accompanied by a greater tone in muscles, an increase of muscle bulk, better posture, and a decrease in pendulous flesh in the older group.

DISCUSSION

In this study, the immediate effect of isometric exercise was an increase in systolic and diastolic blood pressures and an

TABLE 2

Effects of Isometric Exercise on Blood Pressure and Pulse Rate

Group	No. of Subjects	Systolic B.P. (mm Hg)	Weeks	Diastolic B.P. (mm Hg)	Weeks	Pulse Pressure (mm Hg)	Weeks	Pulse (min.)	Weeks
Controls: normal B.P.	3	106 ± 2	15	58 ± 6	15	48 ± 8	15	86 ± 6	15
		112 ± 6	15	70 ± 4	15	41 ± 5	15	64 ± 8	15
		116 ± 4	15	73 ± 3	15	44 ± 2	15	75 ± 3	15
		111.3 (4.32)*		67.0 (4.50)		44.3 (5.57)		&5.0 (6.03)	
Controls: normal B.P., isometrics	4	103 ± 4	33	59 ± 5	33	48 ± 6	33	72 ± 8	33
		110 ± 4	25	69 ± 5	25	43 ± 7	25	67 ± 3	25
		102 ± 4	38	62 ± 6	38	42 ± 6	38	72 ± 8	38
		104 ± 4	38	65 ± 7	38	39 ± 3	38	66 ± 8	38
		106.0 (4.00)		63.8 (5.81)		43.0 (5.70)		69.3 (7.09)	
Elevated B.P.: isometrics	8	140 —18	5	90 — 6	5	50 —12	5	74 — 2	5
		140 —20	8	96 —16	8	44 — 4	8	—	
		144 —16	8	84 — 8	8	60 — 8	8	72 —10	8
		146 —30	8	90 —24	8	56 — 6	5	86 — 4	8
		158 —32	5	98 —24	5	60 — 8	8	88 —12	5
		160 —40	8	80 —10	8	80 —30	8		
		182 —40	5	78 — 8	5	104 —32	5	60 + 4	5
		190 —42	5	80 — 2	5	110 —40	5	72 + 2	5
		157.5 (31.4)		87.0 (16.9)		70.5 (21.9)		75.3 (6.88)	
Hypertension: hypotensive drugs, isometrics	5	142 — 4	2**	86 — 2	2	56 — 2	2	68,0	2
		144 —12	10	96 —14	10	48 + 2	10	—	10
		148 —14	5	82 —14	5	66 —10	5	66,0	5
		152 —20	3	86 — 8	3	66 —12	3	84 —10	3
		152 —28	5	88 —12	5	64 —16	5	78 —12	5
		147.6 (18.1)		87.6 (8.21)		60.0 (10.1)		74.0 (7.81)	
Hypertension: previous drugs isometrics, no drugs	2	150 —22		110 —16		40 — 6		88 — 8	
		160 —36		110 —32		50 — 4		76 —10	
		128 — 6		94 — 8		34 + 2		80 + 6	
		124 — 8		78 — 2		46 — 6		66 + 4	
	maintained lowered blood pressure for 11 months to date								

* Standard Deviation.
** Abdominal and buttocks, isometrics, only.

increase in the heart rate. A 5-8 week training period in isometric exercise demonstrated a decrease in resting systolic and diastolic pressures in hypertensive subjects, but no significant change in the heart rate. It is noteworthy that isometric exercise had no long-term effect upon resting blood pressure, as is evident from the standard deviation values for the control group and for the control group taking isometric exercises, in which blood pressure levels were normal.

During isometric muscular contraction, the release of adenosine triphosphate energy may cause sweeping of cross bridges against a greater resistance, thereby causing greater tension on the Z line. According to Huxley's (1,2) filament sliding hypothesis, the isotropic band of the sarcomere remains unchanged in length; thus an explanation must be sought within the sarcomere. Actin filaments may be oriented in a more orderly way in their two-chained twisted double-helix formation, and may be stretched to make contact with cross bridges situated more centrally between A bands. With training, actomyosin hypertrophy may result. If actin filaments stretch, relaxation may require only recoil. Stretched actin-filament penetration between A bands may account for the apparent increased circumference of isometrically contracting muscles in the resting stage.

Isometric exercise increases muscle strength and endurance by the development of tension but not by the development of anoxia (3). The maintenance of isometric contraction without fatigue may be associated with continuous blood supply to msucle because the capillaries are not occluded (virtually no sarcomere change) and because the arterial blood pressure is increased during isometric exercise.

In this study, involvement of the sympathetic nervous system, epinephrine, and norepinephrine was indicated in the short-term experiments by pupillary dilatation, tachycardia, and increased diastolic pressure through increased arteriolar vaso-constriction.

An hypothesis (4–6) is offered as an explanation of the lowering of blood pressure during isometric training in the long-term experiments:

1. With less mechanical pressure on the muscle capillaries, an increased venous return may stimulate low baro-receptors. This reflexly leads to peripheral vasodilatation by reducing vasoconstrictor tonus. The increased venous return produces an increased cardiac output against less peripheral resistance, thereby lowering diastolic and systolic blood pressures.

2. Stimulation of the high baro-receptors in the carotid and aortic sinuses intermittently during isometric exercise may cause an immediate reflex slowing of the heart, which in turn may reduce blood pressure.

3. Repeated daily isometric exercise over a long period may cause growth of the capillary bed in muscles and thereby increase the volume of blood in this area, which in turn may decrease arterial blood pressure.

Confirmation of the findings of this study would con-tribute to the prevention of cerebrovascular, cardiovascular and peripheral vascular diseases.

CONCLUSION

Maximal, extensive, brief isometric exercise over a period of 5–8 weeks lowered blood pressure in hypertensive subjects and in subjects treated with a constant dosage of hypotensive drugs, and maintained low blood pressure in subjects previously treated with hypotensive drugs.

Addendum

In follow-up studies on the subjects who performed 6-second isometric exercises, there have been no detrimental side effects such as the arrhythmias, discomfort or dizziness which others have attributed to isometric exercises of long duration.

REFERENCES

1. HUXLEY, H. E., AND HANSON, J.: Changes in the cross striations of muscle during contraction and stretch, and their structural interpretation, *Nature* (London) 173: 973-976, 1954.

2. HUXLEY, H. E.: The mechanism of muscular contraction, *Sc. American 213:* 18-27, 1965.

3. GERSTEN, J. W.: Isometric exercise in paraplegia and quadriceps and hamstring weakness, *Arch. Phys. Med. 42:* 498-506, 1961.

4. RODDIE, I.C., AND SHEPHERD, J. T.: Receptors in high pressure and low pressure vascular systems; their role in the reflex control of the human circulation, *Lancet 1:* 493-496, 1958.

5. DOWNEY, J. A.; DARLING, R. C., AND MILLER, J. M.: Effects of heat, cold, and exercise on the peripheral circulation, *Arch. Phys. Med. 49:* 308-314, 1968.

6. REITSMA, W.: Skeletal muscle hypertrophy after heavy exercise in rats with surgically reduced muscle function, *Am. J. Phys. Med. 48:* 237-258, 1969.

BRIEF, MAXIMAL, EXTENSIVE ISOMETRIC EXERCISE AND CIRCULATION

A SUMMARY

The concept of using regimen of brief, maximal, and extensive isometric exercise in lowering blood pressure in hypertension has been published by B. Kiveloff, M.D. and O. Huber, Ph.D.[1] from New York Infirmary.

It has become apparent that the lowering of blood pressure results from increased peripheral circulation, as demonstrated in studies on the treatment of intermittent claudication by B. Kiveloff.[2,3]

. Letters by Kiveloff and Huber on isometrics in hypertension were published in Medical Tribune,[4] and Chronic Disease Management[5] in 1972, and 1973 in JAMA[6,7] and Lancet.[8] A letter by Kiveloff on avoiding amputation appeared in Hospital Tribune in 1973.[9] Hypertension Bulletin,[10] a Ciba Service, published "Isometrics to Reduce Pressure" in 1973. Abstracts and excerpts of the two main publications appeared in Physical Therapy,[11] Internal Medicine Digest,[12] Every inch and 1/2,[13] R.N.[14] The two main publications have become part of the bibliography for physical therapy students at N.Y. University.[15]

Overwhelming requests for reprints have been received from four continents.

The concept of isometric exercise and circulation has been extended to increasing venous flow for prevention of venous thrombosis in letters by Kiveloff in 1975.[16,17]

A study in Chest in 1975[18] on 140 patients with known or suspected coronary artery disease states that "isometric exercise alone is much less likely to produce myocardial ischemia than vigorous dynamic exercise. Higher arterial diastolic (coronary perfusion) pressure may retard the development of myocardial ischemia during isometric . . . exercise in coronary patients".

A New York Infirmary team is studying the effect of isometrics on skin temperatures. Preliminary results with skin thermometry and thermography demonstrate an increased peripheral blood flow by rise of skin temperatures.

REFERENCES

1. Kiveloff, B., and Huber, O.: Brief, maximal, isometric exercise in hypertension, J.Am. Geriatrics Soc. 19:1006 (1971).
2. Kiveloff, B.: Letter to the Editor, Arch. Phys. Med. & Rehab. 54:149, 1973.
3. Kiveloff, B.: Brief, extensive isometric exercise in the treatment of intermittent claudication, J. Am. Geriatrics Soc. 12:133 March 1974.
4. Kiveloff, KB. and Huber, O.: Isometric exercises, letter to the editor, Medical Tribune IX, 13,72.
5. Idem: Letter to the Editor, Chr. Dis. Management XII, 72.
6. Idem: Isometrics in lowering blood pressure, J.A.M.A. 523: 559,29,73.
7. Idem: Exercise vs. drugs for treatment of hypertension, JAMA 225:314,6/16/73.
8. Idem: Isometric exercise and hypertension, The Lancet 212, 1/27/73.
9. Kiveloff, B: Avoiding amputation, Letter to the Editor, Hosp. Tribune 7/23/73.
10. Isometrics to reduce pressure, Hypertension Bulletin, A Ciba service, May 1973.
11. Physical Therapy, 1007 September 1974.
12. Internal Medicine Digest 15, October 1974.
13. Every inch and 1/2, Vol. 5, #12, December 1974.
14. R.N., 102, June 1974.
15. E40, 1409 P.T. Proc II, R. Whipple, October 2, 1974.
16. Kiveloff, B.: Improving Venous flow, letter to the Editor, Orthopedic Review: Vol. IV, No. 5, May 1975.
17. Idem: Prevention of thromboembolism, letter to the Editor N.Y.S.J. of Med. 1832, September 1975.
18. Kerber, R. & al: Myocardial ischemic effects of isometric, dynamic and combined exercise in coronary disease. Chest, 388,67, April 4, 1975.

BRIEF EXTENSIVE ISOMETRIC EXERCISE IN THE TREATMENT OF INTERMITTENT CLAUDICATION

BROINO KIVELOFF, MD*

*Department of Physical Medicine and Rehabilitation,
New York Infirmary, New York, N.Y.*

ABSTRACT: In 7 cases of intermittent claudication due to peripheral vascular disease, pain was relieved and walking ability improved after brief extensive isometric exercise. This form of exercise may be useful in the prevention of intermittent claudication.

The beneficial results of a simple regimen of brief maximal isometric exercise in patients with hypertension was reported in 1971 by Kiveloff and Huber (1). The improved peripheral circulation observed with isometric exercise suggested that this form of therapy might be of benefit also in intermittent claudication. Conventional methods of exercise have not proved of much value in this peripheral vascular disorder.

METHODS AND RESULTS

The brief maximal extensive isometric exercise applied in this study consists of stiffening all the body muscles simultaneously for six seconds, three times; this procedure takes place three times daily — in the morning, at noon, and in the evening. It is essential to maintain normal breathing throughout;

the Valsalva maneuver should not be permitted. The patient should be lying down or standing.

In our previous studies on hypertension we did not observe any arrhythmias or other side effects such as the dizziness and discomfort associated with long-sustained isometric exercises. Electrocardiograms taken before and after a program of brief maximal extensive isometrics showed no changes.

Seven subjects with intermittent claudication were studied — 2 men and 5 women whose ages ranged from 50 to 78 years. Their ambulatory capacity was greatly limited because of pain in the calves of the legs. There was no color change in the skin of the feet. In all cases there were no popliteal and pedal pulses.

With brief maximal extensive isometric exercise, all the subjects experienced relief of pain and return of good ambulatory function. No recurrence of claudication was observed. Three of the 7 cases are discussed in detail:

CASE REPORTS

Case 1

H. C., a 77-year-old female physician, was an excellent walker and hill-climber until April 1971, when intermittent claudication developed bilaterally. In 1954 she had a history of coronary disease and hypertension. The distance she could walk without pain was limited to one or two blocks. On physical examination, no pedal and popliteal pulses could be felt. The feet were warm and not discolored. Vasodilator therapy was ineffective. She refused angiography. On June 2, 1971, a program of brief maximal extensive isometric exercise was begun. After several weeks her blood pressure, which was 180/90 mm Hg before the exercises, fell to 150/76 mm. Pain on walking gradually disappeared. During more than two years under observation, she has had no pain on walking and her blood pressure remains at the lower

* Chief Physiatrist, New York Infirmary.

Address: Department of Physical Medicine and Rehabilitation, New York Infirmary, Stuyvesant Square East and 15th Street, New York, N.Y. 10003.

NEW YORK INFIRMARY   FOUNDED 1853

Stuyvesant Square East &
15th Street,
New York, New York 10003
(212) 228-8000

INSTRUCTIONS FOR BRIEF, MAXIMAL, EXTENSIVE ISOMETRIC EXERCISE

The exercise regimen developed by B. Kiveloff, M.D. and O. Huber, Ph.D., from New York Infirmary, proved effective in lowering blood pressure in hypertension and in alleviating symptoms in intermittent claudication.

Brief isometric exercise of 6 seconds repeated 3 times with a few seconds interval, 3 times a day, *maximal* — to stiffen the muscles as much as possible within isometric limits, *extensive* — to involve all voluntary muscles simultaneously, and *isometric* — to limit joint motion, accomplishes the objective. *Normal breathing* must accompany the exercise to prevent untoward pressure effects.

The optimal position for performing isometric exercise is a relaxed standing position.

BRIEF ISOMETRICS FOR THE PRESERVATION OF GOOD HEALTH

by

Broino Kiveloff, M.D., Olive Huber, Ph.D.,
Jerry Friedman, B.A., Participant

Presented at:

The 29th Annual Scientific Meeting of the
Geronotological Society in a Poster Session
October 13-17, 1976, New York Hilton, N.Y.

Observations of animals, including humans, as they awaken from sleep indicate that brief maximal isometric contraction of all voluntary muscles affects muscular and circulatory conditioning. After awakening, isometric contractions occur as a reflex, but can be performed voluntarily.

To determine whether a regimen of brief isometrics of the body musculature can promote improved circulation, studies were carried out concerning the effect on blood pressure and pulse rate.

Brief isometric exercise of 6 seconds and 3 times with a few seconds interval 3 times a day, maximal — to stiffen the muscles as much as possible within isometric limits, extensive — to involve all voluntary muscles simultaneously, and isometric — to limit joint motion, accomplishes the objective. Normal breathing must accompany the exercise to prevent untoward pressure effects.

The optional position for performing isometric exercise is a relaxed standing position. Experimentation demonstrated that after a five to eight week period of isometric performance in hypertension, a lowering of as much as 42 mm. Hg. in systolic blood pressure and as much as 24 mm. Hg. in diastolic pressure was observed. No detrimental side effects such as arrhythmia, discomfort, nor dizziness, as others have attributed to sustained isometric exercises, have occurred.

Studies in subjects with intermittent claudication after a regimen of isometric exercises have demonstrated considerable relief from pain and improved ability to walk without pain for long distances. It is postulated that isometric exercises assist in increasing peripheral circulation. This hypothesis is supported by a few critical experiments in which circulation to the hand increased as indicated by thermographic studies, after isometric exercise, and the warmth of the hand increased with isometrics after vasoconstriction produced by smoking, which indicates that the increase in peripheral circulation with isometrics is sufficient to overcome the vasoconstriction of smoking. For maintenance and preservation of good health, a functioning cardiovascular system capable of supplying nutrients and oxygen to tissues and removing waste is important. Cardiovascular adaptation is a process of peripheral circulation. Isometrics assist in improving muscle tonus and muscle strength probably through building of muscle hemoglobin which is instrumental in receiving oxygen for muscle recovery.

Improvement of posture is evident with isometrics; this has esthetic value, affords a sense of well being, and contributes to better cardio-pulmonary function. With aging muscle cells become pale through loss of sarcoplasm and muscle hemoglobin. Isometrics may possibly delay this process of aging.

It is recommended that isometric exercises serve as an alternative for hypotensive drugs in the treatment of high blood pressure; as a releif from pain and improvement of function in intermittent claudication; and to foster good muscle tone and strength for a more healthful and productive life.

REFERENCES

1. Kiveloff, B., and Huber, O.: Brief Maximal Isometric Exercise in Hypertension. J. AM. Geriatrics Soc. 19:1006 (1971)
2. Kiveloff, B.: and Huber, O.: Isometrics in Lowering Blood Pressure. J.A.M.A. 223: 559 (Jan. 29) 1973
3. Kiveloff, B., and Huber, O.: Isometric Exercise and Hypertension. The LANCET 212 (Jan. 27) 1973
4. Kiveloff, B.: Brief Extensive Isometric Exercise in the Treatment of Intermittent Claudication. J. AM. Geriatrics Soc. 12:133 (Mar) 1974

* Broino Kiveloff, M.D., Director, Department of Physical Medicine and Rehabilitation, New York Infirmary.
** Olive Huber, Ph.D., Professor Emeritus, Department of Physiology and Health, NCUNY, Hunter College, New York, N.Y.
*** Jerry Friedman, B.A., Chief Physical Therapist, New York Infirmary.

BROINO KIVELOFF, M.D.

OLIVE HUBER, Ph.D.

Stuyvesant Square East &
15th Street,
New York, New York 10003,
(212) 228-8000

NEW YORK INFIRMARY FOUNDED 1853

11 December 1980

Professor Wen-Shan Huang
President,
American Academy of Chinese Culture, Inc.
1493 Galveston Street
Los Angeles, CA 90026

Dear Professor Huang,

Thank you for your letter of November 27, 1980, and your interest in our method of isometric exercise in lowering blood pressure in hypertension.

In answer to your questions:

1) The basic idea of our method is the increase of peripheral circulation because of vasodilation.

2) In our original study of 1971, after trying different time spans, six seconds repeated three times, three times a day was used; and it is efficient. Our own experience for the last years allowed us to do the exercise more than three times a day with no side effects.

3) We have chosen six seconds in order not to raise blood pressure too much while performing the exercise.

4) The several seconds of relaxation allow for circulatory adaptation for the resumption of the following six seconds tension.

Enclosed is our original paper of 1971.

We were happy to hear from you about your friend, Mr. Edward L. Lai; I (Broino Kiveloff) enjoyed immensely meeting him in New York.

Please do not hesitate to contact us as you wish.

Sincerely,
BROINO KIVELOFF, M.D.
OLIVE HUBER, Ph.D.

Dr. Broino Kiveloff, M.D.

Stuyvesant Square East &
15th Street,
New York, New York 10003
(212) 228-8000

NEW YORK INFIRMARY FOUNDED 1853   9 April 1981

Dr. Wen-shan Huang,
Book Department
American Academy of Chinese Culture, Inc.
1493 Galveston Street
Los Angeles, California 90026

Dear Dr. Huang,

Together with Dr. Olive Huber, we thank you for your letter of 3 March, 1981. It was very kind of you to remember me by sending me your Fundamentals of Tai Chi Chuan. It will certainly add much to my understanding of Chinese culture.

To answer your question: The meaning and definition of isometric exercise is the tensing of the opposit (agonists and antagonists) muscles without moving the joints, so that the length of the muscle fibers is not changed during the exercise.

Your translation of Mr. Lai's article is probably correct. It is *important* to add that, during the six-second exercise, normal breathing *must* be maintained. This means that one inhalation at the start and one in the middle of the exercise can be considered normal.

We would be honored to see our work cited in your book.

I am enclosing my latest short publication, in which my concept on aging is expressed.

My kindest regards to Mr. Lai.

Sincerely,
Broino Kiveloff, M.D.

THE NEW YORK INFIRMARY
BEEKMAN DOWNTOWN HOSPITAL

Stuyvesant Square East &
15th Street,
New York, New York 10003,
(212) 228-8000

April 28, 1981

Professor Wen-shan Huang
American Academy of Chinese Culture, Inc.
1493 Galveston Street
Los Angeles, California 90026

Dear Professor Huang:

Fundamentals of Tai Chi Chuan will become for me a source of inspiration from which I will draw more knowledge for my own creativity. It is a pity that due to my physical incapacity (hip fracture) I am unable to learn how to perform the art of Tai Chi Chuan. I hope it would be of interest to you to note that when I invented the method of brief, maximal extensive isometric exercise, my first and primary motive was to "slow down the aging process and to stretch out a healthy life span". That's why the first target was hypertension, the number one enemy. Later the method was developed for more applications. It seems to me that there is no end to the usefulness of my method, as is the case with the Tai Chi Chuan, if I may dare to compare the two.

In his first letter to me Mr. E. L. Lai asked me "why this remarkable treatment of high blood pressure has not been widely used even in the U.S.A., it seems it has not been recommended by physicians or hospitals?" I am asking the same question, but I do have the answer. Despite all of my efforts to get some official recognition of my method, my attempts have been futile. It is easy to understand and it is painful to say that such a simple method to treat hypertension is a big blow to the pharmaceutical and medical industry, and this is most probably the answer to Mr. Lai's question. I am satisfied that tens of millions read of the exercise and probably throngs are performing it for their benefits. I am not bitter but disappointed that the media is not interested in something that is good for the people.

Once again, thank you for the book you sent to me. I would appreciate it if you could send me a xerox copy of the article by Mr. Lai published in the Central Daily News. Please forgive me if I have taken too much of your time. With best wishes for success . . .

> Sincerely,
> Broino Kiveloff, M.D.

THE ROYAL SOCIETY OF HEALTH JOURNAL
PATRON : HER MAJESTY THE QUEEN
SECRETARY: J. AUDREY ELLISON,
B.SC., F.I.F.S.T., F.R.S.H.

Telephone 01-235 9961
Telegrams ROSOPH LONDON SWIX 7EN

VOLUME 100 NO 6 DECEMBER 1980

R.S.H. 6 1980

LETTERS TO THE EDITOR

Dear Sir,

Exercise for a healthy life span

Being a physician for more than 50 years, my thoughts in gerontological terms are directed toward ways of delaying the ageing process and building up body resistance to diseases mainly affecting the elderly. The human body is like a plant. When there is not enought moisture it withers; when the blood supply to the body tissues and vital organs is impaired a loss of vitality, early ageing and cardiovascular diseases fllow. Cardiovascular adaptation is a process of the peripheral circulation. When this is diminished the balance of blood supply is disturbed. The musculature is big source of blood reserves. With ageing, msucle fibres with its vascularity disappears and is replaced by connective tissue.

We invented and developed a method of one minute a day exercises which prove to be effective in lowering blood pressure in essential hypertension after six to eight weeks, ·and in alleviating symptoms in intermittent claudication in a few weeks. The exercise maintains muscle tone and muscle bulk. The exercise is brief, maximal extensive isometrics and it consists of tensing all the voluntary body muscles simultaneously, face included, for six seconds, repeated three times with a few seconds interval, three times a day. Normal breathing must accompany the exercise. In our experiments we demonstrated that the exercise results in peripheral vasodilation with increased blood flow.

More than a decade of experience convinced us of the safety and efficiency of our method of exercise. By maintaining a well functioning cardiovascular system, a healthy longevity may be accomplished.

We urge the readers to join millions of people around the world performing this exercise.

Yours truly,
BROINO KIVELOFF,
M.D., F.R.S.H.

REFERENCES

KIVELOFF, B. and HUBER, O. Brief Maximal Isometric Exercise in Hypertension, J.A.G.S., 19:1006-1012, 1971.

KIVELOFF, B. Brief Extensions, Isometric Exercise in the Treatment of Intermittent Claudication, J.A.G.S., 12:133-134, 1974.

KIVELOFF, B. and HUBER, O. Isometric Exercise and Hypertension, The Lancet, p. 212, 1973.

KIVELOFF, B. Coronary Heart Disease, R.S.H.J., Volume 97, # 4, 1977.

太極拳要義後序

余自一九四九年底到美，飄泊於東西兩岸者幾二十年。自一九六八年東歸後，把積年稿件，次第刊布。這本太極拳要義爲拙著英文寫作之一。此後尚有「文化學與中國文化」、「文化學導論」，將繼續問世。本書先行發表，次題爲「歷史、哲學、方法、實習與應用專論」。全書分三部分，第一爲歷史與哲學的，共分六章，包括：一、說明什麼是太極拳，認定太極拳爲人生藝術，以養生健身，延年益壽爲主要，武藝爲末技。二、敘述太極拳之歷史發展，對於這種武藝之演進，畧有所考證。三、易理與拳理，本屬奧妙難講，本文先說明易理，再說明易理與拳理之對應關係。四、說到太極拳的原理，有人以少林爲佛家拳（外家），太極爲道家或儒家(內家)拳。作者則以爲太極拳與儒，道、釋（禪宗）均有關係。而分別作原則上之說明。五、在研究太極拳與健康方面，則根據生理學、生物學、醫學爲之闡幽抉微，說明其具體的結合。六、在現代哲學與科學觀照之下，作者對於太極拳，則以現代最新的有機哲學與物理等科學，爲之解釋。第二部分爲理論的與方法的。七、解釋太極拳的基本姿勢，以楊澄甫所傳的定型架子爲主體。八、對於太極拳之原則和方法，作概括和系統之敘述。九與十、說明太極拳之呼吸體系，同時對於這種體系作科學的闡釋。第三部分爲技術的與應用的。十一、採用圖解，說明太極拳的連續姿勢（形式）。十二、對圖解所表示的太極拳之序列，詳爲解說。十三、太極拳本來是一種武藝，本章把它的自衞技術，在運作上，分別予以表達。十四、說明推手與大攦之實習概要，均附圖解。十五、畧述太極拳自衞論理與法則之精義。

本書附錄亦分三部份，一爲對王宗岳、武禹襄的太極拳論等之翻譯，對於古典學說，作簡單之介紹。作者對於各種太極拳譜，則另篇爲之述評。第三部份爲健康的藝術。這是作者根據中國民族的智慧與針灸學的理論：一、介紹「均衡的文化運動」——十段錦。二、介紹「自我按摩術」，着重穴道的對應。三、介紹氣功的養生方法。這些都是中國民族文化的遺產，試爲挖掘，整理，使其與太極拳配合，更好地爲世界人類健康服務。第三部份，附錄舊作中文二篇。一、「中國文化與太極拳」，對於易理與太極拳之道，作進一步的解析與說明。二、「東西壽命學合論」，乃是根據西方之壽命學或老年學與東方道家之長生學，印度瑜伽哲學與技術對於長生之要求與希望，作一貫的綜合。最後就是現在的「后叙」。

本書除作者英文自序二篇外，有克怡（ Preston K. Caye ）博士，新墨西哥大學石東（ Justin Stone ）教授與美國創造教育學院恩格伯遜（James C. Ingebretsen）院長等所寫之序文。本書附列太極拳圖式二百餘張，以美國思敏（ Janice Seaman ）夫人的表演，作爲示範。夫人精太極拳，同時也是瑜伽與空手道的教師。至推手與大攦圖式，則請楊澄甫先生高足鄺允征氏領導，表演示範。鄺氏畢業國立中山大學，紐約大學碩士，任工程師多年。在台灣的及門弟子，不下數千人。現任非洲象牙海岸國總統貝尼氏（ Houphone Poigny ）個人太極拳教師，經已數年，常常來往於非洲與巴黎之間，對中國文化之宣傳，貢獻至大。

二

我生平有四大志願：其一、希望追隨革命先進與國人之後，把中國建立一個自由獨立的新中國，成爲二十一世紀世界社會之共同模型。其二、把東方的人本主義、自然主義、大同主義與西方的科學主義，自由社會主義，融合貫通，由理論層面踏進行動層面。其三、建立文化學體系，尋求文化的理念，類型與變遷法則，解決現代面臨的文化危機，爲未來文化舖新路。其四、就是要跑進象牙塔裡，把陳思王嘆爲「今之介弁，反恥而不言」的太極拳之道理，予以現代化，體系化的說明，使這種人生藝術，由貴族化變成平民化，由中國化變成國際化，由少數人的武藝成為多數人的健康藝術。前三種志願，在此處毋須細說，就最後一種論，我在下面說到本書寫作的目的時，更願有進一步的說明。

我本來是學習哲學、社會學、歷史學、人類學、民族學和文化學的，對於武藝既不是內行，也不是專家，但我本孔子志道據德依仁游藝的精神，對於中國藝術（包括美術和武藝而言），向來是愛好的。自從民國八、九年在北京大學參加武術會，並由該會聘專師返齋舍指導練習外，其後奔走海內外數十年，向當代名師請益，交情在師友之間，而就記憶所及者有姚馥春（中央國術館）、董英傑、蔡鶴明、熊養和、梁勁予、太虛法師（佛法）、南懷瑾（內功）、韓振聲、蕭天石（養生學）、鄭曼青、楊守中、董虎嶺、郭連蔭、王延年、張唯中、歐陽竟無、忍慧法師（六字口訣）、韋達（易學）、劉百閔（易學）、程達材（太極尺）、劉曜廷、鄺允征、曾昭然、蔣維喬（靜坐法）、劉培中（內功）、郭廷獻（散手），盧鴻賓（八卦拳）、蔣仲雲（八卦掌）先生等。他們對於我學習道家、易家、禪家的哲理，太極拳，八卦拳，太極尺，推手，散手，氣功與玄門太極長生功等等，給予不少的經驗與指導。如果我對於易理，佛法，太極拳和養生學的精義與功用，能有多少了解，提高和發展，這些除却自己研究與讀書心得外，大部都是他們引路口授的結果。

我練習太極拳，當初的目的不外本諸陶侃運甓，祖逖起舞的精神，希望對於身體健康，有所補益，從來沒有想到為太極拳講解。六十年代，我在紐約新學院講學告一段落之後，遷居羅安琪（Los Angeles），並應友人端美（C. L. J. Damme）之約，共同創立華美文化學院，以宣揚中國文化為職志。其時美國醫生克怡（Preston K. Caye）博士伉儷，知余每天練習太極拳及從事靜坐，堅邀傳授，未便固拒，因此隨同練習者，日漸增加。羅安琪加州大學（U. C. L. A.）分校學生且組織學社，分頭學習，一時成為風尚。

到了一九六六年，由於習者日衆，乃函聘專家董虎嶺師兄由港前往任教，此後傳授之範圍，日益擴大。余因鑒於學者慕學之誠，於是除擇眼爲講解太極拳之哲理與拳理而外，乃另編講義，這是本書寫作的一段因緣。至寫作的目的，卑之無甚高論，約有下列數端：

（一）指出易家，道家，新儒家的「自然有機體論」（Concept of Natural Organism），爲現代生物科學，物理科學之根據者，實非歐洲思想的產品，而是易學與老莊哲學的結晶。迄十七八世紀始由耶穌會士傳入西歐。德國大哲萊勃尼士（Leibnitz）首先接受，後經黑格爾，馬克思，以至當代之懷德海（Whitehead）而蔚成巨流，不料這就是太極拳者宇宙觀之所由來。

（二）指出我的「整合太極論」，與前輩如王宗岳、武宇襄、李亦畲之各種拳論和歌訣之專着重武術，以練勁爲第一義諦者者畧異。我因此自己妄稱我的太極拳論是一種「整合太極論」。（其要端見本文第四段）。根據這種理論來說（已見英文原文），太極拳不但以易理爲根據，而且其根本原則實出自儒家、道家，且與禪家的義諦符合；而在醫理上，則又以針灸學爲基礎。它以這樣的民族哲學，民族醫學爲背景所建立的均衡運動，當然成爲人生藝術；只要鍊之有恒，自能平衡陰陽，調和血氣，疏通經絡，培養眞氣。

（三）指出太極拳姿勢恬靜，美妙，均勻，如能配合呼吸，靜中有動，外靜內動，動中有靜，外動內靜，作到動靜合一，使習者能達到仲尼所謂游于藝的情趣，自無須參加西洋式的筋疲力竭之運動，而可以收養生全生的目的。

（四）指出太極拳的歷史的淵源和演變，認爲這種人生藝術乃是中國民族最高智慧之結晶。到了現階段，其原理與技術，均可以現代的有機哲學，整合哲學和新物理學，文化學爲之闡釋與發揚，與傳統的針灸學術一樣，殊途同歸，可以登上世界學術之林，爲人類造無窮之福祉。

太極拳，照我們的立場看來，旣然是一種人生藝術，同時也是一種健康科學——包括自衞之技藝在內。這種科技的理論之發展，已經過三個明顯的階段。第一是胚胎階段：由漢唐開始，大抵認爲這種技術，以養生鍛鍊爲最高原則，華佗五禽之戲與李宣平之「三世七」，均其先導。第二是長成階段：到了宋代張三丰起來，一方注重「吐納導引」，重視「意」和「氣」的鍛鍊，希望養生延年，另一方則改進少林之文化遺產，在技擊上，以本來的「着勢」做根據，但原理上，却走向老子所謂專氣致柔的一條道路之上。第三是成熟階段：由王宗岳建立太極拳的理論體系之後，自十六七七世紀以至今日，對於十三勢的行功，雖未忘懷於「益壽延年不老春」的初旨，但究竟側重由「着熟而漸悟懂勁，由懂勁而階及神明」，以能在技擊上「牽動四兩撥千斤」，達到超人的偉績，爲無上絕技。我們生在二十世紀的七十年代，因爲原子武器之出現，認爲這種技擊目的，早已變成次要了。原來張三丰、王宗岳之創立太極拳，一本于道儒之太極圖（原圖見英文易學部份）。周子說：「聖人定之以中正仁義而主靜，立人極焉。其行之也中，其處之也正，其發之也仁，其裁之也義，一動一靜，莫不有以全太極之道，而無所虧焉」，因此我個人的意見，認爲太極拳的理論，到了今日的第四個階段，自應以中道法則爲根據，通過其在技藝上的鍛鍊，以能夠保持健康，增強體質，預防未老先衰，延緩自然衰老，爲最普遍之要求，至於武藝則僅屬末技罷了。

本着這種原則，我所以提出「整合太極論」作爲現階段的太極拳之理論基礎。

☰

我寫這本書時，曾面臨着兩個不易解答的問題：其一、太極拳創自何人，其發展演變的過程如何？其二是太極拳的拳架甚多，究以何種爲標準？

關於第一個問題，我把大部份的參考資料差不多都看過。本來武藝與繪畫有同樣的重要性，這是人人皆知的，但國內學人，一向對前一方面，甚爲忽視，大有數典忘祖之慨；至拳術家則把拳理視同奧秘，不肯公開示人，結果便成固步自封，不求光大，使世人無從一窺奧奧，故有關武藝的歷史，向來很少有人作系統的整理，截至今日，自然非常凌亂，這是很可惜的事情。

十年前我起草本書時，曾把太極拳的發展史，分爲三個階段，予以敘述。第一階段由華佗的五禽戲說到唐許宣平之「三世七」，程泌之「小九天」與殷利亨之「後天法」。第二階段則從宋元之際的張三丰開始。他本儒家的易理，融合道佛各家哲學之長，納五行八卦於拳術步法當中，運動行氣，以虛靜勝人；而由於其能傳陳希夷之學，得太極圖說，而衆理始達一貫，拳術乃達到新的綜合。張氏之學，初時只有十三式，其後經過相當時間，始傳至明之張松溪、王宗岳，特別是王氏，他悉心體會，豁然貫通，作太極拳論，於是太極拳之名始著。王氏之學，明末清初傳至陳州同……黃百家，由山陝而浙東，遂演成南派之「內家拳」與少林派之稱「外家拳」者，分途並進，此則黃梨洲先生已有論述，（看「王征南墓誌銘」，見南雷文集），而且言之鑿鑿，無可否認。可惜內家拳中絕，故第三階段，在北方應從陳王廷（長興）說起。陳氏籍出河南陳家溝，受到王宗岳拳論之影响，兼採外家（戚繼光拳經）着勢之長，才有陳家太極拳之創興。河北永年楊露禪受學於陳氏，盡傳其秘，教學北京，復多所發明與改進，其後更由其孫楊澄甫傳播全國，迄至今日，此種拳藝，已遠播歐，美，非，澳各洲，成績斐然。

二十年代，唐豪（范生）、徐震（哲東）等受了『五四運動』時代的疑古思潮的影响，主張採取科學方法，把武藝史上的神怪迷信之談，澈底消除，予以客觀的整理，其志趣見解，自屬高人一等。唐氏且於一九三二年親到陳家溝調查，因見陳氏家譜中，沒有談到太極拳的來源，更沒有談到張三丰與太極拳有關的歷史，因此認定傳統的說法，均出諸僞造。他說：「根據我在陳家溝所得的實際調查，這種拳術係由戚繼光（一五二八──一五八七）的**拳經**採取而來。這書的編造，以該地所傳的**拳法爲根據**」
。他因此**斷**言太極拳的淵源，來自民間，而也是長時間發展的綜
合結果。後一論**斷**，我們當然樂於接受，但他否定張三丰與太極
拳的關係，甚至認王宗岳爲清乾隆間人。徐哲東及近來有許多太
極拳名家，均附其說，一時成爲氣尙，甚至有認爲不易之論者。
余十年前起草本書時，亦不免爲其說所掩蔽。近來細玩其書，始
知他的武**斷**主義和形式主義，實有再度檢討之必要。

太極拳的來源，楊露禪在王宗岳太極拳論註說：「右係武當
山張三丰先師遺論，欲天下豪傑延年益壽，不徒作技藝之末也。
」這話極爲扼要，因王宗岳之理論，是出自三丰的。而楊澄甫在
太極體用全書原序（民二十二年）也說：「先大父（指其祖父楊
露禪）詔之曰：『太極拳創自宋末張三丰，傳之者，爲王宗岳，
陳州同，張松溪，蔣發諸人，繼承不絕。陳長興師，乃蔣發先生
唯一弟子。其術本於自然，而爲形不離太極。爲式十三，而運用
靡窮，運動身而感及心靈，故非習之旣久，驟難得其奧妙……」
。以上兩段文字，我以爲比較可靠，因爲楊露禪的學術淵源來自
陳家溝，如果陳長興對他絕不曾提到張三丰，他是一位來自農村
的老實人，斷然不會自創此說來騙人。近人翻案，只是「五四運
動」後疑古思潮時期的一種反映而已。茲分別說明如次：

（一）唐豪自己說，陳王庭（長興）遺有長短句，內有「閒
來時造拳」一句，「但家譜和注均未說明所造者爲太極拳」。又
謂「陳家溝人只肯學祖先傳下來的十三勢，不肯學習外來拳法」
（均見唐著「內家拳研究」、「王宗岳太極拳研究」、「少林武
當攷」等書）。唐大抵未知十三勢創自張三丰。在太極拳之名未
經成立時，一般人只知有十三勢，而十三勢從現在看來，就是太
極拳的前身和骨幹。這種拳術如沒十三勢還能成其爲太極拳嗎？
我認爲張三丰所傳，而爲王宗岳所撰的太極拳論，開口便說：「
太極者，無極而生，陰陽之母也」，此殆後人稱此拳爲「太極拳
」之始。至王氏的十三勢論，十三勢歌，十三勢行工心解（或云

武禹襄作），十三勢名目等，無非爲說明太極拳而撰作的。

（二）太極拳在着勢上與外家拳有相同之處，這些着勢有些傳自少林，而有些可能由陳氏採自戚氏拳經，但太極拳在由陝西傳入江浙時，則有「內家拳」之名。內家是指儒家，而與外家拳（少林拳，指出家人所習的）不同。其差異處在前者側重「勁「，而後者則重「着」，「蘊于內者爲勁，形于外者爲着，着其體也，勁其用也，勁其氣也，着其質也」，「外家拳精於着，內家精於勁」（黃百家語）。這實在是雙方的分別處。我們不能以陳氏拳法，雜有戚氏的着法，便斷定它的全形，均出自戚氏。

（三）明史「方伎傳」載張三丰傳，對於其生卒年月，沒有說明。如果張氏是生於宋徽宗宣和二年間，則到了明英宗順天年間，可能已達三百三十多歲，這似乎是很難置信的一點（這點因無實證，不妨存疑）。近人董力行曾親到張氏曾居住的寶雞金台觀，發見張氏遺跡甚多，也說到張氏內功，古今第一，長壽亦有可能云云（見所著「明日黃花錄」，第二集，香港天人公司一九七〇年出版，頁九一——一〇七）。但因爲明史說到張居金台觀，一日自言當死，留頌而逝。縣人共棺殮之，及葬聞棺內有聲，啓視則復活」。而黃梨洲先生以一代名史家，在王征南墓誌銘說：「少林以拳勇名天下，然主於搏人，人亦得以乘之。有所謂內家者，以靜制動，犯者應手即仆，故別少林爲外家，蓋起於宋之張三丰。三丰爲武當丹士，徽宗召之，道梗不得進，夜夢元帝授之拳法，厥明以單丁殺賊百餘」。唐氏對於這段紀載，目爲怪誕。我以爲人死入棺復活，印度習瑜伽術者多能之，張氏既爲丹士，如能做到這一步上乘工夫，自不足爲奇。至黃梨洲先生所記載，關於夜夢授拳一事，似屬傳聞，未足爲據。但四百年前，由於其時代尚未脫離神學與玄學思想階段，故其論証方法，亦未能股離「人神同形論」（anthropomorphism）的色彩，所以有夜夢元帝授拳的說法，亦猶之乎夏禹所處的時期，爲圖騰文化時代，夏以龍爲圖騰，此乃當時之一種制度，我們不能因此斷定夏禹爲無其人，或更說禹是一條蟲。由此可見我們如果根據歷史上的傳說的記載，便連其人與技之眞實性，亦全部加以否認，這種方法實在不是客觀的科學方法，而簡直是一種新的武斷主義罷了。此外亦有以太極拳爲技擊，不應由一位丹士張三丰開創出來爲說者。其實丹士只是鍊丹之士，中國數千年的科學技術，大部是由道家經過鍊丹的操作，才創造和發明出來。這點有英科學家李約瑟（Joseph Needham）所著的「中國之科學與文明」（Science and Civilization in China），（看拙譯第一冊，「譯者導言」，台灣商務印書館一九七二年出版）的闡發，可資佐證。李約瑟並且推崇道家哲學爲「未來的哲學」，反觀國內太極拳名家，有些即在今日，仍拾數十年前的陳說，以太極拳乃是拳術，不應說到「陰陽怪氣者」。這種思想顯然也是受了到唐、徐一流人的影响，我們實在應該予以辨正。

（三）黃梨洲先生以：「三丰之術，百年以後，流傳於陝西，而王宗爲最著。温州陳州同，從王宗受之，以此敎其鄉人，由是流傳於温州」。說者謂王宗與王宗岳並非一人，唐范生甚至因武禹襄等發見之王宗岳之拳譜，寫上乾隆年間字樣，便認王宗岳爲乾隆年間人。其實王宗與王宗岳應該同是一人，例如唐書唐太宗時，有王世充作反，史書亦常書作王充（見唐嵩岳少林寺碑），故梨洲先生父子把王宗岳寫作王宗，實不足爲奇。據許禹生之說，張三丰之技傳於陝西，「元世祖時，有西安人王宗岳者，得其眞傳，名聞海內」（見太極拳圖勢解，頁九），而倪清和著內家拳技擊圖解，有陳州同跋，謂：「余游王師之門三載，同門者有薛省三、蔣幼之等，獨承吾師恩慈，將心傳付余，余將心傳載之南歸；願再傳之萬年」等語，寫明爲大明正德十五年。由此可以證明王宗岳實爲元明之際的人物。他是太極拳理論的建立者，也是太極拳南宗（稱爲內家拳，由黃百家傳至甘鳳池，遂中絕），與北宗（稱爲太極拳，由蔣發傳陳長興，再由陳氏傳楊露禪）的開創者，而其淵源則來自張三丰。（又按唐氏在北平得陰符槍譜，有乾隆乙卯五十九年佚名氏叙一篇，便斷說此譜出自王氏之手，又說王氏爲乾隆年間人。其實以余所見，此亦　會之談，不足爲據。（看所著王宗岳考，頁一二——一三）。

　　我因在「太極拳的歷史背景」（本書第三章）上，對以上史實沒有切當的說明和辨白，今對此問題，特爲解答如上述。

　　關於第二個問題，即是拳架應以何種爲標準的問題。我相信張三丰留傳下來給王宗岳做演繹的根據之架式，就是十三勢。十七八世紀時，陳家溝的架式，有新舊兩種。楊露禪從陳長興學的是老架子，是以十三勢爲根據的，武禹襄由陳淸萍學得的是新架子，相傳爲陳有本所創。十九世紀以來，太極拳有三大派，即是陳派、楊派、武派，而架式又分六派，即是（一——二）陳家新舊架式；（三）楊家所傳架式，到了楊澄甫又有了改進；（四）吳全佑架式，後經吳鑑泉加以改進；（五）郝爲貞架式，把武禹襄所傳的改進；（六）孫祿堂學於郝氏，把形意，八卦，太極架式均有改進。一九二九年儲民誼把太極拳與西洋體操配合，當時雖藉政治之力，但亦無法推行。鄭曼青在三十年前，以太極架式太繁，不易普及，乃刪減爲三十七式，已較原有十三式增多廿四式，聞陳微明氏亦表同意。一九五六年北京體育委員會，採取楊澄甫架式，編了簡化太極拳，以健身爲主，把技擊部份約署刪除。一九六二——四年，李英昂以楊架左右不分，複式太多，主張改正，因而有精簡太極拳架出現。最近（一九七一）台灣中國太極拳研究會鑒於初習者易患陰陽不分，虛實不淸，腰胯不鬆，椿步不穩諸病，乃又定出基本運動法兩段：（甲）主練輕靈，（乙）主練功勁。又訂定初級架十式、中級七十一式。

　　本來學術進步，在於通變。武藝不但是文化的結晶，而也是一個民族在時間上前人與後人共同經驗的壘積。一本文化史表現出一切科技都不斷在變，太極拳自非例外。所以楊澄甫評陳微明以其口授者刊成的一書時有說：「顧陳子之書，僅述單人練習之程序，且翻閱十數年前之功架，又復不及近日，於此可見斯術之無止境也」，如此可見太極功架，本無固定不變之架式。習者熟習右式之後，自亦可練習左式。每式十五分鐘，半小時可畢，自能獲收均衡之益，否則加練本書所介紹之十段錦及文化按摩，文化內功等，亦可相助爲理，得到互濟之效。

四

最後，我應該進一步說明什麽是「整合太極論」，來結束以上的研究了。

我向來承認太極拳是中國民族最高智慧的結晶。爲什麽呢？這是因爲普通的健身運動只是注重身體肌肉訓練的層面之運動，對個人以及人類的福祉，沒有提供有力的統一原則，沒有注意到宇宙觀，人生觀，社會觀，文化觀，更沒有注意到把健康運動與精神生活和社會生活打成一片。太極拳不然。它不但是一種健身的運動體系，而也是一種人生的藝術；其整部思想，是以易家、儒家、禪家，新儒家的哲學爲根據，而且可以給現代人有一個安身立命，身體力行的指鍼，馴致可以把現代人的野蠻生活，鬥爭生活進一步而予以純淨化，昇華化。易說：「文明以止，人文也……觀乎人文可以化成天下」。從這方面看，太極拳對於未來文化，可能成爲一種很大的事素，這是可以預斷的。

分析來說，太極拳的體系，就目前所知的，係包括三種成分：

甲、運動姿勢——有的是原始的「十三勢」（方法），以及後來添上的三十七種基本模式或八十八種或甚至可以分爲一〇八種的姿勢。

乙、吐納導引——一切動作姿勢均可與呼吸作韻律的配合。這就是以心行氣，以氣運身，純任自然，不費着力的吐納導引。

丙、技與道——太極拳是技而進於道的，故道技必須雙修。所謂技只是「運勁如百鍊鋼，無堅不摧」的技，但它在本質上是注重「沾，連，黏，隨」，「捨己從人」的技，而不是一種「搏擊」的末技而已。何謂道？道是原理，是哲學也是它的最高原則，本身包含着宇宙觀，自然觀，人生觀，社會觀與文化觀。

我的「整合太極論」，也可說是新太極拳論，是以道為中心。我的說法，可以分為以下的犖犖大端，而畧予簡述：

第一點：「自然有機體論」。自然有機體的概念，由易學與老莊發端，經過唐代的慧能，宋朝的朱熹，方才到達哲學思辨之最高的綜合。易說：「在天之道，曰陰與陽，在地之道，曰柔與剛，在人之道，曰仁與義」。天人是合一的，所以莊生說：「天地與我並生，萬物與我為一」。禪家說，「一即一切，一切即一」，而宋儒張載也宣稱：「天地之塞吾其體，天地之帥吾其性，民吾同胞，物吾與也」。這種自然有機體論，與超越的「創造主」說，固無關係，而與機械論亦絕不相同。現代歐洲科學思想，得力於中國的「自然有機體論」，寢且成為現代自然科學的理論基礎。這恰好就是「整合太極論」的宇宙觀。

第二點：道陰陽論。「道」是宇宙的最高原則，是天地間永存不變之至理，而也是斯賓格勒（Spengler）所說中國民族文化的原始象徵（prime symbol）。易說：「一陰一陽之謂道」，道就是太極。老子說：「天下萬物生於有，有生於無」。又說：「道生一，一生二，二生三，三生萬物，萬物負陰而抱陽，冲氣以為和」。可見依照古人觀念，任何事物由道，或太極產生。道包含陰陽兩勢力，但是陰陽却在一種看不見的「氣」中得到統一。本來陰陽之說，早已應用到中國文化的任何方面，莫之能外，而尤為中國醫學特別是針灸術之基本原理。從科學來講，陽陰也可以說是代表兩種符號；但它們的起源與所含蘊的智慧曾經一度迷失於現代西方科學文明的衝擊中。其現代的意義，由於元子之包含陰電與陽電，早已重新顯現。太極拳論說：「太極者無極而生，動靜之機，陰陽之母也。」所以太極拳着着勢勢，均含一〇圓形，其動而陽，靜而陰，循環無端，生生不息，由此而來。這是「整合太極論的自然觀。

第三點：理氣論。整個宇宙是一個有機的統一體，而其組織的原則，就是理。至於氣，從現代科學講，也就是能。文化學者有主張唯能論的，認爲文化演進，不外由物能和心能所推動，自屬正確。中國古人一向認爲全宇宙都是一氣，人生於氣的運行，所以說人以氣而生，氣絕而死。黃帝內經說：「恬澹虛無，眞氣從之，精神內守。病從何來」。「呼吸精氣，獨立守神，肌肉若一」。故中醫治病，防病，注重培養元氣。鍼灸能扎到穴道爲「得氣」，可見氣與身體各種器官都有關係。明代張景岳早就說過：「生化之道，以氣爲本，天地萬物，莫不由之……四時萬物得以收藏，何非氣之所爲，人之爲生，全賴此氣」。古人說，「生化之道，近人則說「氣化作用」，有氣化然後可以除舊更新，自我調整，自我修復，祛病延年。大抵古人之善言養氣者，當推孟子，他說：「我善養吾浩然之氣」。又說：「其爲氣也。至大至剛。以直養而無害，則塞乎天地之間」。太極論者尚氣之法，受孟子這話的影響，亦「以氣直養而無害」。關乎氣者，有曰：「以心行氣，以氣運身」。「牽動往來氣貼背」。「氣宜鼓盪」，「氣若車輪」，「行氣如九曲連珠，無微不到」。「氣遍周身不少滯」，「意氣君來骨肉臣」，「氣斂入骨」，「氣沉丹田」，「外錬筋骨皮，內錬一口氣」。極其至者「第一能專氣致柔」，第二「能煉氣化神」，所以進言「意在精神不在氣，在氣則滯，有氣者無力，無氣者純剛」。到了這個地步，精氣之氣，化爲神力，所謂技而進於道，此其一端。這又豈祇祛病延年而已。這是「整合太極論」的理氣論。

第四點：運動論。易說：「天行健，君子以自強不息」。華佗作五禽之戲，詔吳普說：「人體欲得勞動，但不當使極耳。動搖則谷氣得消，血脈流通，病不得生。譬如戶樞，終不朽也」。故太極拳論說明，一動無有不動，但動却以宇宙運行的模式作根據，有圓形，有曲線，有螺旋形，在技術上則稱「運動如抽絲」

。抽絲的運行與各種運動之有稜角者有別。而也由於圓形運動，乃產生內勁，所謂「勁以曲蓄而有餘」，這是「整合太極論」的運動論。

第五點：均衡論。宇宙運行，循環無端，其所以不致破壞毀滅者，端在均衡。中庸說：「致中和，天地位焉，萬物育焉」。中和也就是均衡。中國人的生活理想方式，在於「唯精唯一，允執厥中」，執中就是中庸，就是均衡之道。孔子說：「質勝文則野，文勝質是史，文質彬彬，然後君子」，這是文質雙方得到均衡，而均衡與中和，不外孔子所謂「無太過與不及」。老子亦說：「多言數窮，不如守中」。希臘人（以亞里士多德為代表）與佛教的基本觀念是中道。守中與中道，目的亦在均衡。太極拳論者主張虛靈頂勁，氣沉丹田，故一切運動，以中定為中心，以中定為出發點，能中定然後能均衡。這是「整合太極論」的均衡論。

第六點：變化論。易家與道家知道宇宙一切事物，都是對立的，矛盾的，所以有剛必有柔，有上必有下，有前必有後，有左必有右。這種矛盾對立的道理，總結起來，叫做陰陽。由於剛柔相摩，八卦相盪，便生變化；但無論如何變化，第一是陰不離陽，陽不離陰。第二是對立是相互轉化，向着相反的方面發展，所以老子說：「反者道之動」，這與易繫辭：「天下同歸而殊塗，一致而百慮」，中庸：「道並行而不相悖，萬物並育而不相害」的意義相同。太極拳論者認識「動之則分，靜之則合」，「動急則急應，動緩則緩隨，雖變化萬端，而理為一貫」。又說：「偏沉則隨，雙重則滯，欲避此病，須知陰陽」，因為有陰陽對立，才生變化，由變化而得到統一。這是「整合太極拳論」的變化論。

第七點、柔弱論。中庸之道，本是剛柔互濟，但老子從自然與人文現象中，窺探出「弱者道之用」的法則，所以說：「天下莫柔弱於水，而攻堅強者，莫之能勝」。「堅強者死之徒，柔弱者生之徒」，「強梁者，不得其死」，說到反面，則「柔弱勝剛強，魚不可脫於淵」，「專氣致柔，能嬰兒乎」，「聖人後其身而身先，外其身而身存」，故拳論最高道理，莫若「牽動四兩撥千斤」，而語其關要，也不外乎老子所說：「天下之至柔，馳騁天下之至堅」。至於掤、攦、擠、按、採、挒、肘，靠各勁，豈能離乎「周身彈簧力，開合一定間，任彼千斤力，飄浮亦不難」。這種無所畏懼的精神，就是「整合太極論」的柔弱論。

　　第八點：技藝論。拳術之起源，本由於搏鬥。人類愈野蠻，愈是要身法靈活，手法便利，知當斜閃，然後可以招架，然後可以獲勝。到了文明進步，機械百出，所謂赤手肉搏，以爭生命於呼吸，此種情形，萬中難遇一二，所以戚南塘雖以拳經名天下，而竟說：「此藝無預於兵」，又說拳法是一種「似無預於大戰之技」。而現代技術學發展的結果，一切傳統的英雄主義也根本改變。我們雖然不否認太極拳在自衛方面，以其至柔，既能「吞天之氣，接地之力」，猶復「舍己從人」，「不丟不頂」，故「英雄所向無敵」，而天下莫之能勝。但這還不能出乎「善鬥者不武」，「佳兵不祥」的批評以外。故楊露禪述張三丰之主旨，以太極拳的最大目標，在使天下英豪延年益壽，而非徒在技藝之末。這是「整合太極論」的技藝論。

　　第九點：法則論。人類的生命與宇宙是有密切關係的。道家的生命學說，以易家的理論做基礎，認爲在自然方面，生命的普通變化，因受外在物理條件的制約，與內在精力的消耗之結果，所以人生由少而壯而老而死，乃必然的過程。現代文化形態學者丹尼拉維斯基（Danilevsky），斯賓格勒（Spengler），湯恩培（Toynbee）認文化是一種有機體，故斷言每種文化的壽命約爲五六百年，過此以後，即趨沒落，同一道理。然而生命的另一種變化，根據道家所謂「宇宙在乎手，萬化生乎心」的道理，只要我們採取各種方法，來突破現象界的約制，奪天地之造化，則生命的過程自然可以延長。這些方法，在生理方面，如太極拳之「一動無有不動，一靜無有不靜」，「尾閭中正神貫頂，滿身輕利頂頭懸」，篤行做去，身體自然節節貫串，氣通可期。在心理方面，既能「內固精神，外示安逸」，復藉吐納導引，與動作配合，達到「煉精化氣，煉氣化神」之最高境域。人生到此，縱然不能絕對脫離現象界之限制，亦可以袪病延年，非所謂「油盡燈枯」者可比。此理，推而廣之，應用到文化方面，亦可使文化不受有機體的法則之限制，所以克魯伯(Kroeber)和本人在文化學上均主張「文化再造說」(Theory of Cultural Reconstitution)，雙方自有相通之處。邵康節深明周易一陽來復之理，所以說：「卷舒萬世興亡手，出入千重雲水身……這般事業權衡別，振古英雄恐未聞」。而太極拳論則說：「意氣君來骨肉臣，益壽延年不老長」，可見拳家把握易家與道家生命與宇宙關係的法則，所以能發揮生命中生生不息的功能。這是「整合太極論」的法則論。

第十點、大道論。太極拳論者，認為是技而進於道，所以主張道技必須雙修，方不失技，亦不失道。在技方面，多數習者之動機，約有三點，（一）為競技而學；（二）為健身而學；（三）為自衛而學。一旦技藝成熟，便算心滿意足，對於道方面，全不講求，也即是對於太極拳的哲學與科學之基礎，及其與人生與社會之關係，完全置若罔聞。我以太極之道，應該從兩方面說。其一從個人說，岐伯有言：「夫道者，却老而全形，精神內守，病安從來」。極其至，則又說：「筋脈和同，骨髓堅固，氣血皆從」。黃帝的內經素問靈樞，乃是中國數千年之衛生經典，針灸學之寶筏者，就是這樣起源的。所以習太極拳者之道，從淺處看，不外使瘠者肥，羸者腴，病者健。然而從深處看，太極拳之目的，還在能養生，還在能成為至人。何謂養生？中國古代思想家之善言養生者莫若莊子。莊子秋水篇說：「量無窮，時無止，分無常，終始無故」。蓋莊子知宇宙之無窮無盡，人生是非，善惡，窮通，得失，成敗之無定無限，現象終始之無故，故其宇宙觀止於齊物，人生觀止於逍遙，而以此為養生之要道。現代人以長生不老法就是容忍，樂觀，「人老心不老」，同是此理。何謂至人？莊子說：「至人神矣，大澤焚而不能熱，河海沍而不能寒，疾雷破山風振海而不能掠，若然者乘雲氣，騎日月而游乎四海之外，死生無變於已，而況利害之端乎？」這種理想，雖然懸得太高，然而瑜伽學者以超人的智慧自許，亦多以此為鵠的，有些且早已相信達到這種境界。太極拳者「內固精神，外示安逸」，「泰山崩於前而色不變」，一樣是以超人的智慧自許，如此則至人之目的，自非永遠不難到達。然這種目的，縱使達到，還不外是個人主義「小道」的成果。所以其二，從社會方面說，我們認為「大道」，却是儒家禮運所說的「大道之行也」，推其極致則以「貨惡其棄於地，不必藏於已，力惡其不出於身，不必為已」為最高境界。而老子也說：「生而不有，為而不恃，長而不宰，功成而不居」，所以主張「損有餘而補不足」。周易說：「君子以裒多益寡，稱物平施」。佛家則主張「無緣慈，同體悲」。綜合以上種種，這才是太極拳者的「大道」。為什麼呢？這是因為我們知道個人的生存與社會的生存是相互依倚的，中國文化的生存與中西文化的會通是不可以終止的，良好的生活，必須「已欲立而立人，已欲達而達人」，並深刻地認識着個人之身體與心理健康與羣體之安寧與秩序究竟是不可分的。近人說：「如你的人生哲學是放在為大衆而生存的基礎上的，你將不只生活得快樂，而可以長命百歲」，正是此理。這是「整合太極論」的大道論。

整合太極論是二十世紀六七十年代的產品，當然與過去三四百年前許多先哲的太極拳論，在重點上，有很大差別。然而我個人以管窺天，以蠡測海，對於中國最高的文化價值與倫理精神，能否達致綜合的目的，則又殊不敢必；錯謬之處，唯希高明恕其狂妄，有以正之，幸甚幸甚。

五

本書自一九六二年開始着筆，至一九六六年左右早經脫稿。今年（一九七二年）以因緣會合，在港付印，而又適值現代印度聖哲奧魯濱鐸(Sri Aurobindo)生辰百週年紀念，故以此書奉獻。

我于一九六一年在羅安琪設立華美文化學院時，常常約請「東西文化中心」的主持人狄寶（Judith Tyberg）博士到院講演奧魯濱鐸的整合哲學和「整合瑜伽」。伊亦常請我到該中心講中國哲學，及「整合太極論」。她曾在印度國際大學讀書，爲奧氏的高足，精梵文，乃近年在美傳輸印度文化之有名人物。余獲此機緣，因而研究奧氏的生平及學說，深覺他一生的行動與思想體系，有使我注意者約有二端。他自少年時代就學英國，歸國後即從事印度獨立運動，因此被英人囚禁者數年，在幽居當中，經過一種神秘經驗，故出獄之後，即從事精神生活與人類統一運動。當印度於一九四七年八月十五日宣告獨立時，適值他七十五歲生辰，他宣布生平參加的五種世界運動，希望終歸能達到最後底目的：（一）爲着自由與統一的印度而奮鬥；（二）爲着亞洲復興而努力；（三）爲着世界聯合而向世界呼籲；（四）把印度的精神文化輸進歐美；（五）把人類在目前演進的步驟中，更推進一步，使人類達到更高更大的意識性，以便進入人類統一的階段。這可算是他生平的行動綱領。他在南印度潘狄舍利（Pondicherry）設立的「國際大學」，頗引起全世界人士的注意。在思想體系方面，曾先後發表過，「神聖的生命」（The Life Divine）（一部世界最長的史詩，用英文寫成），「世界之謎」（The Riddle of this World），「人類的循環」（Human Cycle），「人類統一的理想」（The Ideal of Human Unity），「瑜伽的綜合」（The Synthesis of Yoga）等鉅著。至其思想的路線，則在把各種瑜伽（Hatha Yoga, Rāja Yoga, Yurna Yoga）綜合起來，作爲「整合瑜伽」，並把西方科學與宗敎之有價値的部分，加以吸收，融會貫通，構成自己的體系。過去的瑜伽，對於宇宙與人生視作空相，故對世界事情，多取消極態度。整合瑜伽則視物質性乃是「眞正的實在」，也是上層心靈（Supermind）之低層形式。他認爲人類進化，截至如今，只走過三個步驟，即是由物質到生命，由生命到心靈，今後則要進一步，由心靈而到達「上層心靈」（Super-mind），然後整個世界演進，方能趨向到「神聖化」。人生的神聖化，其目的不只在達到個人的超越的自由，而在使整個人類神聖化，因而使人類達到集體的自由。最後，則在這個地球之上，建立一個神聖的天國（大同世界）。

整合瑜伽固然相信身體姿勢的訓練爲超人的精神凝集之重要部分，但却不相信它的目的，可以完全由宗敎情感，儀式，咒語，祈禱可以達到，更不相信可以由暴動或善行，甚至虔誠，博愛，智慧和知識可以達到。他以爲這種目的，必須把東西的哲學的，宗敎的，科學的主流，作「意理上」的整理，才有達到的希望。它的最後目的，所以寄託在精神上面，這也可說是「唯心論」。人類未來的希望，依他說的，在於一種人道的精神宗敎之建立。但這不是指通常的世界宗敎——一種體系，一種敎條與知識信仰與外部生活的一致而言。人類老早已企圖採用這種方法來統一世界，但終歸還是失敗。因爲這個世界不能因爲有了世界的宗敎體系，便能使到心理信條與生活形式完全一致。內部精神，誠然是要統一的，但精神生活却是自表的，自由的，多樣的，其發展的方法也有種種不同。人道的宗敎相信人類是同胞。由於人類內心覺悟到人與人之間是統一的，故同胞之愛，才成爲我們一切生活之主要原則。這不單是互助合作的原則之實現，而也是一種深度的同胞愛，一種統一的，平等的與眞正的內在感覺之到達。這就是奧魯濱鐸所說人類進化的最後步，在「上層心靈」之完成的義諦，雖然他沒有否認它的下層物質基礎之功用。

今年是奧氏生辰一百周年紀念。「聯合國文敎科學組織」（UNESCO）在巴黎把他的著作搜集起來，作公開展覽。同時印度與各國的「奧魯濱鐸學會」在潘狄舍利建立一個「曙光之城」（Auroville），作爲世界統一的象徵，爲他紀念。這個小城到了一九八八年可以完成。其設計以偉大的星雲的金色區域爲中心，週圍包括四大區域——住宅、工業、文化與國際。在文化區中，藝術與科學院歡迎全世界的藝藝家與科學家前往參加，至國際區則建立世界各民族館，作爲每個國家文化、藝術與手工藝的大使館。這個城市的設計，在使世界各種文化集合在一個諧和的環境中，作爲大同世界社會的模型，並向這種文化推進，而這也是整合瑜伽的終極目的。

我雖然不是他的信徒，但覺得「整合太極論」在「大道之行」的目的上，與奧氏的「整合哲學」和「整合瑜伽」是完全一致的。印度民族曾以佛教傳給中國，而由慧能在六世紀起來把儒釋道融合，創造成中國的禪宗，使到中國人的心靈昇華化。禪宗思想，早已由中國傳到韓國，日本，現在更由日本推廣到歐美。整合太極論底目的在把儒道釋的體系與西方的現代哲學、科學，綜合起來，今日方由中國開始輸進到歐美，將來再進一步自可推廣到全世界，爲會通東西文化之橋樑，最後更可藉此來使人生昇華化，把文化由獸性化（如戰爭等）進而爲澈底的人道化，達成世界大同的理想。西方諺語說：「光鋩自東方來」。今日世界的危難已到了極端，我們希望中印兩大民族，重新努力，負起當前拯救世界文化危機的重任。這是本人所以把這書奉獻給奧魯濱鐸一百周年紀念的微願。

最後，這本書的出版，獲得許多朋友的幫忙，我在本書英文序論已經說過。但在原序中，因爲有許多意思未曾澈底表達，故以此后叙來補充。這裡值得一提的，就是如果沒有香港南天書業公司李吉如先生以及和記印刷公司的宋叙五先生、珠海書院溫心園教授的共同幫忙，這書是不會與世人見面的。謹誌數言，表示衷心永遠的感激。

一九七二年十二月除夕　凌霜黃文山於九龍危樓萬里心齋

附言：此后叙寫完後，看見李樂俅君在人文世界，三卷三期（1973，三月）發表「中國三絕」一文，謂年登耋耄之美國名醫懷特建議：『美國人宜向中國專心致志學習者：「針灸」其一也；「太極拳」其二也；「靜坐」其三也。』本書除研究太極拳外，對于針灸學原理與靜坐氣功，多所介紹，目的無非希望此三者成爲東西文化整合之橋樑，謹綴數言，以誌感想。

太極拳參考書目（中文之部）

Bibliography in Chinese

(一) 理論　考據

梁啓超，中國之武士道。台灣中華書局。
卞人傑，國術概論。台北武林出版社。
何去非，武經七書。台北商務印書館。
戚繼光，戚氏武藝全書。台北五洲出版社。
宋更新，國術論畧。台北五洲出版社。
金一明，中國技擊精華。武林出版社。
金恩忠，國術名人錄。同上。
季光甫，武術名家談武術。同上。
張三丰，道術滙宗。台北眞善美出版社。
盧煒昌，拳術意見百則。香港出版。
唐　豪，內家拳研究。香港麒麟公司。
唐　豪，太極拳宗師王宗岳。同上。
唐　豪，王宗岳太極拳經研究。同上。
唐　豪，少林武當考。同上。
徐　震，太極拳考信錄。同上。
徐　震，太極拳譜理董辨僞合編。同上。
徐　震，國技論畧。中華武術社。
鄧澤霖，漫談太極拳養生功能。台北出版。
許卓修，太極拳原理與太極拳。台北出版。
吳孟俠，太極拳之要訣。香港太平書局。
黃元秀，太極拳經驗談。上海出版。
白　羽，太極拳掌故。香港勵力書店。

（二）陳家太極拳

陳績甫，陳氏太極拳入門總解。台北眞善美出版社。

陳品三，陳氏太極拳圖說。同上。

陳　鑫，陳氏太極拳圖解。同上。

（三）楊家太極拳

楊澄甫，太極拳體用全書。民三十七年楊守中重刊。

楊澄甫，太極拳使用法。台北中美文化經濟協會太極拳學術研究會。

楊澄甫，楊式太極拳。香港太平書局。

楊澄甫，太極拳用法圖解。香港華聯出社版。

楊澄甫，楊家太極拳體用全書。香港新文書店。

許振武，廖國雄，楊氏太拳圖解。台北華聯出版社。

許禹生，太極拳勢圖解。民十北京版。香港錦華出版。

宋書銘，太極拳譜。北京版。

楊守中，太極拳用法及變化。香港洛克道三一五號。

陳微明，太極拳術。上海致柔學社。

陳微明，太極拳答問。同上。

董英傑，太極拳釋義。香港英傑太極拳學院。

董虎嶺，太極拳應用法。同上。

熊養和，太極拳釋義。台灣宜蘭市舊城東路十二號。

姜容樵，姚馥春，太極拳講義。上海武學書局。

陳炎林，太極拳刀劍散手合編。上海國光書局。台北新醫。

黃耐之，張三丰和他的太極拳。香港上海印書館。

鄭曼青，鄭子太極拳十三篇。香港新聯出版社。

鄭曼青，太極拳自修新法。同上。

蔡鶴朋編，太極拳。香港致柔學社。

郭連蔭，太極拳譜。台北廣信書局。

顧留馨，楊式太極拳。香港太平書局。

吳志靑，正宗太極拳。上海出版。

吳志靑，太極拳法。香港華聯出版社。

田鎭峯，太極拳。濟南世界書局。

愼先媚，太極拳術。香港華聯出版社。

曾昭然，太極拳全書。香港友聯出版社。

曾昭然，太極拳圖解。同上。

陳泮嶺，太極拳敎材。台北眞善美出版社。

宋志堅，太極拳學。台北太極拳研究會代售。

楊振聲編，太極拳研究專集一至十一輯。台北中國太極拳研究會
　　　　　印行。

陳微明，太極拳答問。同上。

李英昂，精簡太極拳。香港麒麟圖書公司。

李英昂，太極拳譜。同上。

李英昂，太極拳使用法。同上。

李英昂，正宗太極拳。香港國術太極拳社。

王鳳亭，最新太極拳圖說。香港新聯出版社。

萬籟聲，太極拳敎材。香港出版。

宋史元，太極拳蘊眞圖解。華聯出版社。

居　浩，楊氏太極拳。台北眞善美出版社。

王延年，楊家秘傳太極拳圖解。台北。

施調梅，太極拳譜內外功研幾錄。台北。

戚靜之，太極拳體用集。香港出版。

鍾道武，簡化太極拳圖解。香港得利書局。

鄭天熊，太極拳精鑑。香港出版。

龍子祥，太極拳學。同上。

關百益，太極拳經（油印本）。

王新午，太極拳拳技。

吳孟俠，楊氏太極拳散手。澳門大成公司。

王新午，太極拳法實踐。陝西人民出版社。

王新午，太極拳法精義。太平書局。

張文元，太極拳常識答問。同上。

李壽籛，武當嬌派太極拳術。重慶業餘太極拳社。

太極拳圖說（一）（二）（三）。香港太平書局。

太極拳運動（一）（二）（三）。人民體育出版社。

甲組男子長拳圖解。香港藝美公司。

乙組長拳圖解。同上。

（四）吳家太極拳

吳鑑泉，太極拳圖。上海九福公司。

吳公藻，吳家太極拳精義。

吳圖南，科學化太極拳。

徐致一，太極拳淺說。上海精武會。

鄭榮光，吳派太極拳指引。

陳鎮民，馬岳樑，吳鑑泉太極拳。麒麟公司。

鄭夢痕，太極拳基本拳式。新加坡肇慶會館太極拳班。

（五）其他各派太極拳

倪清和，王宗先生南傳太極拳。麒麟公司。

吳圖南式太極拳。香港藝華公司。

馬永勝，新太極拳。香港出版。

（六）太極兵器及其他

熊養和，太極劍法圖解。台灣宜蘭市（見上）。

李英昂，太極十三槍譜註。麒麟公司。

陳洪鎮，太極刀圖說。

吳圖南，太極劍圖說。

張祥三，太極劍。

孫明德，太極十三劍。

李英昂，七十二把擒拿原理。華聯出版社。

(七) 形意、八卦拳及其他

姜容樵，形意母拳。台北五洲出版社。

李存義，形意五行連環拳。同上。

靳雲亭，形意拳譜。同上。

凌桂清，形意拳圖說。同上。

孫祿堂，形意拳全書。麒麟公司。

竇顯匡，形意拳譜。武林出版社。

孫錫堃，八卦拳學（黃氏鈔本）。

倪清和，內家八卦拳學。眞善美出版社。

孫祿堂，武當八卦拳學。自由出版社。

韓金鏞，八卦拳。

黃柏年，龍形八卦拳。

藍素貞，綿拳。新文書店。

吳志青，查拳圖說。武林出版社。

程達材，先天氣功太極尺。香港太極尺研究會。

孫劍雲，太極拳。人民體育出版社。

姜容樵，八卦掌練習法。太平書局。

陳亦人，六合八法拳。華嶽心意健身社。

(八) 內功、氣功

白雲霽，道藏目錄詳註（上下）。上海商務印書館萬有文庫。

蕭天石編，養生長壽秘訣集成（一至十）。台北自由出版社。

蕭天石編（伊藤光遠著），養生內功秘訣。同上。

南懷瑾，禪海蠡測。自由出版社。

張洪陽註解，玄宗內典。同上。

周潛川，氣功藥餌療法全書。太平書局。

焦國瑞，氣功强身法。學林書店。

因是子，呼吸習靜養生法。太平書局。

蔣維喬，中醫師談氣功治療。同上。

劉貴珍，實驗氣功療法。同上。

王先青，養生新論。台北柳州街七號。

洪萬馨，五大健康修練法。眞善美出版社。

Bibliography in English

A. Books

Beck, William. "Modern Science and the Nature of Life", New York, Harcourt, Brace & Co., 1951.

Bonner, John Tyler, "The Idea of Biology", New York, Harper & Bros., 162.

Chen, Yearning K. "Tai Chi Ch'uan, Its Effects and Practical Applications", Shanghai, 1947.

Cheng, Man-Ch'ing, Tai Chi Ch'uan, "A Simplified Method of Calisthenics or Health and Self-Defense", Taipei, 1961.

Cheng Man ch'ing & Robert, W. Smith, "Tai Chi", Rutland, Vt. Charles E. Tuttle Co., 1967.

Da Liu,"Tai Chi Ch'uan and I Ching, a Choreography of Body and Mind", Harper and Row, N. Y., 1972.

Delza, Sophia, "Body and Mind in Harmony", N. Y. David Mckay Co., 1961. Paperback by Cornerstone Library, affiliated with Simon and Schuster, Pub. 1972

Feng, Giafu and Kirk Jerome, "Tai Chi — A Way of Centering and I Ching", 1970.

Gould, George, M. & Walter L. Pyle, "Anomalies & Curiosities of Medicine", N. Y. The Julian Press, 1950.

Lin Yutang, "The Importace of Understanding", N. Y. The World Publishing Co., 1960.

Lin Yutang, (ed), "The Wisdom of India and China", N. Y. Random House, 1942.

Maisel, Edward, "tai-Chi for Health", Englewood Cliffs, N.J. Prentice Hall Co., 1962.

Poller, Charles Francis, "The Great Religious Leaders", N. Y. Simon & Schuster, 1958.

Stone, Justin, T'ai Chi Chih, with Forward by Wen-Shan Huang, Sun Publishing Co., P.O. Box 4383, Alburquerque, New Mexico 87106, 1974.

Tang Mong Hun, "The Fundamental Exercises of Tai Chi Ch'uan", Singapore, 1966.

Tseng Chiu Yien, "The Chart of Tai Chi Ch'uan, with English Illustration", Union Press Ltd., Hong Kong, 1965.

B. Articles

Biery, James, "Tai Chi for Four Muscles", Popular Mechanics, Oct. 1960, 196—157.

Curtis, Charlotte, "UN Members Adopt Exercise from China", N. Y. Time, 1962 (only date available).

Cheng Man-ch'ing, "Tai Chi Boxing", Lecture recorded by Liang Tung-Chai, W & E Monthly, Vol. VII, No. 4, 1962, Taipei.

Delza, Sophia, "The Art of the Science of T'ai Chi Ch'uan". Journal of Aesthetics & Art Criticism, XXV, 4, 1965.

Gosta Olander, "Today's Health", vide Reader's Digest, 1964.

Huang, Wen-shan, "Tai Chi Ch'uan and I Ching, or The Book of Changes", Chinese Culture, Taipei, Vol. V. No. 1, March, 1969. Also in Special Research Collections on Tai Chi Ch'uan, Nos. 33—34, 1969, Taipei.

Henning, Stanley E., "An Introduction to Tai Chi Ch'uan, A Branch of the Inner School of Chinese Boxing", Special Research Collections on Tai Chi Ch'uan, No. 52, 1971, Taipei.

Liu, Y. T., "Chinese Martial Arts and Tai Chi Ch'uan", Chinese Kung Fu Wu Su Association, N. Y., 1971.

Lin, Y. T., "Tai Chi, The Ancient Chinese Program of Body and Mind, Conditioning for all Men and Women who hate Exercise", Magnum Royal Publications, Inc., N. Y., 1970.

"Physical Therapy: A Poetic Gesture", Newsweek, Sept. 25, 1961, 105.

"Tai Chi Ch'uan", The New Yorker, Dec. 15, 1962, 32—33.

Tai Chi Ch'uan .— based on Huang's Fundamentals of Tai Chi Ch'uan, Jade, Vol. I, No. 2, 1974, Los Angeles, Calif.

Wiemer, Robert,"The UN Twist", Newsday, April, 1962.

Cheng Man-ch'ing, "Thirteenn Chapters on Tai Chi Ch'uan"

Huang, Al Chung-liang, "Embrace Tiger, Return to Mountain — the essence of T'ai Chi," Real People Press, Moab, Utah 84532, 1973 (in cloth and paperbound book form).

C. Pamphlets

Liu, Y. T., "How to Live Longer, Better and Healthier", based on a speech delivered in Palo Alto, Calif., Nov. 25, 1966.

Liu, Y. T., "Tai Chi Ch'uan: Health Exercises for Advanced Pupils", 1965.

Tsao, T. C. ed. "Tai Chi Ch'uan: Body and Mind", Tai Chi Association, N. Y., 1968.

D. Periodicals

"Black Belt," 1845 Empire Avenue, Burbank, Calif. U.S.A.

"Inside Kung-Fu" — The Ultimate in Martial Arts Coverage, 7011 Sunset Blvd, Los Angeles.

"Tai Chi Magazine", published by Magnum-Royal Publications, N.Y.C., U.S.A.

Index

A

B

H

N

R

S

T

Z

Comments on Wen-shan Huang's Fundamentals of Tai Chi Ch'uan

(1)

"I find the book excellent, as far as I have read into it. The material is marvelous—so full—probably covering the total ground necessary for a real knowledge of what Tai Chi Ch'uan is all about —after one masters it. It is a rich book for anyone interested in its philosophy, history and development."

> Sophia Delza
>
> The first Western professional exponent of this exercise as well as the first Western writer to write a book on the subject: *Body And Mind In Harmony: Tai Chi Ch'uan,* D. McKay CO., N.Y. She teaches Tai Chi Ch'uan at the United Nations and has a school of Tai Chi Ch'uan at Carnegie Hall in New York. Sometime guest instructor at University of Hawaii, New York University; Royal Theatre at Stockholm.

(2)

"Professor Wen-shan Huang's *Fundamentals of Tai Chi Ch'uan* is, to the best of my knowledge, the only book which explains the rationale of Tai Chi Ch'uan on the basis of the metaphysical truths taught in the *I-Ching* or *Book of Changes.* As a culturologist, scholar, and adept in Tai Chi Ch'uan, Professor Huang explains in a lucid and detailed manner the principles of mutation governing the evolution of the universe and the development of man's physical and mental faculties: principles of polarity, of periodicity, and the conversion in extremism. Such knowledge will enable the practitioner of this system of physical culture to perform to perfection the multifarious body movements and their permutations. It gives them confidence in their ability to achieve that perfection and will promote their health and well-being. Such is the unique value of Professor Huang's excellent work."

Wei Tat, M.A., F.R.S.A.
Visiting Professor of the Chinese Culture
Institute, Republic of China;
Academician, China Academy.
Author of *An Exposition of the I-Ching, or Book of Changes,* Institute of Cultural Studies, Taipei, 1971.
Translator of *Ch'eng Wei-shih Lun by Hsuan Tsang,* Hong Kong, 1974.

(3)

"Professor Wen-shan Huang's latest book *Fundamentals of Tai Chi Ch'uan* opens the door to the rich heritage of Ancient China. As one reads this book each page becomes alive and breathes the Truth of the ancient Chinese sages and the reader's mind is renewed and his body filled with new life and vitality."

Preston Kline Caye, Ph.D.

(4)

"I have read through the newly published great work *Fundamentals of Tai Chi Ch'uan,* authored by Professor Wen-shan Huang, and found it to be most valuable for reference of experts of the ancient art of slow-motion exercise for health and longevity (body-mind conditioning) and self-defense by utilizing opponent's own dynamic strength. Its simplified, concise form of presentation will also help laymen and beginners to acquire a quicker knowledge of the art while learning under tuitors. The work, containing excellent English translations of all existing classics of Tai Chi Ch'uan as well as interpretation and commentaries of many renowned grand masters on the subject, is particularly required by those who are not versed in the Chinese language, contemporary and ancient."

> Liu Yao-Ting
> Instructor of Tai Chi Ch'uan,
> Retired Postal Commissioner of China

(5)

"The book is quite fascinating and very well written. I believe it will prove to be very valuable to English-speaking peoples for health and longevity. Not only this, but it is a wonderful demonstration of people-to-people sharing their particular and precious treasures of living (life-ways) and of culture (loving refinement)."

> Joe McCaffree
> Author of *The Comparative Study of the Bible and the I Ching*

（6）

"I have collected over a dozen of books written about Tai Chi Ch'uan mostly in Chinese, and there are quite a few good books. I also have a few written in English: one by Yearning K. Chen, one by Sophia Delza, and one by Edward Maisel. Among the three books mentioned above, I like Chen's the most. But, after a first glance of this new book, I must say that finally I have come across a book in my opinion the most comprehensive one to touch upon the art of Tai Chi Ch'uan both historically and philosophically. To me, it is a must for every student as well as expert to own such a book so masterfully written."

William Moy, M.A.
Founder and
President of Tai Chi Ch'uan Institute,
Flushing, N.Y.

Additional Bibliography

G-hand Chang, Tai Chi Ch'uan for Beginners, 4th Ed, (Taipei, 1976).

G-hand Chang, Push-hand Exercise and Combat skill of Tai Chi (Taipei, 1975).

Da Liu, Taoist Health Exercise Book. (Links Books, New York 10023).

Da Liu, Tai Chi Ch'uan and I Ching, (Harper and Row, 1972).

Andrew Lum, Kung Fu, Combat Tai Chi Ch'uan, Golden Unicorn In Honolulu, Hawaii, 96825.

Andrew Lum, Advanced Tai Chi Ch'uan, same.

Lee, Douglas, Tai Chi Ch'uan, The philosophy of Yin and Yang and its application, Ohara Pub, Burbank, Calif.

Lu Hui-Ching, Tai Chi Ch'uan,

A Manual of instruction

ST. Martin's Press, New York, 1973.

Tseng Chiu-Yen, Marshal Pugilism, Paul H. Crompton Ltd., London, S.W.E. 1977

ADVERTISEMENTS

AN INTRODUCTION TO CULTUROLOGY
VOL. I.

Foreword by James C.
    Ingebretsen

Introduction by
Horace M. Kallen

Foreword by Robert
L. Carneiro

Preface by Wen-Shan
Huang

Editor's Notes

By
Wen-Shan Huang
First Edition,
December, 1980

With Appendices and
Letters from
famous authors

Culturology is the science of culture, or Cultural Engineering. Leslie A. White is considered the "Father of Culturology" by H.E. Barnes White has pointed out the "concept of culture as science." In 1915, Ostwald, a Nobel Prize Winner, in his *System of Science, places culturology at the top of the "pyramid of the sciences." But it has been during recent years when Wen-Shan Huang published his System of Culturology, that a clarification of its principles, methods, theroies, and explanations has emerged.*

In the past, the civilizations of China and of Rome existed side by side; each imagined itself the center of the universe. In recent times, Joseph Needham pointed out clearly the problem which we must solve: the problem of culture synthesis of the West and the East.

THE THREE COMPREHENSIVE PARTS:

1. Introductory Comments:
   "His [Huang's] contacts with A.L. Kroeber, Leslie A White, Horace Kallen, and Pitrim Sorokin helped nourish the early insights which make possible the unique contributions of the present volume..." – James C. Ingebretsen, President of Creative Education institute, Trustee of the Blaisdell Institute for the Study of World Cultures and Religions at Claremont University, California.
   "Wen-Shan Huang's long pondered *System of Culturology* may well prove an event in the history of ideas . . ." – Horace M. Kallen, Graduate Faculty of Political and Social Sciences, the New School for Social Research.

II. Historical Development of Culturology and Prospect
   Hegel seemed to be the founder of the concept of "Kulturwissenschaft." The French positivist Auguste Comte distinguished three great stages in the development of human thought. Culturology, as a system of culture, received the attention of Ostwald. The principal theories relating to culture were expounded by Tylor, Durkheim, Kroeber, Znaniecki, and White. In China, the *I Ching,* or Book of Changes, and various philosophers, such as Fu Hsi, Wen Wang, Chow Kung, and Confucius contributed much. Modern thinkers, such as Danilovsky, Spengler, Toynbee, Liang Shou-ming, and Sorokin continue this tradition.

III. Miscellaneous Compilations

Some aspects of the culture theory of Kroeber and the criticism of White's theory regarding the establishment of Culturology have been written by Huang. Kallen sums up his Philosophy of Cultural Pluralism, etc.

Letters to the author have been compiled. These include letters of White, Kroeber, Horace Kallen, Hu Shih, and Sorokin. These are of historical value.

ABOUT THE AUTHOR – Wen-Shan Huang took his B.A. degree at National Peking University, M.A. at Columbia, and has been conferred Academician by the China Academy. Professor Huang was Dean of the Law School, National Sun Yat-sen University, President of Chien Shek University, and of the Provincial College of Law and Commerce of Kwangtung. As member of the Faculty of the New School in New York and the University of Southern California, he taught in the U.S. for more than ten years. He is the Founder and President of the American Academy of Chinese Culture, Inc., and President Emeritus of the National Tai Chi Ch'uan Association, Inc., in Los Angeles. Recently he has been a Visiting Professor of the New Asia College, Hong Kong Chinese University, National Visiting Professor of the Republic of China, Professor of the Institute of Cultural Research and Dean of the Faculty of Liberal Arts, Chu Hai College, Hong Kong, Dr. Huang was graduate School Chairman of the Department of Arts East and West, College of Oriental Studies in Los Angeles.

He has written many books, among the most famous are the *System of Culturology*, 1968: *Essays on Contemporary Culture*, 1972. He is best known for his translation into Chinese of his teacher's Bertrand Russell's *Problems of Philosophy;*

Roads to Freedom; and his friend Pitrim A. Sorokin's *Contemporary Sociological Theories,* and *Sociological Theories of Today;* as well as Joseph Needham's *Science and Civilization in China,* Vol. 1

ANNOUNCEMENT: A Second Volume, *Culturology and Chinese Culture, is currently printing.*

ABOUT THE PUBLISHER:South Sky Book Company, Ltd., now in its 20th year, is the biggest publisher in Hong Kong. Its products include textbooks, educational materials, and art books. It has produced more than 500 books, many of which are in English, such as Wing-tsit Chan's, *Essays on Neo-Confucianism,* and Tai Chen's *Inquiry into Goodness,* compiled by the Oriental Society in America.

Publisher:	Distributor in U.S.:
South Sky Book Company, Ltd.	**American Academy of Chinese Culture, Inc.**
Prices – Paperback $8.00	1493 Galveston Street
Prices – Hardback Cover $10.00 (5 to 20 copies, 30% off)	Los Angeles, Ca. 90026, U.S.A.

SHIPPING: We are not responsible for books lost or damaged in the mail. Insurance may be prepaid. On domestic shipments, please add 85¢ for the first book ordered. On foreign shipments, please add $1.50 for the first book, $1.0 for each book thereafter for registered shipping. Airmail postage rates on request. Please add 6% local tax. **PAYMENT MUST ACCOMPANY ALL ORDERS** except institutions. No. C.O.D.

ALL PRICES ARE SUBJECT TO CHANGE
WITHOUT NOTICE.

CULTUROLOGY AND CHINESE CULTURE
VOLUME II

Table of Contents

BIBLE AND I CHING RELATIONSHIPS

By

Joe E. McCaffree

I Ching is the Chinese Book of Changes. This venerable classic has been the basis of Chinese civilization for over 3,000 years. Since determination in 1967 that the I Ching was composed by members of the Dan Tribe of Israel, research has shown that it is a gem with each facet a window for viewing the meanings in the Bible and the instrumentality of Israel for the development of various nations with their distinctive life styles and culture systems.

The I Ching consists of 64 sets of principles and patterns that were introduced into the world ages ago by the LORD God for the Godward Cultivation of Humanity. They are the means by which humane awareness and conscience may be inculcated in mankind.

However, it is now known that these 64 sets are composed of the essence and structure of the Bible as it existed at the time of King Solomon. For example, fifty sets in the I Ching are based on the fifty chapters of Genesis and are numbered the same. The present study explains some of these direct relationships.

The I Ching enables individuals, as well as groups of people, to use the patterns and principles of the Bible in planning and striving to fulfil their goals, their justification for existence. Thus, the two classics are interdependent, promoting an inherent and intentional Cosmic Order.

SOUTH SKY
BOOK CO.

U.S. $16.00

BIBLE AND I CHING RELATIONSHIPS

The most important and interesting fact that makes this study of BIBLE AND I CHING RELATIONSHIPS of value to scholars and general public alike is that the Chinese Book of Changes—I Ching—is based directly on the Hebrew Bible. This study presents evidence that the I Ching analyses events and participants of the historical-chronological accounts of the Bible, accurately epitomizing them in terms that show their universal applicability. Since the I Ching was written at the time of Solomon, it now emerges as the world's oldest exposition of the Hebrew Bible as it existed up to that time. It is centuries older than the writing down of the Mishna and Gemara comprising the Jewish Talmud.

ABOUT THE AUTHOR

As this work is a general survey, rather than an intensive systematic analysis, of the very systematic relationships between the Hebrew Bible and the Chinese Book of Changes, a few notes about the writer's qualifications for such a study are in order. Mr. McCaffree has achieved no academic titles, although he has an unused, lifetime teaching credential for vocational training in printing. He has gained no obvious honors, except the respect of his oriental friends, three great teachers: Swami Sivananda of the Divine Life Society of India long ago invited Mr. McCaffree to represent him in Southern California; Roshi Joshu Sasaki of the Zen Order of Rinzai-Ji of Japan invited Mr. McCaffree and trained him to become a monk; Professor Wen-Shan Huang of the American Academy of Chinese Culture invited Mr. McCaffree three times to give talks on the I Ching, urged him to write the present book, and appointed him Vice-President of the Academy. With such a foreground, Mr. McCaffree feels justified in punning allusion to his birth as a "Cheyennese" in the "Wyo-Ming" era.

Otherwise, Joe McCaffree's specific preparation for such research as the present book details was as a stamp collector for about thirty-five years with a collection in more than ninety volumes and as the editor-publisher of Philatelic Consumer for eight years during which era he prepared various analyses and reports for reference of stamp dealers and collectors. In 1967 he wrote and published *Divination and the Historical and Allegorical Sources of the Chinese Book of Changes*. Earlier in the year this was presented as a lecture before the Academy and the National Tai Chi Ch'uan Institute. In it McCaffree detailed his initial perceptions of direct correspondences between the Bible and the I Ching. In 1971 McCaffree prepared and published the report *Assessed Valuations & Taxes on Lands Only, in Kern County*. He now resides in Kern County, California.

ABOUT THE PUBLISHER

South Sky Book Company, now in its 27th year, is the biggest publisher in Hong Kong. For 10 years it has had a branch in Seattle, U.S.A. South Sky's products include about 3 million copies of textbooks, educational materials and art books. It has produced more than 1,000 titles and editions of books. Among the many in English are Wingtsit Chan's Essays on Neo-Confucianism, Tai Chen's Inquiry into Goodness, and Elementary Chinese for American Librarians, compiled by the Oriental Society in America. Writings of Tang Zi-Chang: Principle of Conflict, Poem of Tang, and Wisdom of Dao, as well as Fundamentals of Tai Chi Ch'uan by Professor Wen-Shan Huang, now in its 4th edition, are also South Sky's books. Forthcoming is the lavishly illustrated 'China the Great' which will take readers on marvellous journeys throughout the vast land of China. We will publish CULTUROLOGY AND CHINESE CULTURE, Volume II as soon as possible to commemorate our dear friend, the distinctive author Wen-Shan Huang, who died in Los Angeles, California, in June, 1982.

South Sky Book Co.

Hong Kong — Seattle   1982

Publisher:

South Sky Book Co.,

5-7, O'Brien Road,
Hong Kong
Tel: H-8937608

Distributor:

American Academy of Chinese Culture, Inc.,

1493 Galveston Street,
Los, Angeles, Ca, 90026,
Phone (213) 628-8656

American Branch:

South Sky Book Company, Ltd.,
5501-5503 University Way N.E.
Seattle Washington 98105
U.S.A.

Fifth Edition 1984 Hong Kong.
U.S.$20 (Hard Cover) U.S.$17 (Soft Cover)

太 極 拳 要 義

著作者：黃 文 山

編輯者：華 美 文 化 學 院

出版者：南 天 書 業 公 司

發行人：李 吉 如

發行者：南 天 書 業 公 司

香港柯布連道五至七號
電 話：五—八九三七六○八

美國分公司
South Sky Book Company, Ltd.,
5501-5503 University Way N.E.
Seattle Washington 98105
U.S.A.

印刷者：海 光 印 刷 公 司

香港鰂魚涌英皇道華廈工廠大廈六樓D座
電話：五—六二一○九六 六二一六四一

定 價：

精裝本 港幣一百四十元 美金二十元
平裝本 港幣一百二十元 美金十七元

一九八四年在香港印增訂第五版

650.